METAMORPHOSIS

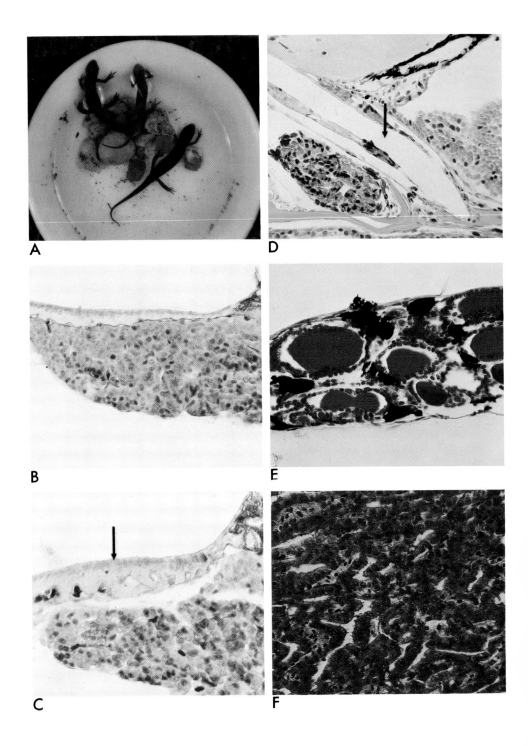

A

B

C

D

E

F

A. Second metamorphosis of the newt (*Notophthalmus* viridescens). Central animal (bright orange) is land phase. Left is animal with pituitary graft not yet effective. Right (dark) is animal transformed under influence of graft, showing change in color and behavior. The animals were dropped into the water and the two "land phase" animals immediately scrambled out, whereas the transformed specimen hid at the bottom. See page 326. (Courtesy of S. Masur)

B. Median sagittal section of pituitary of large thyroidectomized tadpole, showing failure of median eminence development. See page 321.

C. Median sagittal section of animal as in B, but after metamorphosis has been induced by exogenous thyroxine. Note formation of a median eminence in the hypothalamic floor (arrow). See page 321.

D. Hypothalamic-pituitary region of *Ambystoma* larva prevented from metamorphosis by barrier (arrow) inserted between pituitary (left) and hypothalamus (right). See page 319.

E. Thyroid of premetamorphic tadpole. Note flat epithelium and colloid-filled follicles. See pages 309, 317. (Courtesy of A. G. Gona)

F. Thyroid of animal like above but treated with TSH and prolactin. Note activation of thyroid as seen in high epithelium and evacuation of colloid. In spite of this activation, the animal failed to metamorphose. See pages 309, 317. (Courtesy of A. G. Gona)

METAMORPHOSIS

a problem in developmental biology

edited by

WILLIAM ETKIN
Albert Einstein College of Medicine, New York, New York

LAWRENCE I. GILBERT
Northwestern University, Evanston, Illinois

NORTH-HOLLAND PUBLISHING COMPANY—AMSTERDAM

APPLETON-CENTURY-CROFTS—NEW YORK   1968
Division of Meredith Corporation

PUBLISHERS:

NORTH-HOLLAND PUBLISHING COMPANY—AMSTERDAM

Sole distributors for U.S.A., Canada, Latin America, and West Indies:

APPLETON-CENTURY-CROFTS—NEW YORK
Division of Meredith Corporation

Library of Congress Card Number: 67-29170

PRINTED IN THE UNITED STATES OF AMERICA

257329

CONTRIBUTORS

E. J. W. Barrington

Department of Zoology, The University, Nottingham, England

John D. Costlow, Jr.

Duke University Marine Laboratory, Beaufort; Department of Zoology, Duke University, Durham, North Carolina

James Norman Dent

Department of Biology, University of Virginia, Charlottesville, Virginia

William Etkin

Department of Anatomy, Albert Einstein College of Medicine, Bronx, New York

Earl Frieden

Department of Chemistry and the Institute of Molecular Biophysics, Florida State University, Tallahassee, Florida

William S. Herman

Department of Zoology, University of Minnesota, Minneapolis, Minnesota

Jane Kaltenbach

Department of Biological Sciences, Mount Holyoke College, South Hadley, Massachusetts

Heinrich Kroeger

Zoologisches Institut, Eidgenössische Technische Hochschule, Zürich, Switzerland

Joan Whitten

Department of Biological Sciences, Northwestern University, Evanston, Illinois

Gerard R. Wyatt

Department of Biology, Yale University, New Haven, Connecticut

PREFACE

The phenomenon of metamorphosis, as it pertains to both insects and amphibians, has stimulated the thinking of biologists since the time of Aristotle. It exemplifies the most profound general change in form found during the postembryonic development of animals. In recent years increased attention has been focused on metamorphosis by developmental morphologists, physiologists, biochemists, and genticists, and the underlying questions asked by these individuals have been steadily unraveled. There is no doubt that the molecular biologist, who in the recent past has been engaged with phage and microorganisms, will soon apply his tools and knowledge to the problems of development and differentiation, and will utilize animal forms that undergo metamorphosis.

Although there are scattered reviews, and in fact volumes on specific facets of the subject, there is no single up-to-date source that deals with the several aspects of metamorphosis in an integrative way. Because of the importance of this phenomenon we feel that a single source should be available so that students and researchers, whether or not they are at present actively investigating some aspect of metamorphosis, can gain some insight into the innumerable problems of development that studies of metamorphosis deal with. We have attempted to organize this book in such a way that the problems are discussed from many points of view. The contributors have been allowed wide latitude in theorizing on points for which experimental data are sparse. No single format or style was dictated to the contributors of this volume because we hoped that the varied approaches and styles would keep the reader continually interested.

We have planned this book for researchers and graduate students and as an adjunct to any course dealing with development, endocrinology, biochemistry, and physiology. We believe it is admirably suited for all students of growth and development, from the undergraduate junior to the senior researcher.

William Etkin
Lawrence I. Gilbert

CONTENTS

METAMORPHOSIS

part

one

INVERTEBRATES

one

METAMORPHOSIS
IN CRUSTACEANS

John D. Costlow, Jr.

Duke University Marine Laboratory
Beaufort, North Carolina
Department of Zoology
Duke University
Durham, North Carolina

There is general agreement that within the free-living Crustacea the sequence of larval stages and the accompanying changes that ultimately result in the juvenile animal bear little resemblance to the phenomenon of metamorphosis as it normally applies to development in the holometabolous Insecta. Most crustaceans are anamorphic in their postembryonic growth, successively adding new segments and appendages in their progressive development through a number of larval stages to the adult. Some degree of metamorphosis, however, has been superimposed on these anamorphic stages of development. This varies from the relatively simple adaptation of appendages for swimming to a complete reorganization of the animal for a parasitic way of life. Snodgrass (1956) considers metamorphosis in a number of groups of Crustacea, giving examples of the progressive morphological changes, and suggests that from the variety of examples observed it would appear that metamorphosis in the Crustacea has developed separately in each order. From these examples it is not possible to define clearly a common, specific point during development when metamorphosis occurs in all crustaceans. However, if one accepts the more liberal definition of crustacean metamorphosis recommended by Passano (1961)—a change in form at a particular point in the animal's life—and includes the physiological and behavioral changes, it is then possible to consider the gradual and successive changes leading up to this transition, the external factors influencing these changes, the internal reorganization accompanying the more obvious morphological modifications, and the mechanisms controlling and regulating this period of development.

It is unfortunate that any consideration of crustacean metamorphosis is severely limited to a few examples, incomplete within themselves, by the paucity of information on most aspects of development. Within a few of the Cirripedia and Decapoda there have been limited efforts to describe the external and internal changes that occur during larval development and metamorphosis and the mechanisms that regulate these changes. In a consideration of these few examples a brief account of the normal pattern of larval development is necessary, including the point during development at which metamorphosis occurs. Inasmuch as this point is dependent upon definition it will be found that the literature frequently contains conflicting views on the exact stage of development of a particular species that represents metamorphosis.

LARVAL DEVELOPMENT

In the present consideration, the larvae of the Cirripedia, Natantia, and Brachyura will serve as examples of three general types of metamorphosis in the free-living Crustacea. In the Cirripedia, development of the naupliar stages is a gradual progression that is interrupted by the extreme morphological modifications embodied in the cypris. In the Natantia, the gradual and progressive development of the zoeae is uninterrupted, and metamorphosis occurs without any comparable intermediate stage. In the Brachyura, many of the morphological characters of the intermediate stage, the megalopa, appear during development of the later zoeal stages, and metamorphosis to the first crab is neither as abrupt as observed in the Cirripedia nor has it the smooth transition observed in the Natantia.

The larval development of the Cirripedia has been described for a number of species, both from material in the plankton and from rearing the animals under laboratory conditions. There are six naupliar stages which, through successive molts, are distinguished by increased setation of the three pairs of appendages, changes in carapace shape, and the addition of carapace spines (Fig. 1A). The cypris larva, which does not feed, bears little resemblance to the nauplii, having modified antennules for attachment, six pair of thoracic appendages, and a completely different carapace shape (Fig. 1B). Following attachment to the substratum by a cementing substance produced by the cement glands, metamorphosis to the pinhead barnacle occurs and, although molting of the chitinous exoskeleton of the internal soma of the barnacle continues at regular intervals, the formation of external calcareous plates and their continuous growth marks a radical departure from either the nauplius or the cypris.

Larval development within the Natantia, which includes many of the shrimps, follows a variable number of zoeal stages (Fig. 2A). Through a series of molts, the thoracic appendages are added or increase in complexity, abdominal segments are added, and the appendages develop. In the development of *Palaemonetes kadiakensis*, metamorphosis to the first postlarva (Fig. 2B) occurs after six zoeal stages without any intermediate stage comparable to the cypris of the Cirripedia.

Within the Brachyura, or true crabs, zoeal stages progress through a number of molts, at which time appendage setation becomes more complex, segmentation of the abdomen is completed, and abdominal appendages are added (Fig. 3A, B, and C). The final zoeal molt gives rise to a megalopa (Fig. 3D)

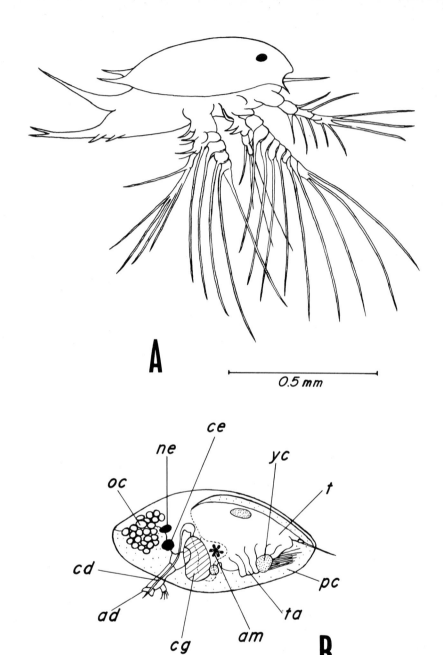

FIG. 1. Side view (A) of a late stage nauplius of *Balanus* and (B) of barnacle cypris. ad, adhesive disc; am, adductor muscle; cd, cement duct; ce, compound eye; cg, cement gland; ne, nauplius eye; oc, oil cell; pc, posterior mantle cavity; t, thorax; ta, thoracic appendages; yc, yellow cells. Fig. 1B adapted courtesy of Dr. L. J. Walley.

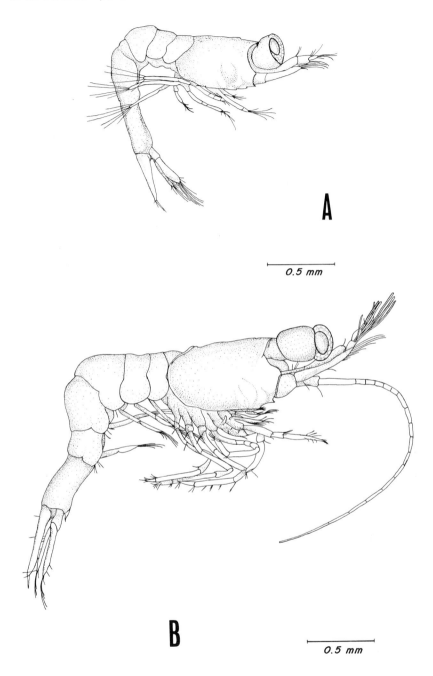

0.5 mm

A

B

0.5 mm

FIG. 2. Side view of first zoea (A) and first postlarva (B) of the shrimp *Thor floridanus* Kingsley. From A. C. Broad (1957).

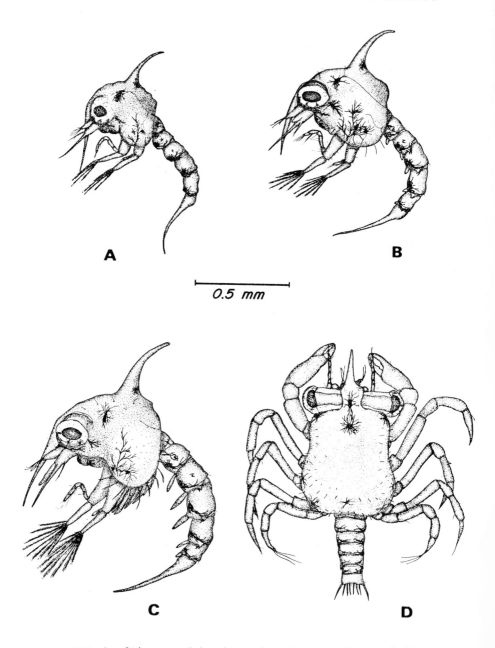

FIG. 3.   Side view of developing larval stages of the crab, *Sesarma reticulatum* Say. (A) first zoeal stage; (B) second zoeal stage; (C) third zoeal stage; (D) megalopa (dorsal view). After J. D. Costlow, Jr., and C. G. Bookhout (1962).

in which the zoeal appendages are further modified, the thoracic appendages become functional, and which, in general morphology and behavior, more closely resembles the juvenile crab. At the next molt the megalopa metamorphoses to the first crab stage.

The number of larval stages within any one species was once considered to be constant, but variability has been observed within the developmental stages of Crustacea representing a number of specific groups. Although there is general agreement on the occurrence of six naupliar stages prior to the cypris stage in development of *Balanus*, a number of authors have described "developmental intermediates" or minor differences in setation of nauplii of some species. Larvae of several species within the Natantia have also been shown to vary in minor morphological features or in number of developmental stages. Within the Brachyura the consistency in number of zoeal stages and morphological detail within any one stage is remarkable for the vast majority of species for which descriptions are available. The few exceptions, as well as the general question of regulation of molting and rate of development, will be considered later in relation to the development of endocrine mechanisms in the Crustacea.

THE EXTERNAL ENVIRONMENT

Crustacean larvae, the distributive phase of the life history, are exposed to and affected by the large number of environmental factors and combinations thereof found within estuarine and marine environments. Until techniques were developed that permitted the culture of crustacean larvae under controlled conditions of the laboratory, our limited knowledge of the effect of light, temperature, salinity, diet, and other physical factors of the environment was restricted to isolated observations on material obtained from the plankton. These observations were frequently made on larvae that could not be identified accurately, the conditions under which the larvae had developed were not known, and frequently the primary interest was some portion of larval development other than metamorphosis.

Although there have been numerous studies on the relationship between surface illumination and settling of barnacles, the actual effect of photoperiod, light intensity, or spectral distribution on larval development or metamorphosis in crustaceans is virtually unknown. Larvae of the crabs *Sesarma reticulatum* and *Rhithropanopeus harrisii* reared in photoperiods varying from 0 to 24 hours of light, but of equal intensity (100 foot-candles), showed no significant variation in time of metamorphosis nor was the survival of the larvae affected (Costlow and Bookhout, 1962).

There have been a number of studies on the effect of temperature and salinity on survival and rate of larval development but, apart from noting the general effect on rate of development, few of these have considered specifically the problem of temperature effects on metamorphosis. Studies on the larvae of the Brachyura have shown that in some species the zoeal stages may develop normally in a wide range of combinations of salinity and temperature, whereas in other species mortality is extremely high at the time of the final zoeal molt to the megalops. The majority of the larvae that attain the megalops stage under these adverse conditions however, do, metamorphose to the first crab. Studies on development of larvae of the blue crab, *Callinectes sapidus*, have demonstrated the way in which the interaction of salinity and temperature can specifically affect the time of metamorphosis to the first crab (Costlow, 1967). As shown in Figure 4, megalops maintained under a variety of temperature-salinity combinations showed a general delay in time of metamorphosis as the temperature decreased. In the lower temperatures, however, this delay in the time of metamorphosis was further accentuated by an increase in salinity. For a series of megalops maintained at 20 and 30° C, the Q_{10} values for time of metamorphosis increased from 2.34 at 20 parts per thousand (ppt) salinity to 3.24 at 40 ppt salinity. For megalops maintained at 15 and 25° C, the values increased from 3.82 to 659 Q_{10}, respectively. From these values it is apparent that the delay in time of metamorphosis is not simply a function of reduced temperature; however, an explanation must await a more complete understanding of the physiological and biochemical changes that accompany metamorphosis.

Studies on the culture of Cirripedia in the laboratory have suggested that there is considerable variability in the nutritional requirements between different species. Thus the nauplii of some species will develop normally to the cypris on a number of different species of unicellular algae and diatoms and metamorphose to the pinhead barnacle. With other species of barnacles, however, there is no development beyond the naupliar stage on an algal diet, and only when food of an animal source is made available will the larvae metamorphose. Within the Natantia some, but not all, species of unicellular algae constitute

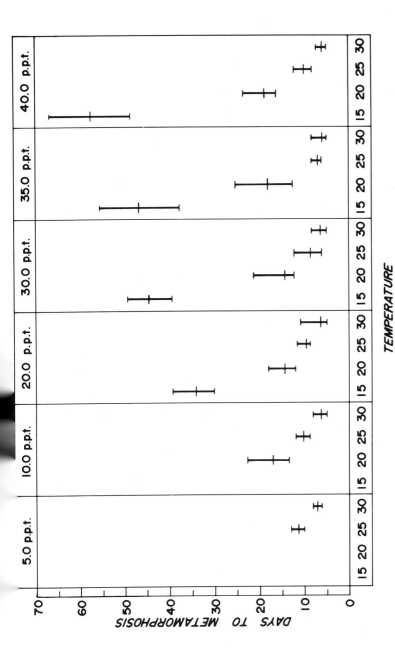

FIG. 4. Duration of megalops stage of *Callinectes sapidus* Rathbun maintained at 23 different combinations of salinity and temperature. The vertical line indicates the range, and the middle horizontal bar indicates the mean time to metamorphosis. From Costlow (1967).

an adequate diet for survival of the larvae and metamorphosis. Broad (1957a, b, and c) has clearly demonstrated that the time required for development and metamorphosis is directly associated with the diet and that use of *Artemia* nauplii as a food source reduces the time required for metamorphosis and also increases survival at metamorphosis to the postlarval stage.

Survival of Brachyura larvae is extremely low on a diet of unicellular algae alone, and metamorphosis rarely occurs. While a mixed diet of algae and *Artemia* nauplii may increase survival, the time required for metamorphosis is still considerably longer than that observed for zoeae and megalops maintained on either *Artemia* nauplii or on fertilized *Arbacia* eggs.

THE INTERNAL ENVIRONMENT

Although there have been detailed descriptions of the external morphological changes that occur at metamorphosis in a number of Crustacea, little is known about the internal reorganization that accompanies them. Descriptions exist of the organ systems of some adult Crustacea, and the cytological changes associated with molting, sexual differentiation, and gonad development are known for representative examples within most of the major groups. Only a few of these have been complemented by studies on the physiological processes involved or the biochemical changes that occur. With very few exceptions these studies have been limited to the juvenile or adult Crustacea and have not considered the complicated changes that occur during larval development or those associated with metamorphosis.

Detailed descriptions of the histological changes and general reorganization that accompany metamorphosis from the cypris to the pinhead barnacle are available (Doochin, 1951; Bernard and Lane, 1962). Walley (unpublished manuscript) has followed the cytological and histological changes during development of the six naupliar stages, the cypris, and the metamorphosed pinhead. The sequence of changes she observed in different organ systems during development and metamorphosis of *Balanus balanoides* is summarized in Table 1. Although there are some differences in the observations of these three authors, it is apparent that metamorphosis in the Cirripedia involves a highly complex series of changes. These changes, as shown in Table 1, are not confined to the cypris stage. Some are initiated during the naupliar stages, to be completed within the cypris stage, while other portions of the complex process of histolysis and reorganization take place during the cypris stage and carry over into the settled pinhead barnacle. These studies, plus the earlier observations by Walley (1964) that reorganization within the cypris stage is accompanied by a sequence of histolysis followed by phagocytosis, emphasizes that some similarities do exist between metamorphosis in barnacles and metamorphosis of holometabolous insects.

Although there have been isolated studies on particular tissues or cells within developing larvae of the Natantia and Brachyura, a complete description of the histological and cytological changes accompanying metamorphosis in these forms is not available.

Size, coupled with the difficulties in providing reasonable numbers of barnacle nauplii and cyprids of known age and stage, has discouraged studies on the physiology of development and metamorphosis in the Cirripedia. Clarke (1947) observed that barnacle larvae maintained a copper concentration that was higher than that found in sea water but also noted that this was not uncommon in invertebrates in which hemocyanins are utilized as a respiratory pigment. Bernard and Lane (1961) used histochemical techniques in an effort to determine changes in the absorption and excretion of copper during settlement and attachment of cyprids of *B. amphitrite niveus*. In the planktonic cypris, copper was concentrated within the loosely organized tissues of the anterior one third of the animal as well as in the food mass of the gut. Although they did not identify the actual mechanisms involved, they suggest that absorption takes place through the respiratory surfaces and excess copper is excreted through the epithelial lining of the hind gut. They further suggest that the high concentration of copper may be indicative of a dynamic exchange and that these same cells may be involved in the concentration of other ions from sea water during the process of metamorphosis.

Although there have not been any studies on enzyme systems in the larvae of the Cirripedia, or possible changes in these systems associated with metamorphosis of the cypris, there is indirect evidence that certain changes do occur. Carbonic anhydrase, associated with respiration in many animals, has been identified in the shell-forming mantle tissue of *B. improvisus* adults (Costlow, 1959). Cypris larvae that had been reared from nauplii under laboratory conditions were maintained in sea water solutions of carbonic anhydrase inhibitors and, while metamorphosis to the pinhead was not delayed, development of the typical six-plate shell of the adult barnacle never

TABLE 1

SEQUENCE OF CHANGES IN DIFFERENT ORGAN SYSTEMS DURING METAMORPHOSIS IN *BALANUS BALANOIDES*[a]

Organ	Naupliar Stages (I II III IV V VI)	Cypris — Free-swimming	Cypris — Settled	Adult
Antennule	Simple 4 segmented	4 segmented, highly specialized	Degenerate	Absent
Antennae	Biramous, swimming and feeding	Apparently	Absent	
Mandibles	Biramous, swimming and feeding	Rudimentary adult	mandible derived	Functional, feeding
Maxillae 1st and 2d	Rudimentary	Incorporated into rudimentary oral cone	Achieve adult form	Functional
Thoracic appendages	Rudiments develop in thoracic region	Function as swimming appendages	Internal histolysis, reorganization	Functional, feeding appendages
Cuticle	Thin and flexible (1–2μ) except on mouth parts	Bivalve carapce, hard (7μ); impermeable: cavities and thorax	thin (1–2μ) on mantle	Heavily calcified shell and cuticle over thorax and mantle
Epidermal and frontal glands	Scattered epidermal glands, 2 gland cells present in each; frontal horn glands similar, become frontal gland in cypris		Histolysis	Absent
Musculature	Naupliar muscles functional until nauplius-cypris molt	Functional cypris muscles	Rudimentary adult	Adult
Nervous system	Pre-oral brain, 2 post-oral ganglia; developing post-mandibular ganglia	Morphological re-arrangement and limited histolysis	Extensive histolysis and regeneration	Adult

Naupliar eye	Single median eye of 3 components:				2 lateral pigmented photoreceptors "ophthalmic ganglion"
	Development				
Compound eyes	Functional		Lost		Absent
Frontal filaments	Attached to lateral lobes of brain	Incorporated with compound eyes		Lost	Absent
Gut	Cuticle-lined esophagus and hindgut; midgut divided by constriction, feeding phase	Esophagus and hindgut closed; some cells sloughed from epithelium and digested, nonfeeding phase	Feeding resumed		
Digestive gland	Absent	Appear at junction of esophagus and midgut as outgrowth and enlarge	Functional		
Antennal glands	Present and functional	Degenerating	Absent		
Maxillary gland	Absent	Rudimentary	Presumed functional		Functional
Yellow cells	Absent	Appear in antennae	Migrate to posterior region of carapace after ecdysis	Disperse	Absent
Oil cells	Precursors around midgut constriction; in haemocoel; multinucleate	Migrate to anterior region of carapace after ecdysis	Gradually reduced and finally lost		
Haemocytes	Present	Become phagocytic	2d phase phagocytosis		?
Cement glands	Rudimentary	Completely developed	Functional		

[a]Adapted courtesy of Dr. L. J. Walley.

proceeded normally. If the metamorphosed pinhead barnacles were removed from the inhibitor to the normal environment within three to six days, normal shell development and growth were gradually resumed. If removal was delayed, however, to eight days following metamorphosis, normal shell development and growth did not occur. These results suggest that mechanisms may be present in the shell-forming tissues of the cypris and pinhead barnacle that determine, initiate, and direct the development of the typical six-plate shell within a ''critical period'' of four to six days following metamorphosis. Four of these plates are defined in the cuticle of recently settled pinheads, but if inhibition of shell growth occurs at this time the determinants may not function; normal development thus cannot be initiated, and the barnacle does not develop beyond the pinhead stage when the inhibitors are removed.

Although certain aspects of the physiology of adult Natantia and Brachyura have received considerable attention, comparable studies on the developing larvae have not been made. Of the few studies on the physiology of these larvae, most have either been made on planktonic forms, with little knowledge of the species or the particular stage of development (Zeuthen, 1947), or have been concerned primarily with changes other than those associated with metamorphosis (Vernberg and Costlow, 1966). Studies on the free amino acids in larvae of two species of Brachyura reared under controlled laboratory conditions have demonstrated a pattern in which the number of amino acids is sharply reduced during the megalops stage. This is followed by an increase immediately following metamorphosis to the first crab (Costlow and Sastry, 1966). In addition to the changes associated with metamorphosis, the relative abundance of a number of these amino acids is directly associated with the salinity and temperature of the environment in which development and metamorphosis occur.

Recent studies on osmoregulation in crab larvae suggest the changes that do occur are not directly associated with metamorphosis to the crab but actually take place late in zoeal development or at the time of the molt to the megalops (Kalber and Costlow, 1966). Working with larvae of *Rhithropanopeus harrisii* reared under controlled conditions in the laboratory it was found that osmoregulation in the final stage zoeae (stage IV) and the megalops is more comparable to that observed in the adult crab than the earlier zoeal stages. Subsequent studies (unpublished) have shown that the larvae of *Callinectes sapidus* show a gradual loss of hyperregulatory ability from the first to the seventh zoeal stage but rapidly regain it following the molt to the megalops stage.

BEHAVIOR

Reese (1964) has recently reviewed the literature on the behavior of marine animals, including the Crustacea. He comments on the extensive literature dealing with aggressive behavior in marine decapod Crustacea, but most of these studies are limited to the adult animals and have not considered other types of behavior. Research on the development of behavior during the larval stages or changes in behavior patterns associated with metamorphosis is very limited.

Most crustacean larvae are usually pelagic for a considerable portion of their development and, during this period, may be attracted to light. Toward the end of their pelagic phase they may either become negative to light or the response to light may be replaced by a positive response to gravity or the substratum. These differences have been observed in the field for many years, frequently with views on their adaptive value (Bousfield, 1954), and Knight-Jones and Morgan (1966) have recently reviewed the effects of pressure on marine animals, discussing in considerable detail the different types of response observed with nauplii and cypris larvae and with zoeae and megalops.

Within the Cirripedia the larval behavior at the time of settling has received considerable attention, and a number of factors are thought to be involved. In discussing the orientation of barnacles at settlement, Crisp and Barnes (1954) point out that the cypris larvae explore the available surfaces extensively before actually settling, and a detailed account of this exploratory behavior is given by Barnes (1955). The cypris settle in grooves and concavities, a tendency to which the term "rugophilic" has been applied (Crisp and Barnes, 1954). When settling in a groove, rugophilic settlement was usually characterized by rugotropism, the orientation of the anterior-posterior axis of the cypris to correspond with that of the groove, and was shown to be a tactile response to the contour of the surface. Established barnacle communities also affect settling, and the stimulus for this gregariousness is thought to be associated with a water insoluble chemical originating in the epicuticle of other barnacles.

Other environmental factors that have been shown to affect settling behavior of barnacle cypris are the bacterial film of the substrate, light, water currents, and surface angle. It should be noted, however, that settling precedes metamorphosis and that nothing is known of the physiological mechanisms underlieing the observed pattern of behavior or the way in which these develop.

Thompson (1903), working with the final larval stage of the hermit crab *Pagurus longicarpus*, found that development of the nervous system was a continuous process but that the musculature was further developed with each molt. At the time of the molt from the final zoeal stage to the glaucothoe, the musculature was complete. From his observations on shell selection he concluded that the response of the glaucothoe to shells was identical to that observed in adult crabs and that they showed a preference for dextral shells. Coffin (1954) observed that the glaucothoe, although not normally occupying the shell until the end of the stage, did behave toward shells in a manner similar to the adult crabs. Reese (1962), working with the glaucothoe of three species of hermit crab reared under laboratory conditions, concurred with the earlier findings. The inception of behavior of selecting shells occurs in the glaucothoe stage and is fully expressed when the animal encounters and enters its first shell. He further concluded that the preference for shells of a certain weight, as well as the ability of the glaucothoe to select between shells of different weights, appears to be innate.

THE MECHANISMS OF CONTROL

There has been very little interest in the mechanisms involved in the regulation of rate of larval development, molting in the larval stages, or metamorphosis. Although the endocrine systems and the processes they are thought to control in adult Crustacea have received considerable attention, little is known of the development of any endocrine system in crustacean larvae, the extent to which these mechanisms are altered during metamorphosis, or if osmoregulation, chromatophores, molting, and metamorphosis in the larval stages are controlled by the same endocrine mechanisms that function in the adult animals.

The zoeae of *R. harrisii* (Gould) have been shown to be isosmotic with seawater of 30 to 40 ppt salinity and to hyperregulate in lower salinities, except during the first diecdysis, when they remain isosmotic (Kalber and Costlow, 1966). Zoeae in the last few hours of proecdysis also hyperregulate against 40 ppt salinity. Eyestalk extirpation during the second zoeal stage caused the larvae to lose the ability to osmoregulate against 10 to 30 ppt salinity within two hours after the operation. Preliminary experiments, however, have shown that the removal of both eyestalks from the final zoeal stage, stage IV, has very little effect on osmoregulation. Inasmuch as osmoregulation during the fourth stage zoea and the megalopa appear to be more comparable to that observed in the adult crabs, one must conclude that the mechanisms within the eyestalks that are associated with osmoregulation have become differentiated well in advance of metamorphosis to the first crab.

Numerous investigators have studied the chromatophores and their control in a number of adult Crustacea (Kleinholtz, 1961; Fingerman, 1965). Chromatophores have been described from the larvae of many species, usually as an aid in identification, but little is known about their control or the manner in which this control may be affected by metamorphosis.

Larvae of the shrimp *Palaemonetes vulgaris* have been shown to respond to background coloration with changes in the chromatophores (Broch, 1960) and, although not specifying the source of the extracts, he further observed that the red chromatophore of an excised thoracic segment of a second zoea contracted on the addition of brain extract, expanded upon the addition of extract from the abdominal nerve cord, and contracted on the addition of eyestalk extract. From these results, Broch concluded that the endocrine control of chromatophores in larval *P. vulgaris* was comparable to that described for the adults.

Eyestalk extirpation in larvae of *P. pugio,* resulting in a response opposite to that reported for the adult animal, produced a pale condition that persisted through metamorphosis and indicated that there is some influence on the chromatophore system by the larval eyestalks (Hubschman, 1963). Further evidence of this influence has been found from injections of extracts of eggs and larval eyestalks of *Sesarma reticulatum* into eyestalkless fiddler crabs, *Uca pugilator* (Costlow and Sandeen, 1961). Chromatophorotropins were first identified within the eggs on the eleventh day of embryonic development. The activity of the chromatophorotropins increased gradually until the time of hatching, remained relatively constant throughout the nine days of zoeal development, and attained a higher level following development to the megalops stage. No appreciable change in chromatophorotropin level was noted following metamorphosis to the first crab, although extracts of adult *S. reticulatum* were found to have an activity approximately three times greater than the activity of the first crab stage.

Cycles of levels of activity of chromatophorotropins from eyestalk extracts have also been reported during the development of *S. reticulatum* larvae (Costlow, 1961). At the time of hatching the total activity was lowest, increased during the next 36 hours, and was reduced at the interval preceding the first larval molt.

During the intermolt period of the second zoea the activity increased again but was reduced immediately prior to and following the second larval molt, increasing again during the intermolt period of the third zoeal stage. This same pattern was observed for extracts of eyestalks of the megalops. It was further noted that zoeae that were delayed in molting usually showed a reduction in total activity of the extracts at the time when molting would normally be expected to occur. If ecdysis did not follow, the total activity of the extracts again increased. On the basis of these results, several hypotheses are possible. First, the chromatophorotropin within the eyestalks of the larvae may fluctuate because of changes in titer associated with molting, but the hormone is not actually involved in the molting process. Although evidence has accumulated since these experiments which suggests that the X organ sinus gland complex of the larvae is not functional, one should not completely ignore the second hypothesis, i.e., that the cycle of activity also applies to the molt-inhibiting hormone. If the X organ sinus gland were functional and concentration of the molt-inhibiting hormone followed a cycle similar to that described for the chromatophorotropins, ecdysis would be preceded by a reduced titer, followed by an increase in concentration of the molt-inhibiting hormone and another larval intermolt period. The pattern of reduced activity or titer prior to molting and increasing titer following molting would be repeated through all larval molts and carried over into the crab stages.

Shedding of the chitinous exoskeleton of the internal soma, the gills, and the mantle tissue occurs every three to five days in adult barnacles of temperate waters, but nothing is known about the mechanisms that control ecdysis. Histological studies of the body and mantle tissue have failed to disclose any tissues that might be associated with the control of molting. Within the Cirripedia, neurosecretory cells have been described from the central nervous system of the adult animals, but their function is not known, nor have comparable cells been described from any of the larval stages. The nauplii and adult animals have been shown to have chromatophorotropins that are similar in activity to those described from the eyestalks of adult and larval crabs, but the function is unknown. Removal of the paired eyes from recently metamorphosed pinhead barnacles, remnants of the naupliar eye that in the adult barnacles constitute the paired eyespots and the ''ophthalmic ganglion'' of Darwin, does not affect the molting frequency, but comparable experiments have not been successful with the late naupliar stages.

In adult malacostracans the efforts of numerous investigators have led to the concept that molting is controlled by two hormones: the molting hormone produced by the Y organ and the molt-inhibiting hormone produced by the X organ sinus gland complex of the eyestalks. Molting is initiated by the release of molting hormone from the Y organ, following the decrease in concentration of molt-inhibiting hormone from the X organ. If both the Y organs are removed, proecdysis is inhibited, but molting can be reinduced by implanting the glands into crabs from which they have been removed. Bilateral extirpation of the eyestalks, thus removing the X organ sinus gland complex, eliminates the molt-inhibiting hormone and molting is accelerated. If, however, both Y organs are absent, molting cannot be induced (Echalier, 1959; Passano, 1960).

Our knowledge of the development of these endocrine systems in the Macrura and Natantia is limited to three studies. Dahl (1957) described the embryology of the X organ in *Crangon allmanni*. No figures or information on the activity of the cells were included, however, and his consideration of further development was limited to the observation that organization of the X organs and the sensory pore complex is essentially similar to that found in the adults. Dahl did comment on the absence of neurosecretory activity in these cells when appropriate strains were used. Pyle (1943), describing the X organ from eggs and larvae of the lobster *Homarus americanus*, posed questions on the development and function of the X organ in the larval stages but did not present any evidence about their function. Hubschman (1963), describing the detailed changes in the larval and early postlarval eyestalks of a number of species of *Palaemonetes*, found that the sinus gland could be recognized by the time of the fifth larval stage but not earlier. Even at the fifth larval stage the sinus gland was not a functional complex, but following metamorphosis it developed its definitive form. During larval life it was not possible to detect the accumulation of secretory material, but by the time of the third or fourth postlarval molt the sinus gland assumed functional importance. In addition, the ganglionic X organs found in the adult eyestalks were not functional during larval development, but secretory activity could be demonstrated in shrimp that completed several postlarval molts. Eyestalk extirpation did not produce any acceleration in the larval molting frequency or in the time of metamorphosis of the *Palaemonetes* larvae. Hubschman suggests that the molting cycle in the larvae, in the absence of a functional X organ sinus gland complex, proceeds uninhibited. He further suggests that the rapid molting cycle in *Palaemonetes* larvae, i.e., every two days, results from the production of a molting hormone by a larval molting gland, "if one exists," but is unable to offer any evidence to its location.

Within the larvae of the Brachyura, and the closely related Anomura, the limited studies on development of endocrine systems associated with larval molting and metamorphosis have also produced a poorly defined picture. Orlamunder (1942) found cells corresponding to the X organ of adults in eyes of developing embryos of *Birgus latro*, and Pyle (1943) described the same structure from eggs and larvae of the crab, *Pinnotheres maculatus*. Because of rearing problems, Pyle was not able to follow the development of the larvae through successive stages, but he did indicate that the sinus gland was not evident in late embryos or in the first zoeal stage. Neither Orlamunder (1942) nor Pyle (1953) considered the possible role of these structures in molting and metamorphosis of the larvae.

As had already been pointed out, the consistency that has normally been ascribed to the number of zoeal stages and molting frequency within any one species of the Brachyura was interpreted to mean that larval molting and rate of development were controlled by the same mechanism. Two exceptions to this consistency were the larvae of *Callinectes sapidus* and *Menippe mercenaria* in which an "extra" zoeal stage was first reported late in zoeal development under laboratory conditions. A zoea, comparable to the "extra" eighth zoeal stage of *C. sapidus*, subsequently has been described from the plankton. Detailed morphological studies on the larval development of *C. sapidus* provided additional evidence that "extra" stages and "intermediate" stages were not unusual and gave some support to the hypothesis that larval molting and rate of development were not necessarily controlled by one mechanism (Costlow, 1965). The three general types of variability that were observed in the study of *C. sapidus* larvae suggested that at least two mechanisms were involved: one that controlled molting and a second, normally synchronized with the first, that regulated the rate of morphological development in the larval stages. In the first type of variability, molting without any perceptible changes in morphology, the frequency of molting was maintained while the mechanism associated with regulation of development was inhibited. In the second type of variability, the "skipping" or elimination of a larval stage, the molting frequency was constant but the mechanism controlling development was accelerated. In the third type of variability, the molt resulted in a larva that combined morphological characters normally attributed to two zoeal stages. In these, the constant molting pattern would appear to have been preceded by normal or accelerated development in the anterior portion of the larvae. In the posterior portion, however, morphological development was inhibited or normal. These observations suggested that the variability in morphology is associated with the malfunction of a regulatory mechanism. The fact that the variability is limited to the later larval stages was attributed to a gradual decline in the secretory activity of an endocrine mechanism rather than an abrupt cessation of activity.

In the absence of a complete description of the structure of the larval eye and any functional endocrine sites that may appear during development, it was necessary to begin with the hypothesis that the larval eyestalks did contain sites of endocrine activity comparable to those found in the adult crabs. If the X organ sinus gland complex of the larval eyestalks were functional, producing molt-inhibiting hormone and thus regulating the frequency of larval molts, removal of both larval eyestalks should result in accelerated molting within the zoeal and megalops stages. Eyestalk extirpation experiments on the larvae of three different species of Brachyura have suggested that the adult endocrine systems thought to control molting begin to function at different times in different species and do not function during zoeal development (Costlow, 1963a, 1966a and b).

In *C. sapidus*, metamorphosis to the first crab stage is accelerated considerably by the extirpation of both megalops eyestalks within twelve hours following the final zoeal molt (Fig. 5). If both eyestalks are removed on the first to fifth days following the final zoeal molt, the time of metamorphosis is not affected. Removal of one eyestalk on zero day of megalops life, the first twelve hours following the final zoeal molt, does not affect the time of metamorphosis, but extirpation on the first to fourth days resulted in a significant delay. That the acceleration observed is not a short-term effect is demonstrated by comparing the time of the first four postlarval molts for crabs that metamorphosed from megalops with both eyestalks removed on zero day, on the first to fifth days, and those that had only one eyestalk removed (Fig. 6). Acceleration of molting continued only in those crabs from which both eyestalks were removed on zero day of megalops life, although the exaggerated increase in size was the same for all eyestalkless crabs. Observations on the metamorphosis of eyestalkless megalops of *C. sapidus* suggest that the X organ sinus gland complex is not functional within the first twelve hours of megalops life. If both eyes are removed during this period, i.e., before secretion of the molt-inhibiting hormone is initiated, metamorphosis is accelerated.

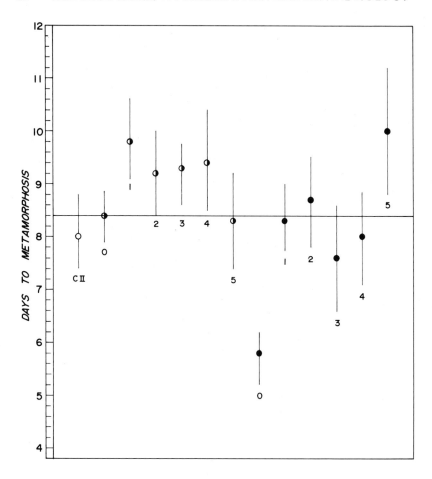

FIG. 5. Time required for metamorphosis of *Callinectes sapidus* Rathbun megalops of control series (horizontal line), megalops with antenna removed (CII), megalops with one eye removed on zero to fifth day following the final zoeal molt (◑), and megalops with both eyes removed on zero to fifth day (●). Vertical line indicates the least significant difference of each series (LSD = SD × T_{05}). From Costlow (1963a).

If both eyestalks are removed after secretion has begun (first to fourth days), the time of metamorphosis is not accelerated. Unfortunately, zoeae from which both eyestalks were removed at any point in development did not survive long enough to provide for a comparison of zoeal molting frequency.

   In an effort to determine the effect of eyestalk extirpation on molting frequency of the zoeae, similar experiments were

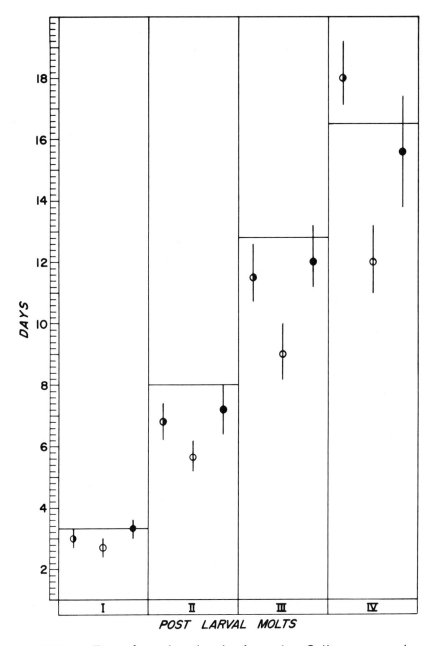

FIG. 6. Time of postlarval molts for crabs, *Callinectes sapidus* Rathbun, which metamorphosed from megalops of control series (horizontal line); megalops with one eye removed (◑); megalops with both eyes removed on zero day following the final zoeal molt (○); and megalops with both eyes removed on first to fifth days following the final zoeal molt (●). Vertical line indicates the least significant difference of each series (LSD = SD × T_{05}). From Costlow (1963a).

conducted on the larvae of another crab, *Sesarma reticulatum.*
In these experiments, however, extirpation was affected as early
as stalked eyes developed in the zoeae, stage II. Removal of
one eyestalk from the zoeae of *S. reticulatum* during any period
of development did not affect the molting frequency or the number
of larval stages. Removal of both eyestalks, simultaneously or
individually at different times of development, resulted in the
acceleration of metamorphosis of the megalops to the first
crab, but only when extirpation occurred prior to a critical
period; fourth day of megalops development. The earlier zoeal
molts were not accelerated by eyestalk extirpation at any time.
The acceleration in the time of the final larval molt was
accompanied by incomplete development, or a "second megalops"
stage. The "second megalops," through a second accelerated
molt, then metamorphosed to a true first-crab stage. The
"second megalops" actually did not represent a discrete stage
in development but rather appeared to be a later period of
development that had been interrupted by the occurrence of
a premature molt. The acceleration of molting within the
eyestalkless megalops and the absence of acceleration in the
zoeal molts suggest that it is within the megalops stage that
the X organ sinus gland complex is first activated in this
species (or possibly late in the stage III zoeae). Initiation is
not as abrupt as that observed in *C. sapidus* megalops, and it
would appear that activity of the X organ increases until a
certain titer of molt-inhibiting hormone is reached. This titer
is sufficient to extend the intermolt period of the megalops
beyond that normally observed for the previous zoeal stages.
Removal of the eyestalks after this level has been reached does
not affect the frequency of molting.

The manner by which this titer is attained is suggested
from the results of removing one eyestalk early in development
and the other later in development and also by the simultaneous
removal of both eyestalks at different periods in larval development. Removal of only one eyestalk did not produce a second
megalops stage, nor did it result in acceleration of the final
larval molt. Thus, the activity of the one X organ sinus gland
is apparently sufficient to regulate the molting frequency of the
megalops if it remains functional throughout larval life. However,
if one eyestalk is removed during the final zoeal stage (stage III)
and the remaining eyestalk is removed at different periods in
megalops development, a sufficiently high level of activity of
the one gland has apparently been reached by the fifth day of
megalops development to regulate metamorphosis and prevent
acceleration even if the remaining eyestalk is then removed.

Also, if only one eyestalk remains up to the fourth day of megalops life and is then removed, a higher percent of second megalops result than if both eyestalks are intact through the fourth day and then removed. The degree of acceleration of metamorphosis is greater in megalops with only one functional eyestalk than in megalops that have intact eyestalks up to the fourth day of megalops life. Thus, it would appear that the activity of the X organ sinus gland of one eyestalk is not equal to the combined activity of two, and the resultant titer of molt-inhibiting hormone at any point prior to the fourth day is not sufficient in one-eyed larvae to completely prevent acceleration of metamorphosis and/or the resultant second megalops stage if the second eyestalk is removed on the fourth day.

While removal of both eyestalks early in zoeal development of *S. reticulatum* did not result in acceleration of zoeal molts, it did result in a small number of zoeae which, at the time of the molt to the megalops stage, molted instead to an "extra" or supernumary zoeal stage. This occurred only in some zoeae from which both eyestalks were removed prior to the first day of the stage III zoeae, whereas others molted directly to the megalops stage. The stage IV zoeae, while continuing to develop toward the more advanced morphological condition of the megalops stage, retained many of the characteristics normally associated with the zoeae. This extra stage cannot be attributed to a change in the molting frequency of the larvae but rather suggests that early in larval development a second endocrine site or storage organ is developed within the zoeal eyestalks. The product of this site would appear to regulate the rate of morphological changes associated with a consistent number of zoeal stages, the transition from the final zoeal stage to the megalops stage, and possibly the changes involved in the metamorphosis of the megalops to the first crab stage. It is suggested that the activity of this second site begins during the final zoeal stage (stage III) and, if both eyestalks are removed prior to this point in development, the normal transition from the final zoeal stage to the megalops stage is not possible. The mechanisms controlling molting frequency in the larvae, however, are not affected, and since morphological development has been retarded, an additional zoeal stage results rather than the megalops.

Inasmuch as *S. reticulatum* normally has only three zoeal stages during its complete development, one may question if there was a sufficiently long period of development to permit detection of any significant reduction in length of intermolt period that might result from removal of both eyestalks. That is, development of the three zoeal stages of *S. reticulatum* is normally completed in approximately 10 days at 25°C. The first zoeal stage does not have stalked eyes and occupies approximately three days of this total period. Only in the remaining two zoeal stages, when the eyes are stalked, can extirpation be conducted. If both eyes were removed on day one of stage II and one day was allowed for recovery of the larvae, a total of approximately five days of zoeal development remain in which acceleration of the additional two molts could occur.

Further evidence for acceleration of molting during zoeal development and the mechanisms that control rate of development and metamorphosis was sought in the development of *Rhithropanopeus harrisii,* a species of mud crab that normally has four zoeal stages and one megalops.

Removal of both eyestalks as early as the first day of the second zoeal stage did not result in a consistent, significant acceleration of any of the larval molts, further substantiating the hypothesis that the X organ sinus gland complex does not contribute to the control of molting in the zoeal stages. Also, there was no acceleration of the time of metamorphosis to the first crab, and the first indication of any decrease in duration of the intermolt period for crabs that metamorphosed from eyestalkless larvae was at the time of the third postlarval molt. Thus, it would appear that the X organ sinus gland complex of *R. harrisii* is not functional until some time after metamorphosis to the first crab and further demonstrates the extent of variability in mode of action and time of endocrine control of molting within larval stages of the Brachyura.

Removal of both eyestalks from zoeae of *R. harrisii* prior to the third day, stage III (Fig. 7), resulted in 45 to 70 percent of the larvae passing through an extra or supernumerary zoeal stage before molting to the megalops (Fig. 8A). From 1 to 10 percent of the destalked zoeae, depending upon the time of eyestalk extirpation, passed through a second extra zoeal stage, stage VI (Fig. 8B). Eyestalk removal after the third day (stage III) did not result in supernumerary zoeae. These results support the hypothesis that the larval eyestalks also provide an additional hormone that is responsible for the control of the rate of morphological development. Since removal of the eyestalks normally delays rather than prevents metamorphosis, the actual source of the hormone is apparently located in a site other than the eyestalks. It has been demonstrated that while larval molting in some insects is under the control of a hormone secreted by the brain, it is the *presence* of a second hormone, the juvenile

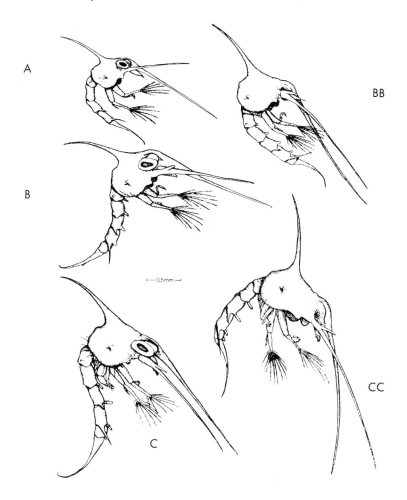

FIG. 7. Normal zoeal of the crab, *Rhithropanopeus harrisii* (Gould), and zoeae from which both eyestalks have been removed. *A*: Second zoea; *B*: third zoea; *C*: fourth zoea; *BB*, third zoea that molted from eyestalkless second zoea; *CC*; fourth zoea from which both eyestalks were moved in stage II. From Costlow (1966b).

hormone, secreted by the corpus allatum that determines the degree of morphological development and metamorphosis (see Chapter 3). If the corpus allatum is removed prematurely, metamorphosis occurs. If it is implanted into a fifth-instar nymph that would normally metamorphose to the adult, nymphal characters are retained following the molt. The appearance of supernumerary zoeal stages in the crabs *S. reticulatum* and

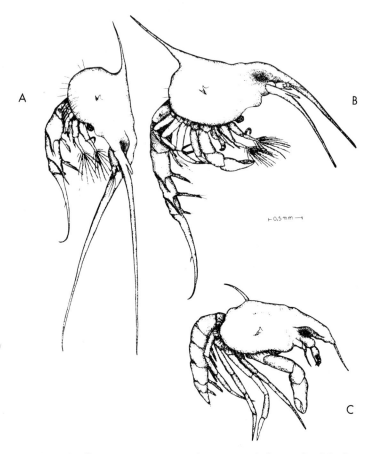

FIG. 8. Supernumerary zoeal stages of the crab, *Rhithropanopeus harrisii* (Gould) produced by the removal of both eyestalks early in larval development. A; First "extra" zoea (stage V); B: second "extra" zoea (stage VI); C: megalops that molted from eyestalkless stage VI zoea. From Costlow (1966b).

R. harrisii is caused by the removal of the eyestalks and thus by the *absence* of some hormone.

The normal rate of morphological development of larvae of these crabs is dependent upon the presence of the eyestalks, and inasmuch as the hormone that they elaborate contributes not to the continuation of larval stages but rather to the progressive morphological changes associated with the adult, it cannot be compared to the juvenile hormone of the insects. Additional studies will be required to determine the source of this hormone, the manner in which its secretion is coordinated with the hormones that control molting in the larvae, and to determine if as in insects the central nervous system and other sites of endocrine activity are influenced by other physiological processes during larval development.

Within the larvae, evidence for the existence of the Y organ that produces the molting hormone in the adult is fragmentary and very indirect. It has not been described in the larvae of any of the Natantia or Brachyura. In adult crabs, the removal of the Y organ results in the inhibition of premolt growth of regenerating appendages, and the implantation of this gland stimulates limb regeneration (Echalier, 1956; Jyssum and Passano, 1957). In some insects that normally lose the ability to regenerate appendages after metamorphosis to the adult, the implantation of corpora allata from larval forms (source of juvenile hormone) restores the capacity for regeneration (Pflugfelder, 1939). Studies on autotomy and regeneration of the chela of megalops of *C. sapidus* have shown that the complete and functional claw was regenerated at the time of metamorphosis if autotomy were induced prior to the fourth day following the final zoeal molt (Costlow, 1963b). If autotomy of the claw occurred later than the fourth day of megalops life, the regenerating appendage first appeared as a limb bud at metamorphosis and was not normally functional until after the first or second postlarval molt. One interpretation of these results is that prior to the megalops stage, only the Y organ is present and functional in the zoeae, providing a molting hormone and maintaining a molting frequency of three to four days throughout zoeal life. Regeneration of the complete claw, if autotomy occurs on or before the third day of megalops life, is possible because either the Y organ is sufficiently active or enough molting hormone is present to initiate regeneration and also stimulate metamorphosis to the first crab on the eighth day. If autotomy occurs after the third day, the titer of the molt-inhibiting hormone produced by the now-functional X organs of the eyestalks has increased to a point where the comparable amount of molting hormone cannot initiate regeneration of the complete claw and also induce molting or

If removal of the source of a hormone that controls molting or rate of morphological development in the larvae interferes with these processes, in theory the replacement of the hormone in sufficiently high concentration at an appropriate period of development should restore the proper endocrine balance, and development should proceed in the normal manner. As shown in Table 2, the injection of extracts from a variety of larval and adult tissues did not reduce the number of supernumerary zoeae of *R. harrisii* that resulted when both eyestalks were

TABLE 2

NUMBER OF ZOEA INJECTED AND EFFECT OF VARIOUS EXTRACTS ON NUMBER OF LARVAL STAGES OF *RHITHROPANOPEUS HARRISII* (GOULD)[a]

No. Zoea Injected	Zoea Sur. Injection		Time of Injection	Condition of Eyestalks	Injection Extract	Concentration in Sea Water[b]	SV Zoea		SVI Zoea		Megalops		Crab	
	No.	Per-cent					No.	Per-cent	No.	Per-cent	No.	Per-cent	No.	Per-cent
60	30	50.0	D2SII	Normal	25% Seawater		0	0.0	0	0.0	20	66.7	20	66.7
60	12	20.0	D2 SI	Normal	Sudan IV + oil		0	0.0	0	0.0	6	50.0	3	25.0
18	9	50.0	D3 SI	Normal	Sudan IV + oil		0	0.0	0	0.0	4	44.4	4	44.4
60	22	36.7	D1 SII	Normal	Sudan IV + oil		0	0.0	0	0.0	18	81.8	17	77.3
50	30	60.0	D2 SII	Normal	Sudan IV + oil		0	0.0	0	0.0	26	86.7	26	86.7
50	24	48.0	D1 SIII	Normal	Sudan IV + oil		0	0.0	0	0.0	18	75.0	15	62.5
50	21	42.0	D2 SIII	Normal	Sudan IV + oil		0	0.0	0	0.0	14	66.7	14	66.7
50	25	50.0	D3 SIII	Normal	Sudan IV + oil		0	0.0	0	0.0	20	90.0	16	64.0
30	25	83.3	D1 SIV	Normal	Sudan IV + oil		0	0.0	0	0.0	17	68.0	13	52.0
30	14	46.7	D2 SIV	Normal	Sudan IV + oil		0	0.0	0	0.0	9	64.3	7	50.0
20	17	85.0	D1 Meg	Normal	Sudan IV + oil		0	0.0	0	0.0	17	100.0	11	54.7
35	10	28.6	D3 SIII	2 off D3 SIII	Sudan IV + oil		0	0.0	0	0.0	0	0.0	0	0.0
56	17	30.4	D2 SII	Normal	D1 SIV EE	10:1	0	0.0	0	0.0	5	29.4	0	0.0
90	24	26.7	D2 SII	2 off D1 SII	D1 SIV EE	10:1	5	20.8	4	16.7	1	4.2	1	4.2
37	9	24.3	D2 SII	2 off D1 SII	D1 SIV EE	100:1	2	22.2	2	22.2	1	11.1	0	0.0
20	2	10.0	D2 SII	Normal	D1 SIV EE	100:1	0	0.0	0	0.0	2	100.0	0	0.0
35	12	34.3	Mixed SII	2 off D1 SII	D1 SIV EE	100:1	5	41.7	2	16.7	1	8.3	0	0.0
20	12	60.0	Mixed SII	Normal	D1 SIV EE	100:1	0	0.0	0	0.0	6	50.0	6	50.0

44	25	56.8	D3 SII	Normal	D2 SIV EE	10:1	0	0.0	0	0.0	18	72.0	8	32.0
10	4	40.0	D3 SII	2off D2 SII	D2 SIV EE	10:1	4	100.0	4	100.0	0	0.0	0	0.0
47	4	8.5	D3 SII	2off D2 SII	Mixed SIV EE	100:1	3	75.0	1	25.0	2	50.0	2	50.0
38	17	44.7	D3 SII	Normal	Mixed SIV EE	100:1	0	0.0	0	0.0	9	52.9	5	29.4
50	19	38.0	D2 SII	2off D1 SII	Mixed SIV EE	400:1	16	84.2	4	21.1	7	36.8	5	26.3
150	87	58.0	D1 SII	Normal	D1 SIII CNS	100:1	0	0.0	0	0.0	59	67.8	44	50.6
120	31	25.8	D2 SII	Normal	D1 SIII CNS	10:1	0	0.0	0	0.0	20	64.5	16	51.6
150	84	56.0	D1 SII	Normal	D2 SIII CNS	100:1	0	0.0	0	0.0	62	73.8	47	56.0
160	54	33.8	D1 SII	Normal	D2 SIII CNS	10:1	0	0.0	0	0.0	37	68.5	33	61.1
80	67	83.8	D1 SII	Normal	D3 SIII CNS	10:1	0	0.0	0	0.0	39	58.2	20	29.9
40	4	10.0	D2 SI	Normal	D1 SIV CNS	10:1	0	0.0	0	0.0	3	75.0	3	75.0
40	8	20.0	D2 SI	Normal	D1 SIV CNS	100:1	0	0.0	0	0.0	3	37.5	3	37.5
30	29	96.7	D1 SII	Normal	D1 SIV CNS	10:1	0	0.0	0	0.0	20	69.0	20	69.0
40	29	72.5	D1 SII	Normal	D1 SIV CNS	100:1	0	0.0	0	0.0	21	72.4	21	72.4
97	39	40.2	D2 SII	Normal	D1 SIV CNS	10:1	0	0.0	0	0.0	10	25.6	10	25.6
27	9	33.3	D2 SII	2off D1 SII	D1 SIV CNS	10:1	3	33.3	2	22.2	1	11.1	0	0.0
45	25	55.6	D2 SII	Normal	D1 SIV CNS	100:1	0	0.0	0	0.0	12	48.0	5	20.0
34	13	38.2	Mixed SII	2off D1 SII	D1 SIV CNS	100:1	3	23.1	3	23.1	1	7.7	1	7.7
20	3	15.0	Mixed SII	Normal	D1 SIV CNS	100:1	0	0.0	0	0.0	1	33.3	1	33.3
130	113	86.9	D1 SIII	Normal	D1 SIV CNS	10:1	0	0.0	0	0.0	74	65.5	44	38.9
45	33	73.3	D2 SII	Normal	D2 SIV CNS	10:1	0	0.0	0	0.0	28	84.8	24	72.7
50	18	36.0	D2 SII	Normal	D2 SIV CNS	100:1	0	0.0	0	0.0	15	83.3	15	83.3
20	8	40.0	D3 SII	Normal	D2 SIV CNS	10:1	0	0.0	0	0.0	3	37.5	2	25.0
14	10	71.4	D3 SII	2off D2 SII	D2 SIV CNS	10:1	3	30.0	2	20.0	1	10.0	0	0.0
15	9	60.0	D3 SII	Normal	Mixed SIV CNS	100:1	0	0.0	0	0.0	4	44.4	4	44.4
20	10	50.0	D3 SII	2off D2 SII	Mixed SIV CNS	100:1	3	30.0	1	10.0	1	10.0	0	0.0
140	73	52.1	D1 SII	Normal	Adult optic nerve	50:1	1	1.4	0	0.0	59	80.8	55	75.3
100	55	55.0	D2 SIII	Normal	Adult optic nerve	85:1	2	3.6	0	0.0	25	45.4	13	23.6
100	53	53.0	D2 SII	Normal	Adult optic nerve	85:1	0	0.0	0	0.0	18	34.0	17	32.1

TABLE 2 (continued)

No. Zoea Injected	Zoea Sur. Injection		Time of Injection	Condition of Eyestalks	Injection Extract	Concentration in Sea Water[b]	SV Zoea		SVI Zoea		Megalops		Crab	
	No.	Per-cent					No.	Per-cent	No.	Per-cent	No.	Per-cent	No.	Per-cent
61	46	75.4	D1 SIV	Normal	Adult optic nerve	120:1	0	0.0	0	0.0	40	87.0	33	71.7
100	72	72.0	D2 SIV	Normal	Adult optic nerve	120:1	0	0.0	0	0.0	49	68.1	39	54.2
60	45	75.0	D2 SII	Normal	Adult "Y" organ	160:1	0	0.0	0	0.0	21	46.7	16	35.6
110	8	0.7	Mixed SII	Normal	Adult "Y" organ	100:1	0	0.0	0	0.0	5	62.5	3	37.5
45	29	64.4	D1 SIII	Normal	Adult "Y" organ	100:1	0	0.0	0	0.0	17	58.6	13	44.8
60	38	63.3	D2 SIII	Normal	Adult "Y" organ	160:1	0	0.0	0	0.0	27	71.0	17	44.7
40	19	47.5	D1 SIV	Normal	Adult "Y" organ	100:1	0	0.0	0	0.0	6	31.6	5	26.3
25	17	68.0	D2 SIV	Normal	Adult "Y" organ	160:1	0	0.0	0	0.0	14	82.3	11	64.7
200	95	47.5	D1 SII	Normal	Juvenile hormone		0	0.0	0	0.0	11	11.6	0	0.0
200	105	52.5	D2 SII	Normal	Juvenile hormone		0	0.0	0	0.0	6	5.7	0	0.0

[a] From Costlow (1966b). D = day; S = zoeal stage; EE = eyestalk extract; CNS = central nervous system.
[b] Number of eyestalks, central nervous systems, optic nerves, or Y organs per cc sea water.

removed. Also, the pattern of development of normal zoeae was not altered by the injection of extracts from larval and adult tissues. The injection of insect juvenile hormone extract of unknown titer into normal, eyed larvae did not alter the pattern of morphological development or the frequency of molting. It should be noted, however, that in spite of the fact that approximately 50 percent of the zoeae survived the injection and completed the normal four zoeal stages, an unusually small number molted to the megalops stage. None of these metamorphosed to the first crab. If the juvenile hormone extract had no effect on the developing crab larvae one might expect survival to the first crab to be comparable to that observed when extracts of sea water or Sudan IV plus oil were used. With the latter extracts, 25.0 to 86.17 percent of the injected larvae did successfully metamorphose to the first crab. Thus, while the injections of insect juvenile homone did not discernibly affect the morphological development of the larvae, it is possible that the inability to metamorphose to the first crab was directly associated with the extract.

CONCLUSIONS

Earlier studies on metamorphosis in the Crustacea were confined largely to observations on material obtained from the plankton, for efforts to culture the larvae in the laboratory had been unsuccessful. Within recent years, however, techniques have been developed that permit the rearing of larvae of most of the major groups within the Crustacea. Development, from early embryology through metamorphosis and into the post-larval stages, can be followed under controlled environmental conditions and, with some species, survival as high as 80 percent has been attained consistently. Thus, it is now possible to consider many aspects of metamorphosis on a level that was not previously feasible with planktonic material.

For purposes of discussion it is convenient to consider the external environment, the internal environment, behavior, and the mechanisms of control, but it is obvious that a study of "metamorphosis" cannot be restricted to any one of these any more than it can be defined as a single point in time. For a more complete understanding of the complex morphological, physiological, biochemical, and behavioral changes that together constitute metamorphosis, it is imperative that we have a clearer picture of the cytological and histological changes as development progresses. This should extend well into the period of embryonic development, since some systems—e.g., the chromatophores—have been shown to develop well before hatching of the larvae. An understanding of the internal morphology of all developmental stages is also essential because, as has been described for the cypris and the megalops, the internal reorganization is not necessarily confined to a particular stage but may represent a gradual progression through a number of earlier stages. Evidence that the X organ sinus gland complex of *R. harrisii* does not begin to function until well after metamorphosis to the first crab suggests that a more thorough examination of the early postlarval stages is also required.

Advances in our understanding of morphological changes must be complemented by comparable efforts toward the elucidation of the underlying physiological and biochemical processes. Using the techniques that are available, or by modifying them to the microlevel, it should be possible to determine the enzyme systems involved during development, the time at which they appear, the role they play in metamorphosis, and changes that may occur during the transition from the pelagic existence of the larvae to the more benthic life of many of the adults. Problems dealing with the synthesis, elaboration, and utilization of proteins, carbohydrates, and lipids during the development of most crustaceans have been neglected, and little is known of the qualitative or quantitative aspects of biosynthesis during embryonic and larval development. At what point in larval development are specific proteins first synthesized, and what tissues are associated with their elaboration? When does heterogeneity first become apparent, and in what way are the larval patterns modified by metamorphosis, early postlarval development, and sexual differentiation? Is the reduction in number of free amino acids during zoeal development followed by an increase at the time of metamorphosis, associated with osmoregulation, or does it represent the utilization of these units in some phase of "metamorphosis" that extends throughout most of the zoeal life?

The interrelationship between the "external" environment and the "internal" environment is an equally important facet to our understanding of metamorphosis. Why, in larvae of some estuarine species, do different optimum conditions of salinity and temperature exist for each stage while survival of larvae of other species is not dependent upon narrow limits of these two environmental factors? In what ways are larval development, as well as metamorphosis, affected by pressure, light of different intensities and wavelength, O_2 and CO_2 tensions, organic and

inorganic constituents of sea water, and differences in quality
and quantity of available food? In what way is development affected
by fluctuations in any one or all of these factors, and is acclima-
tion of the larvae to any one or all of these factors affected by
changes in other parameters of the environment?

The complete picture of metamorphosis will also depend
upon a clearer understanding of the various mechanisms controlling the rate and sequence of larval development, larval molting,
osmotic balance, sexual differentiation, and metamorphosis
itself. Here the studies on internal morphology should contribute
to the picture of where and when these systems develop, the time
at which they become functional, and the changes that may occur
during development through the juvenile animal. This should
involve a clear delineation of the sites or mechanisms that are
present within the larval eyestalks and other portions of the
developing central nervous system. What activates the elaboration
of neurosecretory products or hormones at predetermined
intervals within the regular pattern of larval development?
In what way is the loss or disruption of these mechanisms by
extirpation compensated for by other portions of the nervous
system? Is there an association between the results obtained
from experiments on eyestalk extirpation of larval stages—i.e.,
the production of large supernumerary larvae—and the observations on the natural occurrence of gigantism and neotony
in larvae of some crustaceans? In what ways are these systems
coordinated and, at the cellular level, what is the nature of the
response? Studies on the chemical structure of hormones in
larval Crustacea should provide a more basic understanding of
the origin and evolution of groups within the Arthropoda and
provide for further research on similarities in the synthesis
of the basic chemical components associated with early embryonic
and larval development in many of the invertebrates.

As information on the larval mechanisms becomes available
we should constantly reexamine the existing concepts of endocrine
control in the adult Crustacea. Eyestalk extirpation during a
specific time in the megalops of *C. sapidus* has resulted in
crabs that continue to follow an accelerated molting pattern.
Other crabs, metamorphosing from megalops that had lost both
eyestalks 12 hours later, do not display an acceleration of the
molting frequency. If molting in adult crabs is dependent upon
the activation of the Y organ by a reduced titer of molt-
inhibiting hormone from the X-organ sinus gland complex, has
the Y organ of megalops of the first series remained activated?
If so, what source of molt-inhibiting hormone, in the absence of
both eyestalks, serves to regulate the normal frequency of molting

in megalops of the second series? If an alternate source of molt-inhibiting hormone exists within the central nervous system of the megalops, how is it activated in the megalops of the second series, and why is it not activated in megalops in which both eyestalks were removed only 12 hours earlier? Crabs that metamorphosed from megalops of both series show a much greater increase in carapace size at molting than crabs that metamorphosed from normal megalops. Thus, while molting initially may be controlled by a hormone produced and stored by endocrine sites within the eyestalks, the regulation of size increase, or water uptake, cannot be under the control of this same hormone. If separate hormones are involved, what is their chemical difference and in what way is their action coordinated in normal adults?

Metamorphosis in the Crustacea remains "a problem in developmental biology." The solution to the problem does not lie in isolated studies on the cellular reorganization, the physiological changes, the chemical structure of the hormones, or in the injection of insect juvenile hormone into larval stages, but rather through an integrated approach that recognizes that development involves the animal in all of its parts.

REFERENCES

Barnes, H. 1955. Further observations on rugophilic behavior in *Balanus balanoides* (L.). Vidensk. Medd. Dansk. Naturh. Foren. Kbh., 117:341–348.

Bernard, F. J., and C. E. Lane. 1961. Absorption and excretion of copper ion during settlement and metamorphosis of the barnacle. Biol. Bull., 21:438–448.

_____. 1962. Early settlement and metamorphosis of the barnacle *Balanus amphitrite niveus*. J. Morph., 110:19–39.

Bousfield, E. L. 1955. Ecological control of the occurrence of barnacles in the Miramichi estuary. National Museum of Canada, Bulletin 37.

Broad, A. C. 1957a. Larval development of *Palaemonetes pugio* Holthuis. Biol. Bull., 112:144–161.

_____. 1957b. The relationship between diet and larval development of *Palaemonetes*. Biol. Bull., 112:162–170.

_____. 1957c. Larval development of the crustacean *Thor floridanus* Kingsley. J. Elisha Mitchell Sci. Soc., 73:317–328.

Broch, E. S. 1960. Endocrine control of the chromatophores of the zoeae of the prawn *Palaemonetes vulgaris*. Biol. Bull., 119:305–306.

Clarke, G. L. 1947. Poisoning and recovery in barnacles and mussels. Biol. Bull., 92:73–91.

Coffin, H. G. 1954. The biology of *Pagurus samuelis* (Stimpson). Thesis, University of Southern California, Los Angeles, California.

Costlow, J. D., Jr. 1959. Effect of carbonic anhydrase inhibitors on shell development and growth of *Balanus improvisus* Darwin. Physiol. Zool., 32:177–184.

_____. 1961. Fluctuations in hormone activity in Brachyura larvae. Nature, 192:183–184.

_____. 1963a. The effect of eyestalk extirpation on metamorphosis of megalops of the blue crab, *Callinectes sapidus* Rathbun. Gen. Comp. Endocr., 3:120–130.

. 1963b. Regeneration and metamorphosis in larvae of the blue crab, *Callinectes sapidus* Rathbun. J. Exp. Zool., 152:219–228.

_____. 1965. Variability in larval stages of the blue crab, *Callinectes sapidus*. Biol. Bull., 128:58–66.

_____. 1966a. The effect of eyestalk extirpation on larval development of the crab, *Sesarma reticulatum* Say. *In* Barnes, H., Some Contemporary Studies in Marine Science, pp. 209–224, London, Allen and Unwin.

_____. 1966b. The effect of eyestalk extirpation on larval development of the mud crab, *Rhithropanopeus harrisii* (Gould). Gen Comp. Endocr. 7:255–274.

_____. 1967. The effect of salinity and temperature on survival and metamorphosis of megalops of the blue crab, *Callinectes sapidus* Rathbun. Helgolaender Wiss. Meeresuntersuch.,15: 84-97.

_____, and C. G. Bookhout. 1962. The larval development of *Sesarma reticulatum* Say reared in the laboratory. Crustaceana, 4:281–294.

_____, and M. I. Sandeen. 1961. The appearance of chromatophorotropic activity in the developing crab,*Sesarma reticulatum*. Amer. Zool., 4:191.

_____, and A. N. Sastry. 1966. Free amino acids in developing stages of two crabs, *Callinectes sapidus* Rathbun and *Rhithropanopeus harrisii* (Gould). Acta Embryol. Morph. Exp., 19:44-45.

Crisp, D. J., and H. Barnes. 1954. The orientation and distribution of barnacles at settlement with particular reference to surface contour. J. Anim. Ecol., 23:142–162.

Dahl, E. 1957. Embryology of the X organs in *Crangon allmanni*. Nature, 179:482.

Doochin, H. D. 1951. The morphology of *Balanus improvisus* Darwin and *Balanus amphitrite niveus* Darwin during initial attachment and metamorphosis. Bull. Marine Sci. Gulf Caribbean, 1:15–39.

Echalier, G. 1956. Influence de l'organe Y sur la régénération des pattes, chez *Carcinides maenas* L. (Crustacé Décapode). C. R. Soc. Biol. (Paris), 242:2179–2180.

_____. 1959. L'organe Y et le déterminisme de la croissance et de la mue chez *Carcinus maenas* (L.), Crustacé Décapode. Ann. Sci. Nat. Zool. Biol. Animale, 1:1–57.

Fingerman, M. 1965. Endocrine control of light induced pigmentary changes in Crustacea. Arch. Anat. Micro., 54:565–578.

Hubschman, J. H. 1963. Development and function of neurosecretory sites in the eyestalks of larval *Palaemonetes* (Decapoda: Natantia). Biol. Bull., 125:96–113.

Jyssum, S., and L. M. Passano. 1957. Endocrine regulation of preliminary limb regeneration and molting in the crab *Sesarma*. Anat. Rec., 128:571–572.

Kalber, F. A., Jr., and J. D. Costlow, Jr. 1966. The ontogeny of osmoregulation and its neurosecretory control in the decapod crustacean, *Rhithropanopeus harrisii* (Gould). Amer. Zool., 6:221–229.

Kleinholz, L. H. 1961. Pigmentary effectors. In Waterman, T. H., The Physiology of Crustacea, vol. II, 133–169. New York, Academic Press.

Knight-Jones, E. W., and E. Morgan. 1966. Response of marine animals to changes in hydrostatic pressure. Oceanogr. Marine Biol. Ann. Rev., 4:267–299.

Orlamunder, J. 1942. Zur Entwicklung und Formbildung des *Birgus latro* (L.) mit besonderer. Berucksecktigung des X organs. Z. Wiss. Zool. Abt. A., 155:280–316.

Passano, L. M. 1960. Molting and its control. In Waterman, T. H., The Physiology of Crustacea, vol. I, 473–536. New York, Academic Press.

_____. 1961. The regulation of crustacean metamorphosis. Amer. Zool., 1:89–95.

Pflugfelder, V. O. 1939. Endocrine glands, *Dixippus* (Orthoptera). Z. Wiss. Zool., 152:384–408.

Pyle, R. W. 1943. The histogenesis and cyclic phenomena of the sinus gland and X organ in Crustacea. Biol. Bull., 85:87–102.

Reese, E. S. 1962. Shell selection behavior of hermit crabs. Anim. Behav., 10:347—360.

_____. 1964. Ethology and marine zoology. Oceanogr. Marine Biol. Ann. Rev., 2:455—488.

Snodgrass, R. E. 1956. Crustacean metamorphoses. Smithsonian Inst. Misc. Collections, 131:1–78.

Thompson, M. T. 1903. The metamorphoses of the hermit crab. Proc. Boston Soc. Nat. Hist., 31:147–209.

Vernberg, F. J., and J. D. Costlow, Jr. 1966. Studies on the physiological variation between tropical and temperate-zone fiddler crabs of the genus *Uca*. **IV**. Oxygen consumption of larvae and young crabs reared in the laboratory. Physiol. Zool., 39:36–52.

Walley, L. J. 1964. Histolysis and phagocytosis in the metamorphosis of *Balanus balanoides*. Nature, 201:314–315.

_____. Studies on the metamorphosis of *Balanus balanoides* (L.). Unpublished manuscript.

Zeuthen, E. 1947. Body size and metabolic rate in the animal kingdom. C. R. Lab. Carlsberg, Ser. Chim., 26:17–161.

two

METAMORPHIC CHANGES

IN INSECTS

Joan Whitten

Department of Biological Sciences
Northwestern University
Evanston, Illinois

The aim of this chapter is to set the scene for the detailed accounts that will be given in the following three chapters. Metamorphosis has long been recognized as a characteristic of insects. Even the earliest systems of classification distinguished between those insects that metamorphosed and those that did not. From paleontological records the oldest insects determined with certainty are winged forms (e.g., in Carpenter, 1953). However, it is fairly firmly established that the origins of the insects lie with the symphylan group of the Myriapoda, and that ancestral primitive insects were wingless and therefore would have lacked a metamorphosis.

What exactly do we understand by "metamorphosis"? A dictionary definition may be as follows: "A change in form structure, or function, as a result of development, specifically the physical transformation during postembryonic development, as of the larva of an insect to the pupa or the pupa to an adult or the tadpole to the frog." We speak, within the insects, of the absence of metamorphosis in the groups Collembola, Diplura, and Thysanura, which are described as ametabola since no dramatic changes in appearance occur during development. These insects are wingless and therefore are apterygotes.

The rest of the insect orders are primitively winged or ptery-gote. Of these, the exopterygote insects—the bugs (Hemiptera), the may flies (Ephemeroptera), the stone flies (Plecoptera), the termites (Isoptera), the dragonflies (Odonata), cockroaches, and locusts (Orthoptera), to name a few, have their wings developing externally, hence their name Exopterygota. These are characterized by a series of larval stages or nymphal stages that lack wings and have immature reproductive systems. They show "incomplete" metamorphosis, i.e., a gradual transition to the winged, reproducing adult. Each nymphal stage molts into the next stage, which may have slightly more developed wing buds and reproductive system. However, even here the greatest "jump" or change is generally seen at the last nymphal-adult molt. At this time the most dramatic growth in wings and reproductive systems occurs. The second group of pterygote insects are endopterygotes with wings developing internally and include the scorpion flies (Mecoptera), the alder flies and lace wings (Neuroptera), the caddis flies (Trichoptera), beetles (Coleoptera), moths and butterflies (Lepidoptera), bees and wasps (Hymenoptera), and flies (Diptera). In these insect orders metamorphosis is described as "complete", i.e., the larval stages completely lack any external evidence of wings and reproductive system, and the transformation into the adult is a two-step process, involving first a molt from the larva into a pupa, and then a molt from a pupa into an adult. Often, as in the more specialized forms of the Lepidoptera, Hymenoptera or Diptera, the larva is completely unlike the adult in appearance. Thus, in the Lepidoptera we have the larva or caterpillar metamorphosing into the chrysalis or pupa from which the very different adult moth or butterfly emerges. In this last category there are degrees of change. At the least dramatic, we have cases like *Sialis* the alder fly, or the lacewing or ground beetles, where the larva, pupa, and adult still show strong resemblances, particularly in the abdominal segments and the pupa is capable of movement. Larva and adult differ mainly in the development of compound eyes, wings, and external genitalia.

SIGNIFICANCE OF THE PUPAL STAGE

Much has been written of the "pupal stage" and its significance in the evolution of the insects. One of the more recent discussions is that by Hinton (1963), who compares some of the older theories of Berlese and Poyarkoff. Hinton favors the argument that a pupal stage has been necessitated by the development between larva and adult of flight muscles that require a "mold." He homologizes the various nymphal stages of exopterygotes with the larval or nymphal stages of the endopterygotes, the last nymphal stage of exo- with the pupa of endo-, and the adults of both. Berlese was of the opinion that the endopterygote larval stages corresponded to embryonic forms and that all of the exopterygote nymphal stages were concentrated into the endopterygote pupa. Poyarkoff suggested that the adult exopterygote corresponded to the pupal endopterygote and that the adult endopterygote was an *extra* adult stage.

Hinton draws attention to examples of "pupal" forms among the exopterygote orders—Thysanoptera (thrips), Coccidae (mealy bugs), and Aleurodidae (greenhouse white flies). In these, the general structure of the feeding larva or nymph has departed very widely from that of the adult; the structural differences are bridged in the last two nymphal stages. As the differences between the stages have become greater, this has involved a greater degree of structural reorganization to bridge the gap of the internal tissues. As a result, the last two nymphal instars have become more and more quiescent and have eventually ceased to feed, becoming closely analogous to endopterygote pupae. The structural reorganization required to bridge the gap, in some cases, may be greater than is found in some primitive endopterygotes.

GENERAL CHANGES INVOLVED DURING METAMORPHOSIS

Besides the development of wings, compound eyes, and of external and internal genitalia, one of the other main changes that occurs in metamorphosing insects may be in their feeding habits. Thus, a caterpillar and a moth or butterfly, or a fly maggot and the adult fly, may have completely different habits, and these are reflected in structural changes in the mouth parts, gut, salivary glands, and gut muscles. In some frogs, a change from the larval herbivorous diet to the adult carnivorous one is accompanied by a shortening of the gut at metamorphosis. In a fly, the gut shortens also, and the larval crop, larval caecae, and larval salivary glands all disappear; the very much shorter adult gut develops a crop and an elaborate rectum with characteristic rectal papillae. Clearly, changes in mouth parts accompany changes in feeding habits, as can be seen in a chewing caterpillar and a sucking moth or butterfly. Also, changes in feeding habits and mouth parts are accompanied by changes in gut musculature.

General body musculature may change considerably, as is the case with the higher flies where all larval muscles are replaced, or these changes may be far less extreme, involving only the musculature to the newly developing wings. For example, insects such as the alder fly (Neuroptera), scorpion fly (Mecoptera), or even the generalized members of some of the more specialized families such as Lepidoptera and Diptera, retain essentially larval musculature in the abdomen. The motile pupa of a mosquito or of a chironomid nonbiting midge is very different from the immobile pupa of a higher fly in which all of the larval muscles are broken down.

In the case of an amphibian such as the frog, metamorphosis involves the migration from water to land, and correlated changes in the respiratory system occur (see Chapter 7). In the pterygote or winged insect there are changes in the respiratory system of the terrestrial larval form during metamorphosis to the flying adult form. The elaborate adult thoracic musculature is heavily tracheated, often with an equally elaborate system of air sacs (see Fig. 15). A simpler system of air sacs is also found in aquatic forms, where one function would be to provide buoyancy. Insects appear to have evolved from terrestrial ancestors with well-developed tracheal systems, paralleled today in the Myriapoda. Aquatic forms therefore are secondary and are found with normal tracheal systems that may have closed spiracles; these become open and functional in the pupal and adult stages. Aquatic larvae may have tracheal gills or a superficial dense tracheation beneath the thin body wall, but these are lost during metamorphosis to the terrestrial flying adult form. The tracheal system is intimately involved in the metamorphic changes undergone by the other organ systems. For instance, it has been found within the Diptera that the degree of breakdown of the respiratory system follows closely the degree of histolysis of the abdominal musculature (Whitten, 1960).

The most specialized examples among the Endopterygota will be considered in most detail in the present general survey, for it is here among the specialized lepidopteran, hymenopteran, or dipteran that one finds the extremes in metamorphic change as one proceeds from larva to adult. Not only are reproductive systems, wings, and compound eyes present in adult and absent in younger larval stages, but with changes in the feeding habits extensive changes in mouth parts and gut may occur, and muscle requirements may be drastically different in larva and adult. With the acquisition of a flying habit the sensory environment is completely different (this occurs to a lesser or greater extent in various exopterygotes also) so that larval sensillae are broken down and new adult ones appear. Thus, drastic internal changes are reflected in changes in the respiratory and nervous systems, and recent evidence shows equally elaborate changes occurring in the hemocytes (blood cells), associated with changes in other tissues. In fact, there would appear, in the specialized endopterygote, to be no system that remains unaffected by the metamorphic changes occurring during the pupal stages.

The specialized endopterygote is however best considered first in relation to its generalized relatives, and then to other endopterygotes. Since all of the endopterygote orders cannot be given equal emphasis, the Diptera will be treated in some detail in the present chapter. Within the Diptera, the specialized problems found in the Diptera Cyclorrhapha (higher flies) are placed in better perspective when compared with those of the more generalized forms within the order. The mosquito is a member of the more generalized Diptera Nematocera and it is significant that the extremes of larval tissue histolysis and reorganization are absent here. Clements (1963) has stated for the mosquito that "metamorphosis starts early in larval life with slow development of imaginal buds, compound eyes and gonads, processes accelerated in the fourth instar, and largely completed in the pupa. It is clear that important changes continue to take place in the first days of adult life and that only in the older adult is metamorphosis completed." Pigmentation of the adult eye ommatidia apparently occurs in *Culex pipiens*, by the second larval instar!

The evolution of extremes in metamorphosis is therefore seen in many cases to have occurred within the higher endopterygote orders, just as there has been a general progressive evolution in the insects as a whole from the a-metamorphic apterygotes, through the exopterygotes to endopterygote forms. It should be noted that apterygote, ametamorphic insects have a complement of endocrine organs exactly comparable with those of the "higher" pterygotes (Watson, 1963). It would appear that the juvenile hormone (see Chapter 3) has the same relative role—that of blocking the factors responsible for differentiation of tissues into adult forms, and a second role, that of stimulating yolk deposition in adult females. In all insects ecdysone has the same function also, that of inducing molting.

Changes in hormone balance influence the *progress* of meta-morphosis as will be seen in this and succeeding chapters, but the endocrine organs themselves do not *cause* the differences between a non-metamorphosing and a metamorphosing insect.

The question of why the cockroach begins life as a wingless individual or why a fly has evolved into a form that begins life as a wingless, legless, eyeless maggot remain unresolved. It is possible that, as Berlese conjectured, the latter represents an embryonic form, hatching prematurely. In the vertebrates the old concept of "ontogeny recapitulating phylogeny," where embryonic features tend to be retained while the adult form is more susceptible to change, is seen for example in the transient development of gill arches and circulation in the embryos and early stages of development of higher vertebrates. In an am-phibian such as the frog we find the aquatic tadpole, with its fishlike respiratory and corresponding circulatory systems, "metamorphosing" into the adult, terrestrial amphibian with lungs, no gills, and modified gill-arch circulation. If the an-cestral insect is a symphylan-dipluran type, and the pterygote insect larva is prematurely hatched in the ancestral wingless form, then the acquisition of wings at metamorphosis closely parallels the amphibian condition, with its acquisition of legs at metamorphosis. These are academic questions, the answers highly speculative, but the facts of metamorphosis remain sig-nificant to the biologist, with the insect and amphibian remaining striking examples with which to study the process.

PROBLEMS POSED BY INSECT METAMORPHOSING TISSUES

In a metamorphosing pupa one finds various larval tissues degenerating at specific times. What initiates cell death? Can this predetermined event be experimentally altered, de-layed, or permanently prevented? How far back in time is the process determined? Also, in the developing pupa we have tissues that seemingly regress or dedifferentiate, and new adult tissues redifferentiate from them. Do we know what happens to individual cells? Do cells that are differentiated for a particular function in the larval stage dedifferentiate and then redifferen-tiate into cells performing like or dissimilar functions in the adult stage? Are some adult cells developed from undifferen-tiated "reserve" larval cells? In the metamorphosing pupa we may have tissues that appear as new structures not represented previously. Some of the insect flight and leg muscles come into this category. Since muscles are characteristically mesodermal, can the leg muscles develop from epidermal, ectodermal elements of the imaginal discs or are mesodermal myoblasts present in the discs? It has been shown that radioactive proteins in the cuticle of larval insects reappear in the developing adult cuticle. In this case, how are these materials removed from one and transferred to the other in space and time? The mass of larval muscle in a fly is relatively enormous. At the time of muscle breakdown are the materials lost to the body or is there conservation and use in the buildup of adult tissues? Are the blood cells involved to any great extent in tissue breakdown? Are the cells destined to cell death autocytolyzed or are living cells attacked by phagocytic blood cells? Are there ultracellular components comparable to focal degradation points in other animals, and how general are lysosomes? How does a tracheal system laid down at a previous instar solve the problems of providing respiratory gases, firstly to larval tissues destined to die, secondly to larval tissues to be retained, and thirdly to adult tissues not yet differentiated...all requirements within the same pupal instar? A vital and fundamental problem involves the role of the central nervous system. How much metamorphosis occurs in this system? Are we any further forward now than we were in 1952 when Power, in one of a remarkable series of papers on the *Drosophila* nervous system stated, ''The morphogenesis of the insect's nervous system is still largely unexplored in spite of a large bibliography.'' Among the problems that remained unanswered he named the basic sequence of events in the origin and differentiation of the component parts of the central nervous system, the fate of the peripheral nervous system at the time of metamorphosis, the development of the innervation of the imaginal organs, and the changes that occur in the nervous system correlated with the changes that occur in the various end organs. An understanding of the events occurring in the nervous system is basic to any understanding of metamorphosis of individual organs, yet work on the central nervous system during metamorphosis is far behind that on the endocrine system. Even here it has been shown possible to change, enhance, or retard metamorphic events by altering the hormonal environment, yet we are still left with the basic problem of control of the endocrine organs themselves and, ultimately, of the brain neurosecretory cells. What, e.g., are the controlling mechanisms behind the circadian rhythms of development in the metamorphosing *Drosophila* pupa, shown so elegantly by Harker (1965a, 1965b)?

THE SIGNIFICANCE OF METAMORPHOSIS TO GENERAL BIOLOGICAL PROBLEMS

Embryology

In the more extreme cases of metamorphic change there is a virtual return of most tissues to an embryonic state with the constituent cells in an undifferentiated form. As metamorphosis proceeds, differentiation of individual cells of the various tissues occurs.   Such is the case in a higher fly or bee where the muscular system is entirely broken down and reorganized, and there are correspondingly elaborate changes in the gut, general epidermis and tracheal system, with correlated reorganization of the nervous system.   One of the most valuable aspects of insect metamorphosis is as subject material for study of embryological and general developmental problems. Problems of cell and tissue differentiation, of pattern formation, of cell determination and of cell death can all be studied in the metamorphosing insect. Of primary significance also is the fact that insects are amenable to experimental techniques such as those of implantation (e.g., Bodenstein 1950, and Hadron 1951).

Genetics

Studies using the fly *Drosophila,* and to a lesser extent, the hymenopteran *Habrobracon,* have played a large part in our understanding of genetical problems; these are essentially studies of metamorphic events in these insects.   The various eye mutants or wing mutants or mutants showing abnormal bristle pattern result from the action of various mutant genes. However, an understanding of the steps which intervene between the formation of the initial protein and the manifestation of the visible effect, is in essence an understanding of the events of differentiation within the metamorphosing pupa, at least where the effects are on the adult phenotype. There may be a large number of developmental sequences between the activity of the mutant gene and the expression of for example, "vestigial wing" in *Drosophila.* Studies on the formation of biological "patterns" are often also metamorphic problems, as in the case of bristle patterns in *Drosophila* (e.g., Sondhi, 1963).

Chromosome Structure and Gene Action

Insects have another tremendous advantage over other organisms in possessing giant chromosomes. It is unfortunate that they are known only from the order Diptera among the insects, but at the same time it makes this order of greater interest. These giant polytene chromosomes arise by chromosomal DNA replication in the absence of corresponding cell division. They are best known from larval salivary glands; in *Drosophila* it has been possible to "map" the different bands of the salivary cell chromosomes, so that specific regions represent the positions of particular genes whose action has been determined by genetical means. Giant chromosomes are characterized by regions of intense "puffing" activity. These regions represent areas of active RNA synthesis. The RNA is thought to be messenger RNA which passes into the cytoplasm, where, in association with the ribosomes, it organizes the amino-acids into particular sequences to form specific proteins. In this way the origin of a specific protein could be traced back to the activity of a specific puff at a definite position on the giant chromosome.

Cells other than salivary gland cells may contain polytene chromosomes, although they are relatively smaller. These include cells of Malpighian tubules, male seminal vesicles, nurse cells of the ovary, heart cells, pericardial cells, and even fat body cells. Recently, cells having chromosomes as large as salivary gland chromosomes have been recorded for epidermal cells of the fly foot (Whitten, 1964a). They are responsible for secretion of the various layers of cuticle forming the dorsal surface of the adult foot-pad of the higher flies. These cells are thus intimately involved in general adult "development", whereas salivary gland cells have the disadvantage of undergoing cell death at the beginning of the pupal stage. Changes in salivary chromosome puffing, brought about by changing the hormonal milieu, have been correlated with effects on "general development." Titles such as "Regulation of gene action in insect development" (Kroeger and Lezzi, 1966), and "Chromosome changes associated with differentiation" (Clever, 1965), indicate the extent to which studies of salivary gland chromosome puffing activity have attempted to relate events at the chromosomal level to events at the level of the whole organism, in this case the metamorphosing pupa. Giant epidermal cells, such as those of the foot-pads in the higher flies, should prove of particular interest in pursuing these problems.

Questions of growth by cell division, as opposed to growth by cell size, have also been raised as a result of studies involving metamorphosing insects, particularly the mosquito (e.g., Trager, 1937 and discussed in Clements, 1963). It has been found that, as a rule, cells which increase in size (for example of salivary

glands, Malpighian tubules, rectum, abdominal muscles, trichogen cells, larval oenocytes) are incapable of cell division, and
except for Malpighian tubules are incapable of transforming into
adult organs, so that these then are the cells which histolyse in
the metamorphosing pupa. During growth, replication of chromosomes proceeds without separation and without cell division,
resulting in the characteristic polytene chromosome. On the
other hand cells that multiply by cell division remain small, and
are retained and pass through into the adult; presumably they
are undifferentiated and therefore capable of subsequent differentiation. A seemingly unique condition is found in the various
mosquitoes—that of *endopolyploidy* with somatic reduction. Here,
in the small intestine, and to lesser extent in other parts of the
gut, epidermis, tracheae and neurilemma, cells become polytene
but apparently not differentiated. In *Aedes* the cells may be 16 N
with 48 instead of the normal 6 chromosomes, with the homologues closely associated in a polytene chromosome. However,
at the onset of pupation the polytene chromosome splits up and
cell division occurs, without chromosome replication. In this
way there are produced many small diploid cells which differentiate to reconstitute the small intestine and rectum. An answer
to the question of why this should happen is not at present available.

GROSS MORPHOLOGICAL CHANGES AT METAMORPHOSIS

One of the most striking aspects of insect metamorphosis,
particularly to the casual observer, is the dramatic change
from larva to pupa at the larval-pupal ecdysis. This is all the
more remarkable when one realizes that the pupal "mold"
produced at the larval-pupal molt follows the future adult shape
particularly with respect to the large muscle-filled thorax. Yet
at the time of its formation none of these adult structures may
be developed in some instances, as is the case with the higher
flies. The mechanical aspects have been discussed at length
recently in a review article by Cottrell (1964): The external
shape of the insect is largely limited by the inherent form of
the different parts and more particularly by the extent to which
the outermost layer of cuticle—the epicuticle—can be unfolded.
Then again, the unfolding of the epicuticle and the stretching
of the underlying endocuticle is brought about by hydrostatic
pressures produced by two activities: swallowing of air or
water and the contraction of muscles. The relative importance

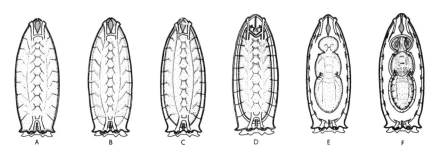

FIG. 1. General sequences in the transformation of the larva to a pupa in the fly, in dorsal view showing cuticular layers and outlines of the tracheal system. A: larva within larval cuticle; B: larva after beginnings of puparium formation, with epidermis of posterior end retracted away from larval cuticle; C: secretion of the so-called "prepupal cuticle" (may be ecdysial membrane) by the larval epidermis; D: a cryptocephalic pupa with pupal cuticle formed and with legs and wings partially everted, but with head still invaginated; E: pupa, lying within the hardened larval cuticle (puparium), "prepupal membrane," and its own pupal cuticle; F: later pupa with newly developed adult cuticle and tracheal system, enclosed within the earlier cuticles. Size ½ in. long. Reproduced with permission from Quart. J. Micr. Sci., 98, 1957.

of these two may differ in different insects. Final form is also attained by the expansion of soft, not yet expanded parts, but not of any prehardened areas. There is a very exact relationship between the two. Köhler (see Cottrell) has shown that the eversion of the wing buds in *Ephestia*, the clothes moth, is brought about by hydrostatic pressures and by muscles opening the mouths of the peripodial cavities. Fraenkel showed that in *Calliphora* eversion of the pupal head is brought about by peristaltic abdominal contractions. Cottrell discusses other examples also. Personal observations with *Drosophila* and *Sarcophaga* have shown the presence of a series of larval suspensory muscles that seem to play a role in attaining pupal form. Typically, the cyclorrhaphan nephrocytes are shown as slung from the two lobes of the salivary glands. In fact, their attachment in both *Drosophila* and *Sarcophaga* (and probably other Cyclorrhapha also) is by way of a muscle that runs along the proximal third of each lobe of the salivary glands, with firm attachment between gland, muscle, and nephrocytes being maintained by the continuous connective tissue basement membranes (micrographs in Whitten, 1964c). These muscles are attached at one end near the spiracles and at the other on the gut. Two other muscles, with origins in the prothoracic region and insertions asymmetrically on the midgut, pass through the body cavity to their points of attachment on the midgut. These muscles show rhythmical contractions and resemble the alary muscles, being clearly striated under phase optics. In the fly, a "cryptocephalic pupa" has its head still invaginated, but leg and wing discs are everted though flaccid and unexpanded; the abdomen is larval in shape being disproportionately long, and larval tracheae are still within the body (Fig. 1D). Simultaneously with eversion of the head, there is extension of the wings and legs and contraction of the abdomen. Contraction of the abdomen must reduce the internal volume and help force blood into the legs and wings and head. A large air bubble present before, and absent after eversion of the head, also probably plays some part. Observations of internal changes reveal a dramatic overall contraction of the entire system of longitudinal visceral muscles and unpaired suspensory muscles. This simultaneous contraction of the muscles effects the shortening of the larval gut to the dimensions of the much shorter adult gut. At the same time, contraction of the longitudinally running visceral muscle through the midgut caecae reduces these to four small knobs on the gut. Their cells later histolyze, and these structures are not represented in the adult gut. At the same time the contraction of the "slinging" or suspensory muscles plays a role in the form of the pupa and future adult. By anchoring the gut and salivary glands they seem to help prevent their being everted into the head along with the brain. This is probably also helped by muscles such as the alary muscles, which also attach to tracheae. At the same time the muscles, whose origins are on the body wall behind the prothoracic spiracles, may help during their contraction to draw in the "neck" region between head and thorax. Nothing is fortuitous, and the establishment of shape in the pupa is a very precise process.

Attainment of adult shape is equally intriguing. Clearly, it is genetically determined that the slightly bilobed saclike pupal leg appendage of the higher fly should develop by epidermal cell retraction, cell division, and differential growth into an adult leg (see Fig. 17 for the fly pretarsus), yet little is known of the factors that determine this shape. There is a suggestion in the development of the fly foot that the ecdysial membrane (c.f. Taylor and Richards, 1965), the *first* secretion of the adult epidermal cells, may play a mechanical role in maintaining shape in the delicate, otherwise naked, cytoplasmic extensions of the various epidermal cells that form hairs of various sizes. Once the adult structures are laid down, it can be seen from Cottrell's account that the adult shape is attained by a dual process—by the prehardening of structures that will *not* expand after ecdysis (the various leg bristles and the terminal pretarsal structures shown in the fly foot in Fig. 17 are examples) and the postecdysial expansion of soft structures that subsequently harden, e.g., the wings and general abdominal cuticle. Evidently, timing is delicate and there are elaborate control mechanisms involved. Again it is with the flies that much work has been done. Fraenkel and Hsiao (1962) and Cottrell have separately found a "darkening factor," named by former "bursicon." More detailed discussion is given in Cottrell's review. It is sufficient here to note that the factor is released after the flies have ceased "digging" their way through the soil and that darkening can be produced in these "digging" flies by injection of blood from air swallowing, darkening flies. The cessation of digging and the onset of air swallowing and darkening are closely interrelated; "shut off" of digging movements is permanent. It cannot be related to the hardening process and, according to Cottrell, the mechanism of "shut off" is probably nervous. Push through the ground is accompanied by and partially brought about by alternate eversion and retraction of the blood-filled sac at the anterior end of the head—the ptilinum. The muscles producing the movement breakdown within three days of emergence, demonstrating the remarkable coordination of events. The nervous stimulation for cessation of digging may well result from signals received (or no longer received) by the tiny tactile hairs dispersed over the surface of the ptilinum (Whitten, 1963c; Fig. 2). Each hair possesses a sensory nerve fiber, and avoiding reactions with soil particles are seen to result from stimuli received by these hairs. When the fly appears above ground, no resistance is felt by the ptilinum, and signals cease to be received by the sensory nerve fibers. This in itself could *initiate* the chain reaction which involves retraction of the ptilinum, air swallowing, darkening, and finally breakdown of the ptilinal muscles. Particularly puzzling is that if the darkening factor is a hormone whose release is necessary for the final synchronous darkening of all areas to be hardened and darkened following expansion, what is responsible for the progressive predarkening of areas such as the legs before ecdysis? This occurs from thorax forward and backward and proximodistally along the legs. The predarkening process has been used as a very reliable aging device, e.g., for general development aging in *Drosophila* (Harker, 1965a, 1965b) and in the development of the fly leg (Whitten, 1968). Are the preecdysial and the postecdysial hardening and darkening processes really controlled and effected by different agents?

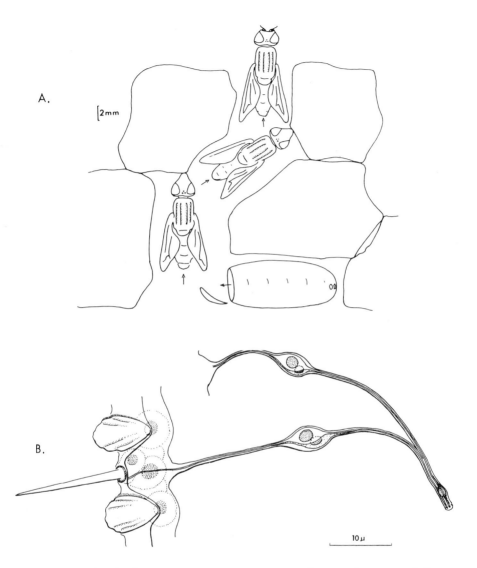

A.

[2mm

B.

10μ

FIG. 2. A: Diagrammatic representation of a newly emerged fly pushing its way through the soil by alternate inflation and deflation of the "ptilinum"; B: one of the sensory hairs occurring between scales on the ptilinum, which may function in triggering off the complex sequence of events leading to the eventual darkening of the adult, cessation of digging, withdrawal of ptilinum, and histolysis of the ptilinal muscles. Sensory nerve fibers, sheath cells, and innervated hair. Reproduced with permission from J. Linn. Soc. (Zool.), 44, 1963.

DEVELOPMENTAL RATE IN METAMORPHOSING
PUPAE: INTERNAL CLOCKS

A very different but equally intriguing aspect of the metamorphic process occurring between larval and adult stages can
be followed in two papers by Harker in a study of developmental
rates and their controlling mechanisms. Working with the
fruit fly *Drosophila melanogaster*, Harker (1965a) first studied
the course of development in two strains in an attempt to
establish the factors affecting the time taken to complete three
stages of: head eversion to yellow eye, yellow eye to wing
pigmentation; wing pigmentation to eclosion. Time measurements were taken for pupae entering each stage at each particular
hour of the day when insects were kept at 12-hour light: 12-hour
darkness; 12-hour bright light: 12-hour dim light; or in continuous darkness. She found that the duration of each stage in
both strains is affected by the time of day relative to the *light
cycle at which the stage is entered*. The duration of each stage
for pupae kept in continuous darkness is affected by the time of
day at which the stage is entered, relative to the light cycle to
which they had been exposed as larvae. She further found that
the time interval curves for all three stages of any one strain
take the same form. Consequently, because of the very wide range
of development rates, dependent on the time within the light cycle
at which each stage begins, a population in which the larvae
all pupate within a 24-hour period will continue to produce adult
flies over several days. The eclosion rhythm is a population effect
and does not reflect the phasing of individuals at a dawn
eclosion; the majority of individuals emerge at dawn because
of the summation effect of circadian rhythms of development
at earlier stages.

In a second series of experiments, Harker (1965b) studied
the time taken for *D. melanogaster* to complete the same three
stages of development for pupae entering each stage at each
particular hour of the day in cycles of 12-hour light: 12-hour
darkness; 4-hour light: 20-hour darkness; 18-hour light: 6-hour
darkness. Similar experiments were carried out on insects in
which the larvae were subjected to the light cycles but the pupae
remained in constant darkness. It was found that the duration
of each stage is affected by the time of day, relative to the light
cycle, at which the stage is entered. When pupae are in constant
darkness, the development rate of each stage is affected by the
time of day at which the stage is entered relative to the *particular
light cycle* to which the larva had been exposed. It was further
shown that the eclosion rhythm, arising as a "summation effect"

of rhythms of development at earlier stages, may become bi-modal in light cycles with suitable photofractions. It was further found that the rate of development of a pupa entering a stage during the light period is related to the time interval since the light "on" signal; the preceding dark period has no effect.

Finally, the development rate of a pupa entering a stage during the dark period is affected by the time interval elapsing since the light "off" signal, but may also be affected by the previous light "on" signal, although there is no simple relationship between them.

Harker concluded that as the development rates are maintained in constant darkness, the rate is affected by factors following a *diurnal rhythm*. The *form* of the rhythm is determined by both light "on" and light "off" signals, but the *timing* of the rhythm is determined by the two signals acting independently of each other.

METAMORPHIC CHANGES IN INDIVIDUAL SYSTEMS

In order to follow the types of problems presented by individual tissues one needs to look at each system in turn, for each presents its own characteristic problems. Cell differentiation and pattern formation may be best studied in various epidermal cell types, cell death perhaps in muscle systems, along with considerations of blood cell relationships, cell determination in the various imaginal rudiments, and controlling mechanisms in endocrine and nerve-tissue relationships. As general a picture as possible will be given in the space available, but slightly more emphasis will be given, in tracing sequences in individual systems, to members of the Diptera Cyclorrhapha, relating them as far as possible to events occurring in the lower Diptera Nematocera and other insects. For each system the same question will be asked. "In what way does the mosquito (Diptera: Nematocera) differ from the fly (Diptera: Cyclorrhapha), and how then do other insects compare with both?"

METAMORPHIC CHANGES IN THE ALIMENTARY CANAL

Changes occurring in the alimentary canal vary from one insect type to the next and cannot be covered comprehensively here. The cyclorrhaphan system again will be taken as an extreme example of the type of changes that occur. The feeding apparatus in larva and adult are quite different: It has been mentioned earlier that the larval gut is longer, possesses a larval "crop" and four midgut caecae and is otherwise more or less a long, straight tube. The adult gut lacks the crop and midgut caecae, and is characterized instead by the development of an adult crop and of a rectum containing four "rectal papillae" of characteristic appearance but until recently of little known function.

The mouth parts of the larva consist of a pair of strong mouth hooks; the adult mouth appendages—labial, maxillary, and mandibular—are highly specialized and arise from the median portion of the frontal sac of the larva, an imaginal rudiment lying between the brain lobes. Changes in the gut during metamorphosis involve degeneration of the midgut epithelium, disappearance of the midgut caecae, disappearance of the labial "crop" and the development of adult crop and rectum from two "imaginal disc" areas located at the junctions of foregut and midgut and midgut and hindgut, respectively. Also, the larval salivary glands break down, and adult salivary glands develop from an "imaginal disc" area located between the base of the larval gland and the duct. From the undifferentiated cells of this area the adult glands arise by cell mitosis, growth, and differentiation. Other imaginal areas may include labial and a ring of peri-anal cells.

Coordinated longitudinal contraction of the gut muscles and those of the midgut caecae bring about shortening of the gut and reduction of the caecae to stumps. This contraction throws the basement membrane into elaborate folds. Slightly later, the basement membrane breaks down as does that of other tissues in the pupa (Whitten, 1962a and Fig. 3), and the gut lining cells degenerate, adult epithelium being formed from small interstitial cells in the gut wall. The age of a midpupa can be fairly accurately followed by determining the length and degree of development of the adult crop. In the cyclorrhaphan pupa the Malpighian tubules are retained throughout pupation and evidently function at least in the late pupa, where they are filled with a milky material. This is passed into, and accumulates in, the rectum and later partially contributes to the gut content or "meconium," which is eliminated from the gut at the time of emergence.

Virtually nothing is known of muscle reorganization. Do the adult visceral muscles arise from dedifferentiated gut muscle cells or do some or all arise from myoblasts, as has been suggested in older literature and again recently by Crossley (1965) for certain of the abdominal skeletal muscle cells in

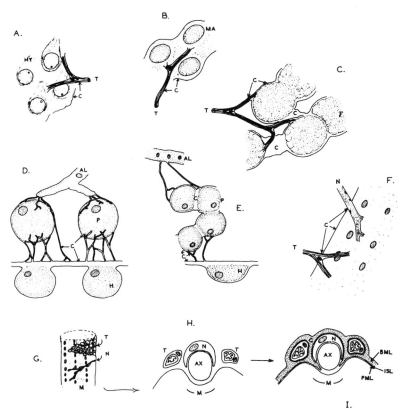

FIG. 3. "Connective tissue" relationships in various fly tissues; larval basement membranes characteristically break down in the early pupal stage to allow growth of the developing tissues; new adult basement membranes (connective tissue) develop in the late pupa when growth and differentiation are completed. Note continuity of the membranes (c). A: larval epidermis (hypodermis) and trachea; B: larval Malpighian tubule and trachea; C: larval fat body and trachea—these cells are released in the early pupa by breakdown of the basement membranes; D and E: alary muscle-pericardial cell-heart connections; membranes are retained during the pupal stage; F: muscle with nerve and trachea; G: developing adult muscle with developing nerve and tracheal air sac; H: cross section of developing adult muscle, nerve with axon sheath cell, and trachea; I: same as H, a little later with adult basement membranes (BML) laid down; PML: plasma membrane, ISL: interspace. Partially reproduced with permission from Quart. J. Micr. Sci., 103, 1962.

Calliphora, and by Daly (1964) for a large proportion of the thoracic muscles in *Apis,* the bee? In the case of the fly gut, the muscles apparently disappear, with adult muscles appearing in the late pupa. However, it is very probable that the muscles dedifferentiate, to redifferentiate later in a fashion similar to the cyclical muscle changes shown in *Rhodnius* by Wigglesworth (1956). Here the muscle fibers disappear between molts, with only the sheath and nuclei remaining; then at the onset of each molt the muscles are completely differentiated again.

Changes in the mosquito gut are essentially similar (Clements, 1963). The phenomenon of endopolyploidy, discussed earlier, is of particular interest.

METAMORPHIC CHANGES UNDERGONE
BY THE HEART

The heart during metamorphosis is an organ that has received relatively little attention. It reportedly ceases to function in many insect pupae, and in some it has been described as reversing the direction of heartbeat. In *Sialis,* the alder fly, a very fine study has recently been made, by Selman (1965), on the circulatory system. In this species he notes that, as is the case in other larvae including those of dipteran flies, the larval heart is not innervated, whereas for some at present inexplicable reason the adult heart is innervated.

In general, the heart changes relatively little during metamorphosis. For instance, in the mosquito (Clements, 1963) the heart and associated pericardial cells are said to pass unchanged from larva to adult.

Personal observations on *Sarcophaga* and preliminary work on *Drosophila* suggest a closely similar pattern of events for these cyclorrhaphans. The heart is seen to pass without dissolution through to the adult stage, but in the midpupa metamorphic changes do occur. Also the larval posterior tracheal plexus is absent. The heart wall itself becomes somewhat thickened, and this thickening does not extend to the aorta. Correlated with the increase in wall material, the intrinsic heart cells become active and display well-developed polytene chromosomes (Whitten, 1963a). The smaller anterior and the large posterior pericardial cells undergo changes in the midpupal stage, and the larger cells also develop well defined polytene chromosomes. The thickening of the heart but not of the aortal region produces a humped effect at the junction of the two regions, and this comes to lie in the raised abdominal region immediately posterior to the constriction between adult thorax and abdomen. In a midpupa the heart muscles have degenerated and degeneration is also seen in the alary muscles. In these latter, there would appear to be events occuring that are comparable with the cyclical muscle dedifferentiation and redifferentiation in the abdomen of *Rhodnius*. In the fly midpupa, heart pumping ceases and there is virtually no circulation of blood. Developing adult nerves can be followed migrating over the heart surface of a mid to late pupa. An attempt to review events recorded for other insects will not be made; the scarcity of information concerning metamorphic changes can be seen from the recent review of Jones (1964). The absence of circulation during the midpupal period would seem to be pertinent to questions of hemocyte relationships in the pupal stages, and these will be discussed later in more detail.

There are many other peripheral issues in connection with the developing adult circulation during metamorphosis, including the development of pulsatile organs, dealt with in current textbooks on entomology. As with all the other systems, the more one looks into the problem the more one realizes how little, relatively, is known of the subject. Few insects have their circulatory systems as thoroughly investigated as has the alder fly *Sialis* in Selman's recent study.

METAMORPHIC CHANGES IN THE FAT BODY, OENOCYTES AND NEPHROCYTES

The fate of the fat body varies in different insects. For instance within the Diptera, in a generalized dipteran such as the mosquito, it is said to pass from larva to newly emerged adult unchanged and little if at all diminished in size (Clements, 1963). Changes in the higher flies are however somewhat more complex. It was formerly considered that the larval fat body of the fly broke down in the early pupa and thereafter ceased to function (e.g., Bodenstein, 1950). However, what happens at pupation is that the connective tissue sheath (basement membrane) that binds the cells into a composite organ breaks down and releases the component cells (Whitten, 1962a; Fig. 3). The breakdown, as with all the events in the metamorphosing pupa, is perfectly timed and coordinated. Breakdown of thoracic segments of the fat body occurs in the cryptocephalic pupa while the abdominal portion breaks down later, in the early pupa. Although appearing diffuse, the fat body arises segmentally and functions as such in later life. A branch of a middorsal nerve has been traced to the fat body in *Sarcophaga,* and the basement membranes of the nerve and fat body are confluent. The fat body in this fly would therefore seem to be innervated.

The cyclorrhaphan larval fat body cells function right into the adult stage. They have been the subject of much recent research, particularly in *Drosophila,* where they seem to play an important part in intermediary metabolism in the developing pupa. Changes in the fat body are characteristic of certain *Drosophila* mutants.

In many insects including flies and moths a separate adult fat body originates within the pupal stage. Older workers have suggested that adult fat body cells may have originated from hemocytes. The whole subject is by no means clear. Evidence in the Diptera Cyclorrhapha recently has suggested that this is not as unlikely a possibility as might at first be supposed (Whitten, 1964b). Phagocytic hemocytes, which at the time of pupation ingest larval fragments, later undergo a second cycle of activity. They persist right into the adult stage, and at this time appear very like the adult fat body cells (Fig. 7). The mosquito is seen not to have a distinct adult fat body, and the larval fat body is said not to histolyse in the early adult (Clements, 1963). Certainly phagocytic hemocytes would be relatively much less active in the mosquito where tissue histolysis is less extensive.

Oenocytes are cells which are thought to be involved in intermediary metabolism, in growth and in reproduction (Wigglesworth, 1965). In many insects including the mosquito and the fly there are two generations- larval and adult. The larval oenocytes in the fly are large cells with polytene chromosomes, located segmentally in groups along the side of the body. Adult oenocytes are smaller, appear in the pupal stage and are often associated with the adult fat body cells. In the mosquito the larval cells grow in size, develop polytene chromosomes, and breakdown in the pupa. The many smaller adult oenocytes appear in the abdomen during the fourth larval instar (Clements, 1963).

In the fly, *ventral nephrocytes* thought to be excretory in function and related to pericardial cells, are slung as a garland between the lobes of the salivary glands (attached by muscles and basement membrane material). They breakdown in the early pupa, at the time of the disappearance of the salivary glands. Comparable cells are present in the mosquito where in some species they also form a chain between the salivary lobes.

METAMORPHOSIS OF THE MUSCULAR SYSTEM

Among the Endopterygota there is a considerable range in the degree to which muscles are retained from larva to adult. In some of the more primitive orders, but also in some of the more primitive members of the more specialized orders including the Diptera, the majority of the larval muscles are carried over into the adult stage. The muscles, particularly of the abdomen, are carried over and changes occur mainly in the muscles of the thorax that are responsible for flight. In the mosquito for example, larval abdominal muscles are used in the pupa for swimming and these degenerate early in adult life. The adult abdominal muscles arise from myoblasts in the pupal stages. However, among the specialized forms there are remarkably few muscles passing through from larva to adult. In the thorax of the honeybee, a very comprehensive survey made recently by Daly (1964) showed that no larval muscles pass unchanged into the adult, that 85 percent of larval muscles are associated with the development of adult muscles, and that 15 percent of the larval muscles degenerate and have no relationship to adult muscles. Some 61 percent of adult muscles arise from aggregations of myoblasts, including those of appendages and direct flight muscles. Crossley (1965), in a recent study on the blowfly *Calliphora erythrocephala,* similarly showed the origin of certain of the abdominal muscles from myoblasts, an observation substantiating the opinions of several of the older workers at the turn of the century (e.g., Perez, 1910). The description by Crossley of the actual invasion of larval muscle sheaths by nuclei that subsequently differentiate into adult muscles in the same location as the larval is difficult to conceive but is all the more fascinating if actually the case.

In recent years interest has centered largely on the breakdown of muscles and the cause of the breakdown. This remains one of the most intriguing problems of insect metamorphosis. Of particular interest is the fact that not all larval muscles degenerate at the same time. Some are retained while their neighbors degenerate. Initial work on this subject was in the Lepidoptera (see, e.g., Finlayson, 1956). More recently, an extremely interesting series of papers have appeared by Lockshin and Williams (1965), also on the Lepidoptera. Whereas the earlier workers concentrated on muscles that were carried over from the larva into the early pupa and then degenerated, Lockshin and Williams studied muscles that passed into the adult and were involved in emergence; these degenerated three days later under normal conditions. Similar differential breakdown occurs in

other insects: e.g., in the cyclorrhaphous Diptera certain
larval muscles do not degenerate with the remainder after
puparium formation (Cottrell, 1964), but they do so some 48
hours later.   Likewise, there are muscles that degenerate in
the early adult, including those of the ptilinum and other
muscles expressly involved in the process of eclosion. The
ptilinal muscles degenerate following the sequence of events
that starts with cessation of digging. Similar controlling mechanisms to those shown by Lockshin and Williams for the lepidopteran may apply in these and other cases. They have concluded that the initiation of cell death in the muscle cells is
brought about by the coordination of several factors — humoral,
nervous, and an ability of the cell to respond to the factors.
Thus, the breakdown of certain intersegmental muscles in the
adult is first potentiated by exposure to the molting hormone
ecdysone during the first few days of adult development. Three
weeks later, when development is completed, actual breakdown
is triggered by a neural mechanism. The muscle cells attain
the capacity to respond to this during the three days before
emergence.

Johnson (1959) has shown that where degeneration of flight
muscles normally occurred in adult aphids this was prevented
by decapitation. Further, the thoracic muscles of decapitated
aphids broke down when they were joined in parabiosis with intact
aphids. The complete story may well be similar to that shown
for the postadult muscle breakdown in the Lepidoptera. Much
has been done and much remains to be done on this subject. It
is an important biological problem because the whole question
of "programmed cell death" is involved.

The problems of muscle dedifferentiation and subsequent
redifferentiation are equally interesting. Why should the muscles
of *Rhodnius* (Wigglesworth, 1956) dedifferentiate between molts,
and shortly before molting redifferentiate contractile muscle
fibers? The same problem is posed in the metamorphosing pupa
by the larval muscles that are transformed into adult muscles,
constituting the 39 percent of the total thoracic musculature in
the adult honeybee (Daly, 1964).

Reorganization of the alary muscles in the fly pupa presents
a similar problem. Another problem is posed by muscles that
develop in the pupal stage and degenerate before emergence. The
functions of muscles of this type are discussed at length by Daly
for the honeybee, and their possible involvement in determining
shape is also considered.

Hinton (1961) has described how the disposition of the
indirect flight muscles of insects can be brought about at the

time of the larval-pupal molt by activity of the epidermal cells. He demonstrates this with *Simulium*, which as a generalized nematoceran member of the Diptera has (unlike the more specialized Cyclorrhapha) its epidermal cells carried over from larva to adult. The indirect flight muscles at the time of the larval-pupal molt are undifferentiated strands, attached to the epidermis but in relative positions quite unlike the relative positions of the corresponding future adult muscle. He concludes that the definitive shape of the adult mesothorax and the final position and orientation of the skeletal muscles are determined by the way the epidermis grows between the time of secretion of pupal cuticle (larval-pupal molt) and the time that the larval cuticle is shed (larval-pupal ecdysis).

THE CONTROLLING CENTERS OF METAMORPHIC CHANGE: ENDOCRINE GLANDS AND THE NERVOUS SYSTEM

Since the endocrine system is the subject of Chapter 3, only the barest mention will be made here. A brief look will be taken of the hormone system that controls the metamorphic changes in the various organs. As was seen earlier, the endocrine system is essentially similar in all of the groups of insects. The corpus allatum secretes juvenile hormone, the prothoracic (ecdysial) gland cells (and the ventral gland cells, their homologues in the apterygote thysanurans) secrete ecdysone, the molting hormone, while the corpus cardiacum, which has been assigned various functions, contains distinct glandular and storage regions. The cephalic endocrine system in the Thysanura Apterygota is seen to resemble closely that of the generalized pterygote (Watson, 1963). It is currently thought that the brain hormone, secreted by neurosecretory cells of the brain, stimulates the prothoracic glands as the principal target organs. The secretion of ecdysone in the presence of juvenile hormone in the winged pterygote insects produces a juvenile form; the secretion of ecdysone in the presence of a reduced titer of juvenile hormone initiates metamorphosis, so that at the time of the last larval molt in an endopterygote insect, a pupa is formed instead of a further larval stage. With relatively few exceptions it has been shown that after emergence the corpus allatum again becomes active, and the hormone secreted stimulates the deposition of yolk in the female.

METAMORPHOSIS OF THE NERVOUS SYSTEM

Along with the endocrine system, the nervous system is the controlling center of the body's activities, so that changes in the nervous system are fundamentally concerned with metamorphic changes in other systems. It has already been seen for example, that the nervous system plays a role in the process of differential muscle breakdown. Also, the neurosecretory cells of the brain are virtually the controlling agents of the endocrine system: through regulation of the release of brain hormone molting is controlled; through regulation of the release of juvenile hormone maturation is controlled (Schneiderman and Gilbert, 1964).   What then happens to the nervous system itself during metamorphosis?   As was noted earlier in reference to Power's work, surprisingly little is known about metamorphosis of the insect nervous system at the individual cellular level. Neurometamorphosis has been the subject of study recently by several workers, e.g., Pipa and Woolever (1965) and Ashhurst and Richards (1964a and b), both for Lepidoptera.   Many older workers considered the fate of individual nerves; evidence is extensive, although often contradictory, and Wigglesworth (1965) should be consulted for major references on the subject.

For *Drosophila* alone (Bodenstein, 1950) there is no detailed account of nervous system changes. What happens to the paired lateral nerves of the larva? Do these disappear in the pupal stage? Are the adult nerves all new developments? How is the relatively longer and narrower ventral thoracico-abdominal nerve mass of the larva converted into the shorter, broader thoracic mass of the adult where the whole abdominal center is reduced to the small posterior region? An answer to some of these questions will be attempted below in discussing metamorphic changes in the cyclorrhaphan nervous system.

Power (1952) drew a graph for the *Drosophila* nervous system development in the pupa, plotting volume increases in the components of the central nerve mass, of cells relative to fibers. He concluded that there was essentially little cell breakdown, but that there was a great increase in neuropile (composed of nerve fibers). Clearly, where larval organs break down their nerve supply is no longer required. Conversely, where new adult organs are formed, a new nerve supply also has to be available. Do the old nerve fibers degenerate? Are the old nerve fibers taken over by other tissues? Do new neurons come into being in the pupa? Do the larval neurons dedifferentiate, their nerve processes degenerating, and later redifferentiate and form new nerve fibers? These are problems touched on but not completely solved for any of the insects in which changes are extreme. The field lies open for investigation at the light and electron microscope levels. Of course the problem is far more extreme in a case like the Cyclorrhapha than in, say, the Diptera Nematocera such as mosquitoes or crane flies, where most tissues and organs are carried over more or less unchanged from larva to adult. In the mosquito, it is said that the central nervous system grows by cell multiplication in the larva, with very slight increase in cell size. Only slight histolysis occurs in the pupa, and in the adult there is again cell multiplication (Trager, 1937). However, even here we will have the large flight muscles developed. How is the new innervation to these developed? How do nerve fibers grow out of and into (sensory) a central nerve mass that is invested in a thick neural lamella? Breakdown of the connective tissue sheath would seem to be one prerequisite for this (Whitten, 1962a, Ashhurst and Richards, 1964; Pipa and Woolever, 1965).

GENERAL METAMORPHIC CHANGES IN THE CYCLORRHAPHAN NERVOUS SYSTEM

Instead of complete breakdown and reorganization of the peripheral nervous system there is actually continuity in the *basic* framework from larva to adult (Whitten, 1965). At the time of puparium formation there are numerous mitoses among the sheath cells of the lateral abdominal nerves (Fig. 4). Similar mitoses are present in the recurrent nerve from hypocerebral ganglion to the midgut junction, and the mitoses are paralleled in the string of cells (mesodermal gonad duct rudiment) arising posteriorly from the testis and ovary. This burst of mitotic activity is followed by the breakdown of the sheaths, thus allowing cell growth and migration to occur. In the ventral nerve mass, growth occurs along the region of arrows shown in Fig. 5, and the net result is a dramatic sweeping backward of the abdominal nerves, aided by a general contraction in length of the abdominal nerves themselves (brought about by the shortening of individual sheath cells now that the sheath has gone). In this way the sheath cells, by cell division, growth, and migration, lay down the skeleton of the adult nervous system (Fig. 5A, B, and C). This system is basically the same as the larval in general plan, but it differs in the details of individual branching. Differences are most extreme in the thorax where tremendous growth of the sheath cells, from the ventral nerve mass, form the framework of the nerves to and from the flight muscles, legs, wings, and halters (Fig. 6). The *external framework* is thus laid down.

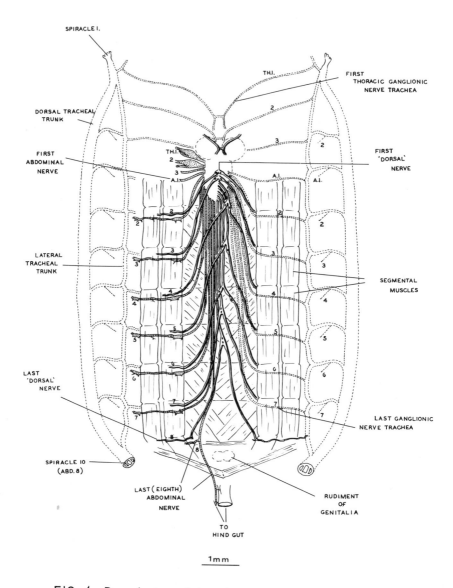

FIG. 4. Dorsal view of larval nervous system in relation to the segmental tracheal system, showing the segmental lateral and dorsal nerves, together with some of the larval muscles, the first and second leg imaginal discs, and the genital disc. *Sarcophaga* and other Cyclorrapha. Reproduced with permission from Quart. J. Micr. Sci., 104, 1963.

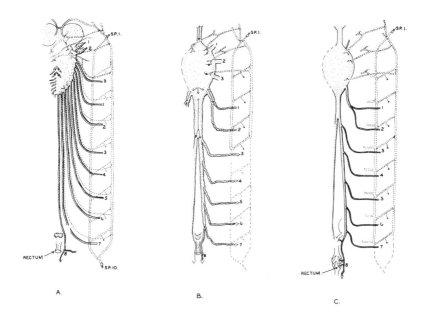

FIG. 5. Metamorphosis of the abdominal nervous system, showing in outline the complex growth changes that transform the segmental larva nerves into the adult condition. The system is shown in relation to the metamorphosing tracheal segments. A: larval condition; B: growth phase in early midpupa; C: adult condition. *Sarcophaga*, but applies equally to *Drosophila*.

Internal to this, individual nerve fibers may degenerate and new fibers regenerate. Evidence so far suggests this and also that there may be dedifferentiation and redifferentiation of fibers of individual neurons. Pipa and Woolever, using electron microscopy, observed little evidence for "axoplasmic degradation," but the situation in the lepidopteran nerve cord may well be less extreme than in the cyclorrhaphan system. Muscle breakdown and tracheal histolysis are certainly less extreme in the former group of insects. Early in pupation, at the time of breakdown of the larval neural lamella, there is a concurrent breakdown in dorsal nerves and in the larval abdominal ganglionic tracheae—the reduction in volume of the abdominal center is such that these tracheae could not even be accommodated in the adult nerve mass. (Fig. 6F). One of the most spectacular observations, which will be discussed in connection with the tracheal system, is the fact that these abdominal ganglionic tracheae *before puparium formation* occurs do not produce pupal cuticular linings. Their fate is already determined at this time. They are empty tracheal tubes, their cells destined to die. Why these? If apparently not innervated, why do they die and other tracheae in the same hormonal milieu survive through to the adult? What changes occur in the abdominal nerve mass that can cause such drastic reductions in respiratory requirements? Late in the pupal stage, when the processes of growth and differentiation are completed, the new adult nerve sheath is laid down. In the meantime, new adult tracheae have been formed, including the air sacs shown in Fig. 6 E and F. Their sheaths are formed at the same time as, and are confluent with, the adult neural lamella (Fig. 3). These events have been followed in *Sarcophaga bullata, Phormia regina* and *Drosophila melanogaster* and are essentially similar in all three. It may be mentioned that staining for neurosecretory material in sections of the nervous system of *Sarcophaga* has revealed the presence of dorsal neurosecretory cells throughout pupal life. They are always gorged with PAF staining material, which does not imply that they are active but does show that they pass through unchanged from larva to adult.

Nerves and tracheae to organs destined to disappear in the pupa, break down; new nerve branches grow out at a time when the innervated organs themselves are still developing. What stimulates the sheath cells of the abdominal nerves to undergo mitosis? The number and location of these mitoses determines the future pattern of the abdominal nervous system. How do the nerves at this stage know where future adult structures will develop and require innervation? This brings us into the realm of cell differentiation and pattern formation, problems that will be considered in more detail later. The coordination of the different metamorphic processes is amazing, as is the realization that all these events occur within, in response to, and at speeds determined by light darkness cycles such as those shown by Harker for *Drosophila* (1965a and b).

HEMOCYTE ACTIVITY IN RELATION TO METAMORPHOSING TISSUES

Older works on the hemocytes were largely concerned with the role of blood cells in relation to developing tissues. More recently, work has centered more on hemocyte identification,

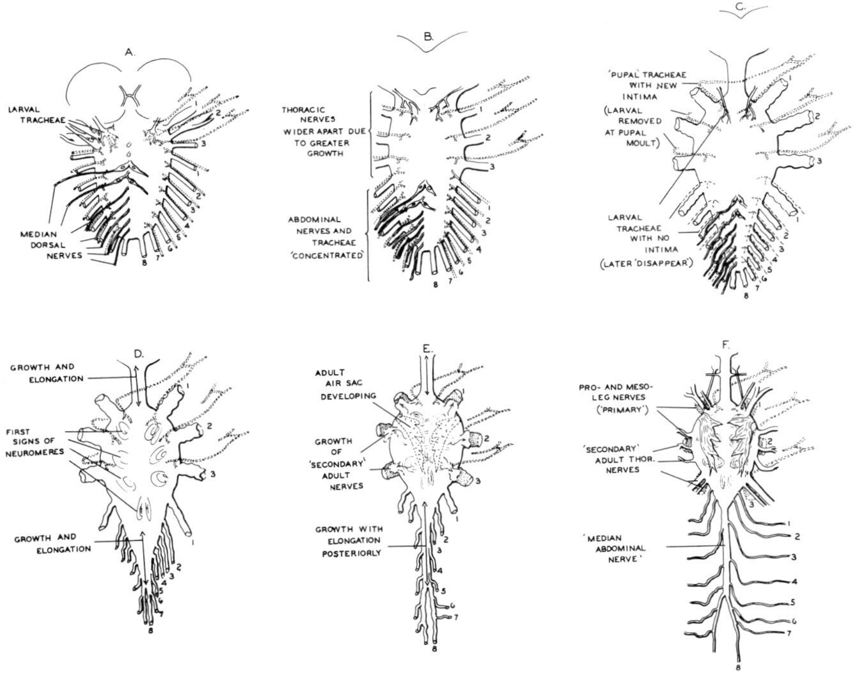

FIG. 6. Metamorphosis of the thoracico-abdominal nerve mass showing general changes in shape due to growth of sheath cells and the formation of adult "neuropile" in the thoracic, and general reduction in the abdominal region. A: larval system in dorsal view, with lateral and dorsal nerves and segmental tracheae (dotted); B: cryptocephalic pupa showing general elongation of the thoracico-abdominal mass; C: first-day pupa showing beginnings of relative enlargement of thoracic and reduction of abdominal centers; D: second-day pupa, showing disappearance of abdominal tracheae and apparently also of the segmental dorsal nerves with neural lamella broken down; growth and elongation occurring in the abdominal region; E: midpupa showing growth and elongation of the abdominal nerves, growth of secondary thoracic nerves and the development of adult tracheal epithelium; F: adult system completed, with lining of air sac secreted and new adult "connective sheaths" formed continuously around nervous system and tracheae. Sarcophaga, but events are similar in Drosophila.

73

origins, and their relative numbers at various stages, together with their role in coagulation. The vast amount of work up to 1962 is reviewed by Jones (1962). Since that time renewed interest has arisen in the part that blood cells may play in relation to the different metamorphosing tissues. Selman, in 1962, described briefly the fate of blood cells during the life history of the alder fly, *Sialis lutaria*. Here, phagocytes were found to ingest all particles freed in the hemolymph as a result of the cytolysis of the cells of the fat body, and in the gills the epidermal cells are ingested by the blood cells also only after cytolysis. The phagocytes or morula cells, as they are later called, were said to disintegrate immediately before darkening of the cuticle. Ashhurst and Richards (1964b) described adipohemocytes in the vicinity of the nerve cord at the time of breakdown of the sheath in the lepidopteran *Galleria mellonella*. The participation of these cells in the breakdown of the neural lamella was substantiated by autoradiographic studies by Shrivastava and Richards (1965), and by electron microscopic observations by Pipa and Woolever (1965) on the same species. The latter demonstrated the presence within the adipohemocyte of neural sheath fibrils. These blood cells were not found to be involved in formation of the later adult nerve sheath. In the Diptera Cyclorrhapha similar conclusions had been reached by Whitten (1964b) in an investigation of the blood-tissue relationships primarily in *Sarcophaga bullata*, with observations also on *Phormia regina* and *Drosophila melanogaster*. It was found that phagocytic hemocytes underwent very complex activities at the time of puparium formation. They were responsible for the ingestion of all tissue fragments in the hemocoele; they were also located in such consistent and characteristic positions in the developing pupae as to suggest that they participated in the transfer of materials to the developing tissues, particularly hypodermal cells of the general body surface and internal tracheae and muscle tendons. As with the lepidopteran nerve cord, these blood cells were not found closely associated with the developing adult neural lamella. The blood picture is outlined in Fig. 7. The sequence of events for cell type 5 shows nuclear and not cytoplasmic division to form enormous phagocytic bodies, which then over an extremely short period of time ingest larval fragments, including whole nuclei. These cells correspond to the granular hemocytes of Jones (1962), and in their later gorged form—as "spherules" (Fig. 7)—they correspond to the "spherule cells" and "spheres of granules" of earlier workers. These cells have recently been followed at light and electron microscope levels (Whitten, 1968) through the pupal to

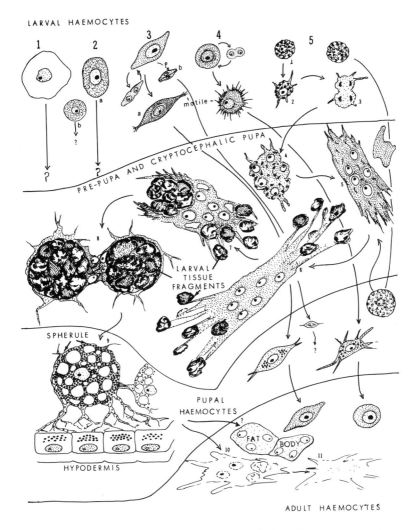

FIG. 7. Diagrammatic representation of the changes occurring in
the hemocytes, accompanying metamorphosis in *Sarcophaga bullata*.
1: hyaline cell; 2 to 4: plasmatocytes, 2-oval, 3-fusiform, 4-round;
5: granular hemocytes that by complex processes undergo nuclear
division, forming multinucleate masses that phagocytose larval fragments and become the pupal "spherules;" these later appear uninu-
cleate but may or may not retain cytoplasmic bridges throughout pupation. They appear again later in the pupal stage to be multinucleate
and enter a second phase of phagocytosis, selectively ingesting adult
hypodermal (epidermal) cells at very specific times. Reproduced with
permission from J. Insect Physiol., 10, 1964.

the adult stage. Their continuing close relationship with the developing adult tissues has convincingly shown the importance of the cells not only in removing larval fragments but also in processing and passing on materials to the developing adult tissues. By the time the adult emerges the blood cell contents are depleted. These cells undoubtedly correspond to the type F hemocytes described by Crossley for *Calliphora* (1964). In a later paper (1965), Crossely described breakdown of type F cells in the midpupa, whereas it will be shown below in a study of coordinated development in the fly foot that the corresponding cells in *Sarcophaga* pass through into the adult stage, functioning even at the time of emergence, in the ingestion of selected epidermal cells (Fig. 20). We have now reached the stage in studies on insect hemocytes where it is clear that phagocytic blood cells play as important a role in tissue destruction as phagocytic blood cells do in a metamorphosing amphibian. There is also no doubt whatsoever, in the cyclorrhaphan dipteran pupa, that the phagocytic blood cells can and do play an extremely important part in providing "processed larval tissues" as raw materials for the developing adult cells.

Blood cells have been variously described as giving rise to adult tissue. Attention may be drawn here to Figure 7, where the possible origin of the cyclorrhaphan adult fat body cells from the phagocytic hemocytes is suggested. This suggestion is not new, having been made by several of the older workers at the turn of the century. Electron microsocopy has substantiated, rather than refuted this suggestion. As with other systems, there is a vast source of information awaiting investigation with modern techniques.

There is no evidence to suggest that phagocytic hemocytes attack normal, healthy insect tissues. Figure 8 shows the beginnings of focal degradation in foot pad tenent hair cells. This occurs before any attack by the hemocytes which only subsequently ingest the pycnotic tenent nuclei and surrounding cytoplasm (Fig. 9). Figure 8 parallels closely micrographs of vertebrate tissue in which focal degradation is occurring (e.g., Swift and Hruban, 1964).

LYSOSOMES

The cyclorrhaphan phagocytic hemocyte provides ideal material for study of lysosome origin and fate and function. DeDuve's article on the lysosome (1963) describes lysosome activity with respect to the tail resorption and tissue breakdown

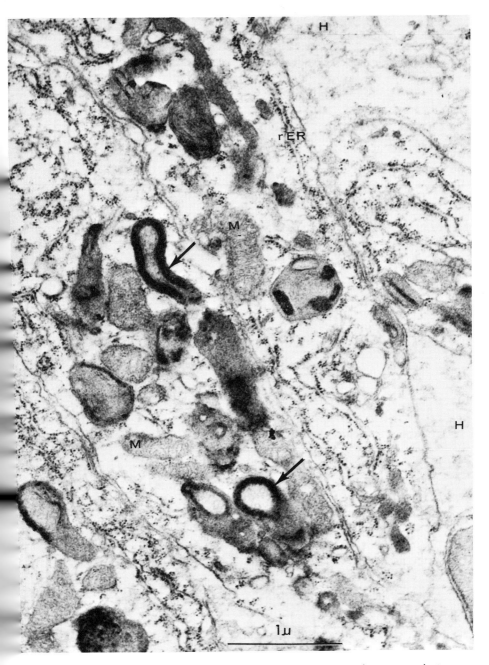

FIG. 8. Areas of focal degradation appearing in the tenent hair cells of the foot of *Sarcophaga* at the onset of "cell death" and before the beginnings of phagocytosis by the blood cells. Compare with Fig. 9. rER: rough surfaced endoplasmic reticulum; H: hemocoele; M: mitochondrion.

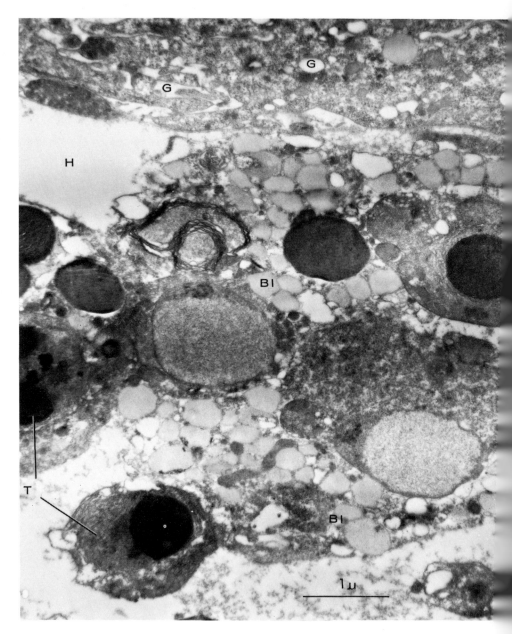

FIG. 9. Electron micrograph of hemocytes of *Sarcophaga* late in pupation, following phagocytosis (Day 9-10 at 25°C) of the tenent cell nuclei and adjacent cytoplasm. Bl: phagocytic blood cell; G: giant cell cytoplasm; H: hemocele; T: ingested pycnotic tenent cell nuclei.

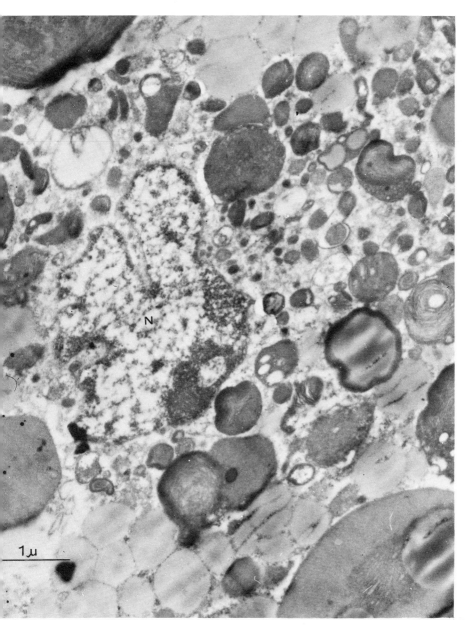

FIG. 10. Electron micrograph through a phagocytic blood cell (spherule) at day four of pupation at 25°C, showing various stages of degradation of larval contents (lysosomes?) in the vicinity of the nucleus in *Sarcophaga*.

in the metamorphosing frog. A similar story can be given for lysosome activity in the cyclorrhaphan phagocytic hemocyte. Figure 10 shows a typical picture of different stages of degradation of *larval* fragments in the vicinity of the nucleus in a day four (at 25°C) pupa. Acid phosphatase has been demonstrated in these cells and in their apparent homologues in *Calliphora erythrocephala* (Crossley, 1964). This is particularly good material for such studies of lysosomes in that within a time span of 12 days at 25°C these blood cells can be followed at all stages of their various phagocytic activities.

THE REPRODUCTIVE SYSTEM

Since the reproductive system matures in all insects regardless of whether they undergo metamorphosis or not, considerations of general development of the reproductive system are not directly relevant to the present discussion. However, certain aspects bear on the subject. In the apterygote ametamorphic insects, the reproductive system is laid down at the time of hatching from the egg, and maturation occurs later, although even in the Apterygota, genitalia may be undeveloped at the time of hatching and develop in later instars. In insects with complete metamorphosis, the larvae may hatch with the reproductive system in an embryonic state. Gonads are present but the ducts are limited to the mesodermal elements that extend from the gonad distally, to end posteriorly in a coelomic sac or ampulla, located in different segments in male and female (see the figures in Imms 1957). During metamorphosis, development of the reproductive system is completed when the genital imaginal rudiment develops both the external genitalia and the ectodermal elements of the internal reproductive system, including median ducts, accessory glands and spermathecae. When growth is completed and ectodermal and mesodermal ducts have met and fused the breakdown of cells and continuity of the ducts to the outside is established. In one of the best-known insects, *Drosophila*, onset of metamorphosis is characterized by immediate and rapid growth of the imaginal discs, including the genital disc. In this same example an anomaly exists in that the ectodermal component is considered to give rise to the entire duct system right to the gonad. This anomaly has recently been doubted in the higher fly *Sarcophaga*, where the mesodermal ducts have been shown to be present in the larva in a typical embryonic state. The ducts themselves represent true examples of "imaginal rudiments" (Whitten, 1965). The onset of pupation is characterized by extensive mitoses in this strand of cells. Subsequent dissolution of the connective tissue "basement membrane" and shortening of the strand (closely similar to events in the peripheral nerves) produces the proximal mesodermal genital duct in both male and female. This meets up and fuses with the ectodermal components derived from the genital imaginal disc. Thus *Sarcophaga* falls into line with other endopterygote insects in which metamorphosis involves passing from the embryonic to the adult condition. It would be surprising if *Drosophila* is really exceptional in this respect.

During metamorphosis, extensive changes occur within the reproductive system. The degree of maturation attained by the time of adult emergence varies from male and female and from species to species. In many cases gametes are fully developed at the time of emergence of the adult insect. Review articles of King (1964) and Telfer (1965) provide interesting and instructive reading on this subject.

THE EPIDERMIS IN THE METAMORPHOSING PUPA

The epidermis and its derivatives have been left for consideration until last because in many respects this is the most important and interesting cell layer to the insect developmental biologist. Included here are the imaginal discs which are essentially epidermal sacs containing nerve and tracheal endings along with the hemolymph and contained blood cells. Strictly speaking, the ectodermal regions of the reproductive system and of the gut also fall into this category, but they have already been considered briefly along with the rest of these systems. The tracheal system is an invaginated extension of the general epidermis and will be considered first.

THE TRACHEAL SYSTEM

The tracheal system is composed of two cell types: the tracheal cell and the tracheolar cell. Essentially, the difference between a trachea and a tracheole is that the former is formed as a layer of cuticle by the tracheal epithelium, while the tracheole is terminal and formed intracellularly by a single cell. At one time it was thought that tracheae possessed the spiral or annular thickenings, whereas the tracheoles did not. However, electron microscopy has shown that tracheoles do also (Fig. 11). A physiological distinction made between tracheae and tracheoles is that little gaseous exchange occurs through the tracheal wall, exchange being mainly by way of the tracheoles at the tissue level. It will be seen below that the metamorphosing pupa may be an exception to this generalization. The pupa has respiratory problems that are unique in that a single system laid down at the larval-pupal molt has to tracheate tissues that are destined to disappear during the pupal stage, tissues that persist through from larva to adult, and more significantly, yet other tissues that develop during the pupal stage and are not in existence at the time that the tracheal system of the pupa is laid down. These demands on the tracheal system will be taken up following a general survey of the development of the system from first instar to adult.

Details can be obtained from Buck (1962) and Miller (1964) on the large amount of work that has been done on the tracheal system; however, problems of development are relatively unexplored. In general it has been thought that at each molt the tracheal lining is replaced but that the tracheolar lining is retained throughout the life of the insect. However, the situation is much more complex than this, particularly in the metamorphosing insect where drastic changes are occurring in other systems. Figure 14 gives a schematic drawing of the types of development that can occur in individual tracheae. In general, the insect tracheal system is divided into 10 pairs of tracheal metameres, occurring in segmentally repeating order and, in the pterygote insects, joined laterally and longitudinally at junction points or *tracheal nodes*. The original segmental pattern can be seen at each molt when the continuous tracheal tube linings "break" at the tracheal nodes, and each segment is removed through its respective spiracle. This occurs even in forms in which the spiracles are physiologically closed and not functional as far as respiration is concerned. The degree of change or growth in the tracheal system from instar to instar is determined by the physiological requirements, so that as far as the metamorphosing pupa is concerned, there is a direct correlation between the degree of metamorphic change in, say, the muscular system and that in the tracheal system. Figure 12 shows the pattern of development in a generalized dipteran, and members of the nematoceran Bibionidae would follow this closely. Here the larval basic pattern is taken right through from larva to adult, and the only drastic change is in the thorax where the tracheation to the new flight muscles, wings, halters, and legs is superimposed on the larval pattern by growth of new tracheal branches at the end of the last larval instar. In contrast, Fig. 13 shows the sequence of events in *Drosophila melanogaster* where there is considerable change from larva to adult, cor-

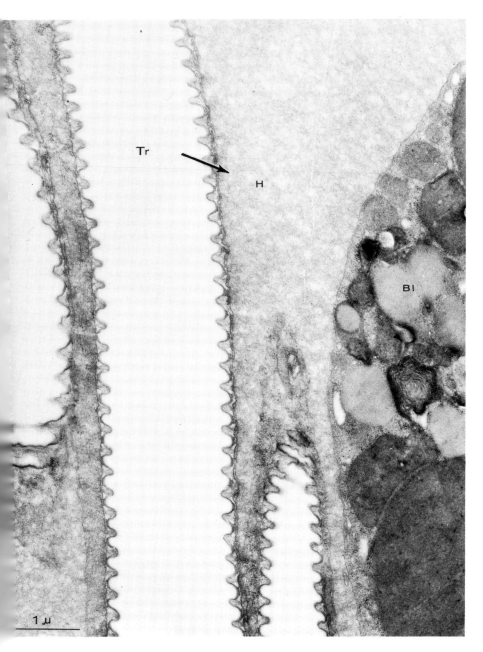

FIG. 11. Electron micrograph of a pupal tracheole from the leg of *Sarcophaga*; note taenidia, the very thin layer of cytoplasm between tracheal lining and hemocoele, and the virtual nonexistence of basement membrane. It is suggested that any gaseous exchange is between tracheal lumen and hemocoele. Bl: adjacent blood cell; H: hemocoele; Tr: tracheole.

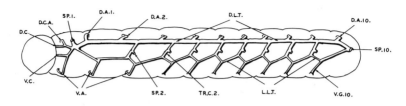

LARVA.

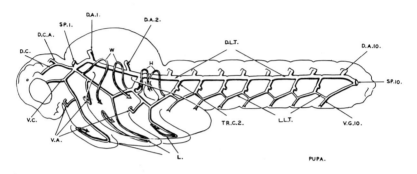

PUPA.

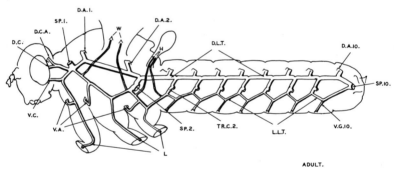

ADULT.

FIG. 12. Diagrammatic representation of the development of the tracheal system in a generalized member of the Diptera. A: larval system in left lateral view; B: pupal system; C: adult system. At each molt the tracheoles are retained, new tracheae developing around those of the preceding stage, with new branches also being formed, particularly in the thorax. Abbreviations: D.C.: dorsal cervical; V.C.: ventral cervical; D.C.A.: dorsal cervical anastomosis; V.A.: ventral tracheal anastomosis; SP.: spiracle; D.A.: dorsal anastomosis; TR.C.: transverse connective; V.G.: ventral ganglionic; D.L.T.: dorsal longitudinal trunk; L.L.T.: lateral longitudinal trunk; W: wing trachea; H: halter trachea; L: leg trachea.

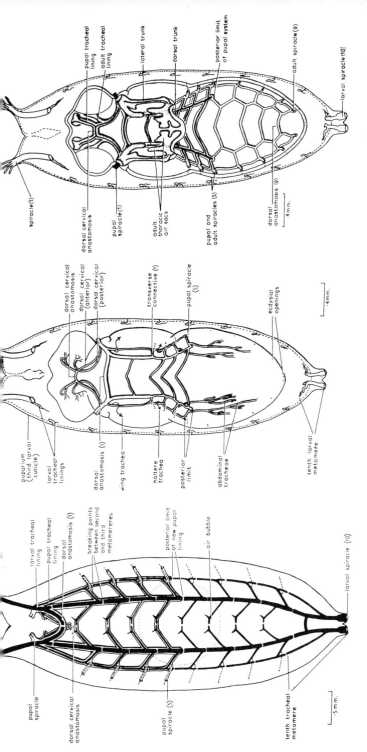

FIG. 13. Diagrammatic representation of the development of the tracheal system in a specialized member of the Diptera – *Drosophila melanogaster*; here development is highly complex. The posterior half of the larval system is histolyzed, being reformed when the adult system is laid down, although the last tracheal metamere is never replaced. The adult thoracic system develops around the preexisting pupal system and by elaborate branching of the epithelium of the basic system. A: prepupal stage with pupal system being formed around the larval; B: functional pupal system; C: adult system being formed around the pupal system. Reproduced from Quart. J. Micr. Sci. 98, 1957.

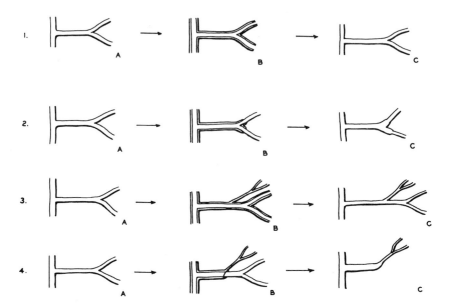

FIG. 14. Diagram showing the different types of fate that an individual trachea can undergo during development. Details can be found
in Whitten (1962b). Reproduced with permission from Ann. Ent. Soc.
Amer., 55, 1962.

related closely with the drastic changes in other systems and with
the virtual reduction of the pupa to an embryonic system. At the
larval-pupal molt the posterior half of the larval system does
not secrete pupal cuticle and is subsequently histolyzed (as are
the ganglionic tracheae of Fig. 6). Later in the pupal stage there
is new growth of adult tracheal epithelium in this region, but
the last metamere is never replaced.

Between these two extremes there are all degrees of
relative histolysis in the abdominal system, and these are
highly consistent within dipteran groups of close affinity. This
whole subject is as intriguing and probably as important in terms
of the control of cell death as are problems of muscle cell
death, particularly as tracheae are generally considered to be
noninnervated. Without a nerve supply, why would an individual
trachea or a whole tracheal segment cease to secrete cuticle
and the cells subsequently die when its neighbor remains and
functions normally? Perhaps the answer lies in physiological
changes in the organ that is tracheated and destined to die.
However, the converse cannot apply to the development of new

tracheal branches to tissues that are not yet developed in the pupa.

It has been said that the elaborate tracheal development of the thoracic region of adult systems bears little relationship to that of the earlier larval system. This is not so. From a survey by the author of the development of the adult system within some 20 families of Diptera, it is evident that the very elaborate system of tracheae or air sacs represents branching of the tracheal epithelium of the earlier basic larval pattern. Figure 15A and B are of *Drosophila* and *Mycetophila*, respectively. Superficially, they look very unlike each other and their corresponding larval systems. However, close inspection shows the same basic pattern of transverse and longitudinal elements, with very constant positions of origin of leg, wing, and halter tracheae. No comparable survey is apparently available for other endopterygote orders.

SOME UNIQUE CHARACTERISTICS OF PUPAL TRACHEAL SYSTEMS

The pupal system of the cyclorrhaphous Diptera, including forms like *Drosophila, Sarcophaga*, and *Calliphora*, is characterized by grapelike bunches of tracheoles suspended in the hemocoele. These arise by mitosis of cells of the tracheal system, and after the larval-pupal molt there is often extension of the tracheal cell cytoplasm toward various organs, including the developing epidermis. The pupal stage has been seen to be characterized by the absence of basement membranes; there is no penetration of individual tissues by the pupal tracheoles which lie essentially within the hemocoele. Some of these tracheoles are shown in Figure 11. They are particularly interesting in that respiratory exchange is apparently occurring between the tracheole and the hemolymph. The lining of cytoplasm, particularly on one side, is infinitesimally thin and so is any basement membrane. These pupal tracheoles are seen to move in later pupal stages to come in closer proximity to developing adult organs such as the reproductive system. For example, an early pupal testis or ovary has no tracheation, whereas later pupal gonads have functional pupal tracheoles associated with them, as well as the as yet nonfunctional adult tracheae and tracheoles. The condition in the Diptera Cyclorrhapha is extreme, but the same condition prevails in at least the thorax of more generalized forms where there is extensive evelopment of muscles in

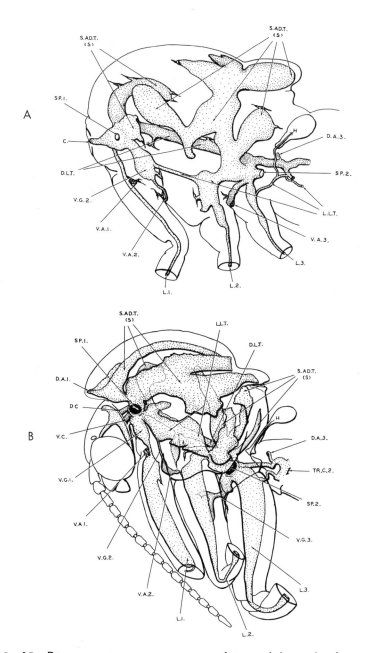

FIG. 15. Diagrammatic representation of two adult tracheal systems that superficially look very dissimilar, yet both arise by growth of the larval and pupal tracheal epithelium around the preexisting pattern. Secondary adult tracheae arise by branching from the basic pattern. A: *Drosophila*; B: *Mycetophila* (Mycetophilidae, Diptera Nematocera). (See Fig. 12 for abbreviations.) S.AD.T.(s): secondary adult tracheae in the form of air sacs.

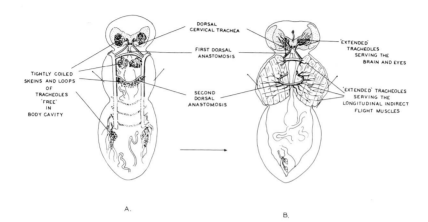

FIG. 16. Diagrams to illustrate the unique condition of the pupal tracheal system in a specialized pupa such as in *Drosophila* or *Sarcophaga*. Except for a few tracheae, such as those to the thoracic nerve mass, pupal tracheation consists of bunches of tracheoles lying free in the hemocoele. Later, many of these tracheoles migrate to become attached to developing adult organs such as gonads, muscles, etc. They are removed and not replaced at the pupal-adult ecdysis. A: early pupa; B: late pupa.

the later pupal stages. Figure 16 diagrammatically represents the situation in an organism such as *Drosophila*. In the present case it is the tracheal cell cytoplasm that extends towards the tissues, whereas in the bug *Rhodnius*, Wigglesworth (1959a) described the drawing of tracheoles, by epidermal cell extensions, to areas requiring oxygen. Epidermal cells at quite considerable distances away would send out processes towards tracheoles, "capture them," and draw them to the deprived area.

By comparison with other epidermal cell types the tracheal cell shows remarkable uniformity, the only distinction being between tracheal and tracheolar. Whether the cells at the tracheal nodes are structurally different seems never to have been investigated. That they are important physiologically in connection with gradients has been shown by Locke (1964). Cells of the spiracular region are not included in this tracheal system since they are most easily thought of as belonging to the general body surface. It would be of considerable interest to understanding of cell differentiation to know whether the same tracheal cell ever produces specific larval, as opposed to pupal, and pupal as opposed to adult, tracheal cuticle. Whether the air sac cuticle is specifically different in an adult is not known.

METAMORPHOSIS OF THE GENERAL EPIDERMIS

The rest of the organ systems differ from the epidermis in proceeding more gradually from larva to adult except in cases where metamorphic changes are involved. The epidermis is, however, characterized by periodic molting and secretion of new cuticular layers, and often the cuticular layers of different instars are characteristically different from those of other instars. Thus, a newly hatched *Thermobia* (firebrat: Thysanaura, Apterygota) that undergoes no metamorphosis during development, is scaleless whereas later preadult and adult instars have scales; a fly pupal cuticle is smooth, while that of the adult consists mainly of small and large bristles and their sockets. There has been a tendency in recent years to talk of the cuticles of metamorphosing endopterygote insects as "larval," "pupal," or "adult" and to relate the appearance of the specific type to the hormone balance between juvenile hormone and molting hormone at a particular period of development. Thus, the larval cuticle has been said to be produced in the presence of high levels of juvenile hormone and low ecdysone; the pupal cuticle is produced in the presence of high levels of ecdysone and lower juvenile hormone; and finally the adult in high ecdysone and virtually no juvenile hormone (see figure in Schneiderman and Gilbert, 1964). In the case of the non-metamorphosing *Thermobia,* a piece of scaleless cuticle from a newly hatched larva, when implanted into an adult, is found to molt and prematurely produce scaled cuticle. The larva has a high and the adult a low concentration of juvenile hormone (Watson, 1963). While there are in most Endopterygota considerable differences between larval, pupal, and adult cuticles, one cannot say, for instance, that bristles are confined to adult cuticles. A particular insect type will have characteristic cuticles at different stages, but whether a larval cuticle is ultrastructurally diagnostic has not been shown for any insect. Certainly the tracheal cuticle appears to be essentially similar at all stages, and the epidermal cells secreting this are every bit as exposed to hormone fluctuations as are the cells of the general hypodermis. That changes are not simple responses to different hormone titers has recently been shown by Krishnakumaran and Schneiderman (1964). They questioned whether perhaps the cells of the lepidopteran adult differ from cells of the pupa in response to juvenile hormone, since it was seen in experiments that adult abdomens could be induced to molt again when joined to pupae, but that the second adult cuticle, although distinctly adult, seldom produced scales. A much older adult did produce normal scaled adult cuticle. A high level of juvenile hormone did not seem to influence the development of the adult cuticle since experimental results were similar with abdomens containing high levels of juvenile hormone (e.g., *cecropia, cynthia*) and others containing low levels *(polyphemus)*. Krishnakumaran and Schneiderman quote a comparable phenomenon from the work of Piepho and his students, who showed that when fragments of adult cuticle were implanted into larvae they did not secrete larval cuticle immediately but required several molts before doing so. It may be of interest to observe in this context that the cells of the imaginal discs in the fly (which will be seen below to be determined but not differentiated), secrete first pupal cuticle (see Fig. 17 for the foot or leg imaginal disc) and *subsequently* undergo extensive mitoses followed later by differentiation into adult cuticle secreting cells. These disc cells in an adult host continue mitoses indefinitely, but implanted into a metamorphosing larva they first secrete pupal cuticle, then further divide, and finally differentiate and produce adult cuticle.

METAMORPHOSIS OF THE EPIDERMAL CELLS

The degree of change occurring in individual epidermal cells varies from insect to insect. In the more generalized endopterygotes or even the more generalized members of the specialized orders, e.g., the Nematocera of the Diptera, the epidermis passes more or less unchanged from larva to adult. On the other hand, in the higher flies, the Cyclorrhapha, there is said to be a complete replacement of larval epidermis by adult epidermal cells that originate from areas of undifferentiated imaginal cells—those of leg, wing, halter, genital, labial, antennal and eye discs, and paired groups of cells segmentally arranged on the abdominal segments. The pupal cuticle is secreted by the larval epidermal cells of the abdomen and small areas of the thorax, and the remainder is secreted by the undifferentiated cells of the different imaginal discs. Only in the cyclorrhaphan tracheal system might it be possible to follow individual epidermal cells through from larva to adult, whereas in the Nematocera this should be possible for general epidermal cells also.

The metamorphosis of the epidermis may best be looked at now from the viewpoint of "imaginal disc" development, since a tremendous amount of thought-provoking and fascinating work has been done on this subject. Following this, the fate of a few individual cells can be traced through from the time of the larval-pupal molt to the time of adult emergence. This will demonstrate the complexities on the one hand and the great potential on the other that the metamorphosing insect epidermal cells have in helping to solve some of the most puzzling of biology's and life's problems—those of nuclear-cytoplasmic relationships and of cell and tissue differentiation. The insect epidermal cell has been the fascinating subject of several articles, including that of Stern (1954) and of Wigglesworth (1959b). There have been new developments involving the epidermal cell, that include gradient studies (Locke 1964) and the discovery of giant polytene chromosomes in the dipteran epidermis; these, along with the fact that the epidermis is undoubtedly the main "target organ" of the molting hormone ecdysone, give the epidermal cell greater importance than ever.

METAMORPHOSIS OF THE IMAGINAL DISCS

In the more generalized Diptera the imaginal discs of wings and legs lie beneath the epidermis and are not withdrawn into the body as are those of the specialized Cyclorrhapha. Also, the cavities connecting with the general epidermis are never closed and the eyes do not develop from invaginated buds. Developing pigmented eyes can often be seen, as in the mosquito, through the semitransparent head capsule of a late larva.

The imaginal discs of a cyclorrhaphan fly include genital and leg discs, (Fig. 4 shows genital and first and second leg discs), wing, halter, labial, eye, and antennal. The groups of cells between duct and larval salivary gland, those at the junctions of foregut and midgut and midgut and hind gut, the mesodermal genital duct rudiment of *Sarcophaga,* and the hypodermal discs of the abdominal segments, are also imaginal rudiments. It is difficult to draw a hard and fast line of distinction between some of these cell groups and those associated with individual systems, such as the tracheal cells that will suddenly at puparium formation undergo intense mitosis to produce the bunches of specialized pupal tracheoles, or the sheath cells of the peripheral nerves, which presumably functioned in the embryo to secrete the larval nerve sheath and now at puparium formation are stimulated into intense mitotic activity to give rise to the cells that form the skeleton of the adult peripheral nerves. Studies on the leg or wing or genital imaginal discs, are essentially studies on epidermal cell lines. Embryos of endopterygotes that undergo complete metamorphosis, such as *Drosophila*, possess two cell types. Firstly, there are those cells that are determined to form the larval body and, in these, differentiation immediately sets in. Secondly, there are those cells that are determined but are set apart and remain in an embryonic state until the time of pupation (Hadorn, 1965). Cells of the imaginal discs come into this category. They do divide and the discs grow considerably in size from their earliest appearance to the end of the larval stage, but they remain undifferentiated. Due largely to the classic earlier works such as those of Bodenstein (see 1950) using transplantation techniques and more recently the fascinating works of Hadorn and his collaborators, some amazing phenomena have come to light with respect to potentialities of imaginal disc cells in the metamorphosing insect. It would seem that the cells of these discs are already determined for "leg" or "wing" or "eye" early in embryonic life, as early as the first to fifth hour, at a time when the imaginal discs are not yet visibly set apart within the still apparently homogeneous blastoderm. There is even determination for particular areas of these discs. There is *determination* at this time but not *differentiation*. This occurs only at metamorphosis. As stated by Hadorn, the change from undifferentiated to differentiated state in holometabolous insects is controlled by hormones. The juvenile hormone somehow in the larval instars blocks any differentiation; a drop in the level of juvenile hormone at the onset of metamorphosis results in a "deblocking" of readiness for differentiation present in the discs throughout larval life. *Perhaps the juvenile hormone acts as a repressor of the sets of genes needed in differentiation,* but here Hadorn warns that much more information is needed before the happenings that clear the path for differentiation in a determined cell can be interpreted in molecular terms. Until details are clearer of the responses by particular cells of known fate and history, it would be good to extend such reservations to work on hormone action, particularly with respect to the influence of the balance between juvenile hormone and ecdysone on the production of specific "larval," "pupal," or "adult" cuticle. The same reservations may be extended to the effects of hormones on chromosome puffing sequences (see Chapter 5). The results with larval salivary glands cannot necessarily explain hormone action on tissues that will undergo metamorphosis.

The exciting results of Hadorn and co-workers involve the maintenance of imaginal discs within adult hosts, where they increase in size by extensive mitosis but do not differentiate. Removal from the adult and transplantation into a metamorphosing larva brings about cessation of cell division and differentiation into adult structures. Of particular interest is the process of "transdetermination" whereby after some eight or nine transplants (from one adult host to another), the disc when allowed to differentiate in a metamorphosing larval host, differentiates into an adult structure different from the original implant. Thus, a genital disc after many transplants may give rise to leg or wing or thorax. Transdeterminations occur in the probability order of genitalia, antenna, leg, palpus, wing, and thorax, the latter occurring in the oldest transfer generations. Reversals were also found. No explanation can as yet be given for these amazing results, but it is suggested by Hadorn that possibly a degree of dilution reached by cell cultures might have a feedback action on gene activation. Instead of the genes that formerly determined the original organ, other genes come into play, resulting in the transdetermination. Some of the transdetermination effects are reminiscent of some *Drosophila* mutants such as *aristapedia* where a tarsus is formed on the antenna. However, most of the transdetermination effects are not known as mutants.

METAMORPHOSIS OF AN IMAGINAL DISC: THE LEG DISC

The type of development undergone by individual elements of an imaginal disc can be seen in the case of the leg (Fig 17: stages 1-12). Details have been followed for *Sarcophaga bullata*, the flesh fly, but development is essentially similar in other Cyclorrhapha, including *Drosophila*. Events followed at light and electron microscope levels demonstrate the complex changes and coordinated development of the different components: various epidermal cells, tracheoles, and phagocytic blood cells. Some of these events have already been discussed in relation to hemocyte activity during metamorphosis. At this point the main concern will be with the development of individual epidermal cells.

The mass of thousands of determined yet undifferentiated epidermal cells (stage 1) first secrete the pupal cuticle of the leg disc. Retraction of the epidermal cells from the pupal cuticle follows and cell division continues (stage 2). Five cells forming the future end of the claw and four future giant cells

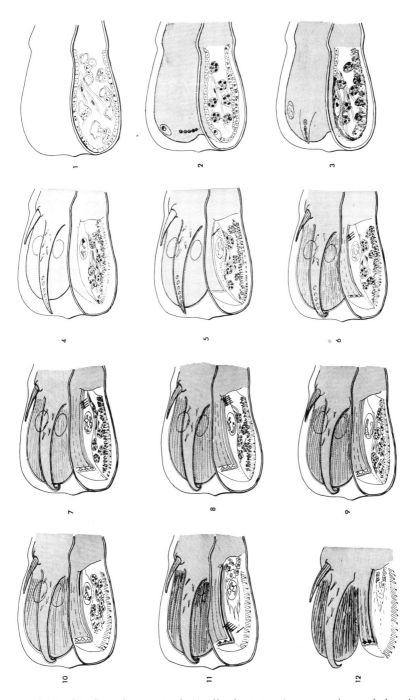

FIG. 17. Development of the fly foot to show coordinated development of dorsal giant, ventral tenent cells and the associated phagocytic blood cells. For details, see text. *Sarcophaga*.

become recognizable at stage 3 while cell growth and continued mitoses occur among "mother" tenent hair cells whose descendants will occupy the future ventral surface of the foot. Growth and cell division thrust the five claw cells into the tip of the forming claw, and the foot pads take shape by progressive growth and median indentation. Dorsally, the two giant cells extend over each foot pad; their nuclei are characterized by giant polytene chromosomes. The tenent cells give out very fine cytoplasmic processes, while the dorsal cells grow in width as broad, flat cells. The tarsal hair cells at this same time form, like the tenent cells, cytoplasmic processes, varying in size according to whether a large or small hair is to be produced. Stage 4 marks the end of growth and differentiation, yet at this time *no* cuticle is as yet deposited. Thus, the future shape of a hair is laid down by cell growth (c.f. Lees and Picken, 1945) and is completed by the time cuticle secretion begins. This is of interest in questions of abnormal bristle development in mutant *Drosophila*.

Cessation of growth and attainment of cell maturity is followed by a well-spaced sequence of cuticle deposition accompanied in the giant cell by constant and characteristic patterns of chromosome puffing activity (e.g., Figs. 17, 18, 19). First is secreted an *ecdysial membrane* (1), followed by a cuticulin layer (2), a layer of dense exocuticle (3), which later becomes darkened and sclerotized, a homogeneous inner layer of exocuticle (4), and a narrow layer of "mesocuticle" (5); each layer is indicated by an arrow in Figure 17. By stage 9 these sequences are completed in giant, tenent, and trichogen cells. Cytolysis is now observable within the tenent cell nuclei and cytoplasm. This is seen at the electron microscope level in Figure 8, in which centers of focal degradation can be clearly seen. The hemocytes, which at the time of first evagination of the legs were gorged with larval tissue fragments, have subsequently been digesting them and passing on the degradation products to the developing epidermal cells. These phagocytic blood cells now, at stage 9, embark on a second phase of phagocytosis. By stage 10 the pycnotic tenent cell nuclei are nearly all engulfed (Fig. 9). In fact, the exact age of the foot can be determined by three means: (a) by close inspection of the extent of the darkening process and actual shade of specific areas, (b) by close investigation of the relative degree of phagocytosis of tenent cell nuclei, and (c) by close inspection of the puffing pattern of the chromosomes. All are equally exact and reliable. The tracheoles and giant cells remain unattacked at this time. Endocuticle secretion within the giant cell cytoplasm occurs after this at a time when darkening

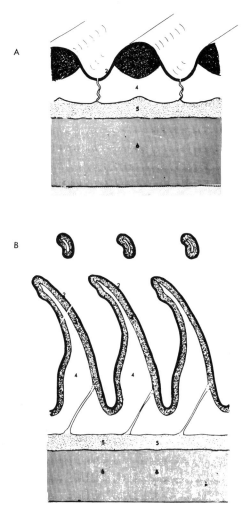

FIG. 18. The cuticular layers determined from electron microscope observations in A, dorsal cuticle, B, ventral tenent hairs which occur in very precisely arranged rows. The same layers are laid down at comparable times in dorsal cuticle, ventral tenent hairs and tarsal trichogen, hair, cells. *Sarcophaga.* Layers—1: ecdysial membrane; 2: cuticulin layer of epicuticle; 3: dense exocuticle, later melanized and sclerotized; 4: homogeneous amber colored exocuticle, not melanized later; 5: "mesocuticle;" 6: extensive layer of endocuticle.

of the exocuticle is occurring over the ridges of the dorsal cuticle. Endocuticle (layer 6) secretion seems to occur by a combination of intracellular secretion and retraction of cytoplasm (and nuclei and blood cells) to the base of the foot, so that the space formerly occupied by giant and tenent cells is now occupied by endocuticle. The position of blood cells in relation to that of giant nuclei and the former position of tenent nuclei can be seen in Figure 20. Even at the light microscope level, association of blood cells with the giant cytoplasm can be seen. The association becomes more close, and at emergence the giant nuclei and cytoplasm also become ingested by the blood cells. The blood cells finally come to lie as a layer over the inner border of the foot pad cuticle, at the base of the pad.

There is no innervation of individual cells in the foot, though possibly a basal stimulus is received that can be transmitted from cell to cell. What determines that cell division should cease in the giant cells and cells of the future claw at a time when mitoses are still occurring among the future tenent cells? What determines the regular pattern and uniform deposition of the different cuticular layers in the various epidermal cells? It can be seen from Fig. 18 that the layers are similar and are deposited at comparable times in tenent, trichogen, and giant cells. The biochemistry must be similar, yet the spatial distribution of the various layers is different, and this is essentially what gives each product its characteristic "differentiation." What initiates cell death among the tenent hair cells? Is it simultaneous or is there a focal point at which the process starts? Focal degradation (Fig. 8) begins before any phagocytosis on the part of the blood cells is to be observed. Does this prompt the blood cells to attack the tenent cells and not the giant or the tracheolar cells? Interestingly, the final deposition of endocuticle by the cytoplasm of the tenent cells is carried out in the absence of their nuclei.

What of the chromosome activity while these sequences of growth, cuticle secretion, and finally death are occurring in the giant cells? For the first time we seem to have a system where one should be able to correlate closely chromosome activity and puffing sequences with the activity of a single cell through growth, various phases of clearly defined activity, and finally cell death (as in Fig. 19). Detailed analysis will be made in Chapter 5 on the vast amount of information that has accumulated as a result of work carried out on dipteran salivary glands and to a lesser extent on the chromosomes of cells of the Malpighian tubules, gut, or seminal vesicles. The Malpighian tubules persist through pupation but are of small dimension while the salivary glands degenerate shortly after pupation. Since epidermal cells

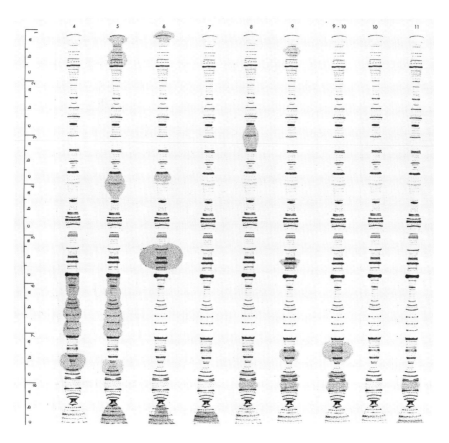

FIG. 19. Puffing sequences in the long arm of chromosome B from the developing foot pad cells; stages 4-11 correspond to stages 4-11 of Fig. 17. *Sarcophaga bullata.*

are specifically the "target organs" for the molting hormone ecdysone, repetition of much of the work carried out on salivary glands should produce particularly interesting results with foot pad cells, particularly work such as that of Karlson and his colleagues (e.g. 1965). It would be exciting to see if and how hormone changes can affect puffing activity and in what way they may alter the biochemistry and ultrascopic structure of the cell.

These discussions might seem to have taken us far from considerations of the whole metamorphosing insect, but in fact it is visible changes in the epidermal cells and their products that constitute external evidence of metamorphosis.

What determines the differences between the various cells of the epidermis of the developing insect? They are variants

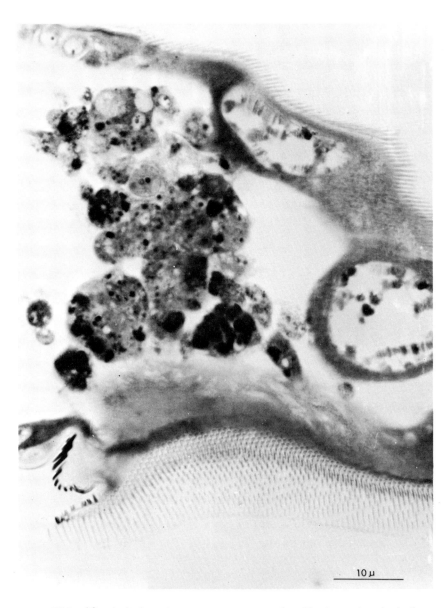

FIG. 20. A light microscope section of a fly foot shortly before emergence. Giant nuclei can be seen dorsally; the former position of tenent cells is still occupied by cytoplasm; the blood cells will shortly ingest the giant nuclei and adjacent cytoplasm, and the cytoplasm of giant and tenent cells will be converted to endocuticle. *Sarcophaga bullata.*

of the same cell type — the epidermal cell. When the layers of cuticle that are secreted are identical in two or more variants, what determines the spatial distribution of these cell products, and what determines the cell shape? If one could answer these questions one would be nearer to answering the problems posed by the phenomena of transdetermination of Hadorn and of the problems of patterns and prepatterns discussed at length by Sondhi (1963) and in a broader context by Waddington (1962).

It will be seen from the foregoing necessarily superficial survey of insect metamorphosis that each system in turn has its own fascinating problems, which, to name but a few, include general considerations of body change, diurnal rhythms, problems of cell determination, cell differentiation, cell death, and cell interaction. Many of the problems are common to those found in other metamorphosing animals, as will be seen in succeeding chapters. Nevertheless, in the insects alone one cannot but be impressed by the infinite number of problems that the one phenomenon of metamorphosis poses to the inquiring developmental biologist.

REFERENCES

Ashhurst, D. E., and A. G. Richards. 1964a. A study of the changes occurring in the connective tissue associated with the central nervous system during the pupal stage of the wax moth, *Galleria mellonella*. L. J. Morph., 114:225–236.
———.1964b. Some histochemical observations on the blood cells of the wax moth, *Galleria mellonella*. L. J. Morph., 114:247–254.
Bodenstein, D. 1950. The postembryonic development of *Drosophila. In* Demerec, M., ed., Biology of Drosophila, pp. 275–367, New York, John Wiley.
Buck, J. 1962. Some physical aspects of insect respiration. Ann. Rev. Entom., 7:27–56.
Carpenter, F. M. 1953. The geological history and evolution of insects, Amer. Sci., 41(No. 2):256–270.
Clements, A. N. 1963. The Physiology of Mosquitoes. Inter. Monograph No. 17, Pergamon Press, pp 1–393.
Clever, U. 1965. Chromosomal changes associated with differentiation. Brookhaven Sympos. Biol., 18:242–253.

Cottrell, C. B. 1964. Insect ecdysis with particular emphasis on cuticular hardening and darkening. *In* Advances in Insect Physiology, vol. II, 175–218, New York, Academic Press.

Crossley, A. C. S. 1964. An experimental analysis of the origins and physiology of haemocytes in the blue blowfly *Calliphora erythrocephala*. J. Exp. Zool. 157:375–398.

———. 1965. Transformations in the abdominal muscles of the blue blow fly *Calliphora erythrocephala* (Meig) during metamorphosis. J. Emb. Exp. Morph., 14:89–110.

Daly, H. V. 1964. Skeleto-muscular morphogenesis of the thorax and wings of the honey bee *Apis melliferra* (Hymenoptera: Apidae), Berkeley, of California Press, pp. 1-77.

deDuve, C. 1963. The lysosome. Amer. Sci., 7:72—80.

Finlayson, L. H. 1956. Normal and induced degeneration of abdominal muscles during metamorphosis in the Lepidoptera. Quart. J. Micr. Sci., 97:215–233.

Fraenkel, G. and C. Hsiao 1962. Hormonal and nervous control of tanning in the fly. Science, 138:27–29.

Hadorn, E. 1965. Problems of determination and transdetermination. Brookhaven Sympos. Biol., 18:148–161.

Harker, J. E. 1965a. The effect of a biological clock on the developmental rate of *Drosophila* pupae.   J. Exp. Biol., 42:323–337.

———. 1965b. The effect of photoperiod on the developmental rate of *Drosophila* pupae. J. Exp. Biol., 43:411–423.

Hinton, H. E. 1961. The role of the epidermis in the disposition of tracheae and muscles. Sci. Prog., 49:329–339.

———. 1963. The origin and function of the pupal stage. Proc. Roy. Ent. Soc. Lond. (A), 38:77–85.

Imms, A. D. 1957. A General Textbook of Entomology, 9th ed., London, Methuen, pp. 1—886.

Johnson, B. 1959. Studies on the degeneration of flight muscles in alate aphids II. Histology and control of muscle breakdown. J. Insect Physiol. 3:367–377.

Jones, J. C. 1962. Current concepts concerning insect hemocytes. Amer. Zool., 2:209–246.

———. 1964. The circulatory system of insects. *In* The Physiology of Insecta, vol. 3, 1–107, New York, Academic Press.

Karlson, P. 1965. Biochemical studies of ecdysone control of chromosomal activity. J. Cell. Comp. Physiol., 66:69–76.

King, R. C. 1964. Studies on early stages of insect oogenesis. *In* Insect Reproduction Symposium. Roy. Ent. Soc. Lond., 2:13–25.

Krishnakumaran, A., and H. A. Schneiderman. 1964. Developmental capacities of the cells of an adult moth. J. Exp. Zool., 157:293–305.

Kroeger, H., and M. Lezzi. 1966. Regulation of gene action in insect development. Ann. Rev. Entom., 11:1–22.

Lees, A. D., and L. E. R. Picken. 1944. Shape in relation to fine structure in the bristles of *Drosophila melanogaster.* Proc. Roy. Soc. Lond. (B), 132:396–423.

Locke, M. 1964. The structure and formation of the integument in insects. *In* The Physiology of Insecta, vol. 3, 380–470, New York, Academic Press.

Lockshin, R. A., and C. M. Williams. 1965. Programmed cell death *111.* Neural control of the breakdown of the intersegmental muscles of silkmoths. J. Insect Physiol, 11:601–610.

Miller, P. 1964. Respiration: aerial gas transport. *In* The Physiology of Insecta, vol. 3, 558–617, New York, Academic Press.

Peréz, C. 1910. Recherches histologiques sur la metamorphose des muscides (*Calliphora erythrocephala* Mg). Arch. Zool. Exp. Gen., 4:1–274.

Pipa, R. L., and P. S. Woolever. 1965. Insect neurometamorphosis II. The fine structure of perineural connective tissue, adipohemocytes, and the shortening ventral nerve cord of a Moth, *Galleria mellonella* (L). Z: Zellforsch., 68:80—101.

Power, M. E. 1952. A quantitative study of the growth of the central nervous system of a holometabolous insect, *Drosophila melanogaster.* J. Morph., 91:389–412.

Schneiderman, H., and L. I. Gilbert. 1964. Control of growth and development in insects. Science, 143:325–333.

Selman, B. J. 1962. The fate of the blood cells during the life history of *Sialis lutaria.* L. J. Insect Physiol. 8:209–214.

———. 1965. The circulatory system of the alder fly *Sialis lutaria.* Proc. Zool. Soc. Lond., 144:487–535.

Shrivastava, S. C., and A. G. Richards. 1965. An autoradiographic study of the relation between hemocytes and connective tissue in the wax moth, *Galleria mellonella* L. Biol. Bull., 128:337—345.

Sondhi, K. C. 1963. The biological foundation of animal patterns. Quart. Rev. Biol., 38:289–327.

Stern, C. 1954. Two or three bristles. Amer. Sci., 42:213–247.

Swift, H., and Z. Hruban. 1964. Focal degradation as a biological process. Fed. Proc., 23:1026–1037.

Taylor, R. L., and A. G. Richards. 1965. Integumentary changes during moulting of arthropods with special reference to the subcuticle and ecdysial membrane. J. Morph., 116:1–22.

Telfer, W. H. 1965. The mechanism and control of yolk formation. Ann. Rev. Entom., 10:161–184.

Trager, W. 1937. Cell size in relation to the growth and metamorphosis of the mosquito *Aedes aegypti*. J. Exp. Zool., 76:467–489.

Waddington, C. H. 1962. New Patterns in Genetics and Development. New York and London, Columbia University Press, pp. 1–271.

Watson, J. A. L. 1963. The cephalic endocrine system in the Thysanura. J. Morph., 113:359–374.

Whitten, J. M. 1957a. The supposed pre-pupa in cyclorrhaphous Diptera. Quart. J. Micr. Sci., 98:241–250.

_____. 1965b. The post-embryonic development of the tracheal system in *Drosophila melanogaster*. Quart. J. Micr. Sci., 98:123–150.

_____. 1960. Tracheal histolysis in the Diptera. Bull. Ent. Soc. Amer., 6:150.

_____. 1962a. Breakdown and formation of connective tissue in the pupal stage of an insect. Quart. J. Micr. Sci., 103:359–367.

_____. 1962b. Homology and development of insect wing tracheae. Ann. Ent. Soc. Amer. 55:288–295.

_____. 1963a. Giant polytene chromosome development in cells of the hypodermis and heart of fly pupae. Proc. XVI Intern. Congr. Zool. Wash., 2:276.

_____. 1963b. The dorsal nerves of cyclorrhaphan larvae: giant cells in which secretory channels appear at the onset of puparium formation. Quart. J. Micr. Sci., 104:217–225.

_____. 1963c. The fly ptilinum: tactile receptors and their function at emergence. J. Linn. Soc. 1 Zool., 44:725–730.

_____. 1964a. Giant polytene chromosomes within hypodermal cells of the developing foot-pads of dipteran pupae. Science, 143:1437–1438.

_____. 1964b. Haemocytes and the metamorphosing tissues in *Sarcophaga bullata*, *Drosophila melanogaster*, and other Diptera Cyclorrhapha. J. Insect Physiol., 10:447–469.

_____. 1964c. Connective tissue membranes and their apparent role in transporting neuro secretory and other secretory products in insects. Gen. Comp. Endocr., 4:176–192.

_____. 1965. Observations on the metamorphosis of the nervous system in the fly *Sarcophaga* and other Diptera Cyclorrhapha. Proc. XII Intern. Congr. Ent. Lond., 148–149.

──────. 1968. Haemocyte activity in relation to hypodermal cell growth, cuticle secretion and cell death in a metamorphosing cyclorrhaphan pupa. J. Insect Physiol. In press.

Wigglesworth, V. B. 1956. Formation and involution of striated muscle fibres during the growth and moulting cycles of *Rhodnius prolixus* (Hemiptera). Quart. J. Micr. Sci., 97:465–480.

──────. 1959a. The role of the epidermal cells in the migration of tracheoles in *Rhodnius prolixus* (Hemiptera). J. Exp. Biol., 36:632–640.

──────. 1959b. The control of Growth and Form: A study of the epidermal cell in an insect. Ithaca, New York, Cornell University Press. pp. 1–136.

──────. 1965. The Principles of Insect Physiology, London, Methuen, pp. 1–741.

three

CONTROL OF
HORMONE PRODUCTION
IN INSECTS

William S. Herman

Department of Zoology
University of Minnesota
Minneapolis, Minnesota

INTRODUCTION

The most casual observer cannot fail to be amazed by the spectacular transformations of wormlike caterpillars into beautiful moths and butterflies, of nondescript grubs into any one of a number of highly polymorphic beetles, or of legless and almost headless maggots into those ubiquitous and rapidly flying pests, the houseflies. The sudden and precisely synchronized emergence of swarms of mayflies, cicadas, and other insects are developmental events of equal wonder, as are the totally different adult individuals that may emerge from essentially identical immature stages of termites, bees, ants and other social insects. These are but a few of the more generally observed morphological and physiological alterations occurring during the life cycles of various insects, but they do serve to illustrate the magnitude and diversity of the developmental pathways found in these animals. These transformations, and most other developmental events occurring in insects, are directed by the activity of the insect neuroendocrine system, and thus a study of the control of hormone production in insects can in a sense be considered a study of the regulation of insect development. As we shall see, this regulation is accomplished by several endocrine centers, and these centers are capable of responding to a wide variety of intrinsic and extrinsic stimuli.

THE NEUROENDOCRINE SYSTEM

The major known components of the insect neuroendocrine system are the neurosecretory cells of the brain and ventral ganglia, the organs serving as release sites for the products of some neurosecretory cells, the corpora allata, and the ecdysial glands.

The Neurosecretory (NS) Cells

A generally acceptable definition of these cells has not yet been formulated. For pedagogical reasons, and with hesitation, we will arbitrarily designate as NS cells those neurons exhibiting glandlike characteristics. Many of these neurons fulfill the classical definition of NS cells, i.e., they are hormonogenic neurons; others innervate endocrine organs, and others have been reported to innervate such structures as the insect epidermis. They are all distinguished from "ordinary" neurons by their glandular appearance, i.e., they contain stainable secretory products and frequently exhibit cycles of accumulation and discharge of these products. Cells of this type are found throughout the insect central nervous system and may also occur in association with, or in the ganglia of, the peripheral nervous system (Gabe, 1966).

Most investigations of insect NS cells have disclosed the presence of several distinct cell types in both the brain and ventral ganglia. These types are typically distinguished on the basis of location, size, and tinctorial properties, and in some insects certain cell types also exhibit cycles of accumulation and depletion of NS material distinct from those of other types.

The most thoroughly investigated NS cells are those found in the pars intercerebralis (PI) of the insect brain. In this area there are generally observed at least four groups of cells, one on each side of the midline of the brain, the so-called medial cells, and one more laterally in each hemisphere, the so-called lateral cells. Careful histological studies of these cells have demonstrated several cell types in each of the four locations and have also disclosed additional types in other areas of the PI. The presence of this multiplicity of types strongly indicates that specific NS cells fulfill specific functions, especially in view of the fact that the PI is known to hormonally regulate numerous processes. Unfortunately, most studies of these cells have either treated all of the PI NS cells as a single group, or have merely distinguished between the medial and lateral clusters. Therefore, in the following discussion we can do no more than implicate medial or lateral clusters in any particular process, although future research likely will show that particular cell types within these clusters, or elsewhere in the PI, regulate distinct functional events.

Although the PI does contain the majority of the brain NS cells, such cells are also present in the tritocerebrum, and possibly elsewhere in the brain. The brain NS cells are generally regarded as functionally the most important NS cells of the central nervous system, but in many insects they are fewer in number than those of the ventral ganglia, and future studies may demonstrate a more important role for the ventral ganglia NS cells than is currently suspected. Since these cells have only been well studied in a few insect species, the available information is still too fragmentary for generalizations as to types and locations. Several distinct types have been observed in specific locations in most ganglia, and the NS cell complement of different ganglia in a single species is usually not identical.

What chemical types of hormones are secreted by the insect NS cells? The best evidence we have suggests that they are peptides or polypeptides, like the NS hormones of vertebrates.

Release Areas for the Products of NS Cells

NS Axons have classically been thought to terminate outside the central nervous system in special storage and/or release organs. These so-called neurohemal organs are now known to be associated with most of the brain and ventral ganglia NS cells. The major neurohemal areas for the brain, the corpora cardiaca (CC), are relatively large organs located directly behind the brain. These structures usually receive three nerves from the brain, each of which is formed partially by the axons of specific NS cells and partially by the axons of "ordinary" neurons. One of these nerves, the NCC I, contains the axons of the contralateral medial NS cells; another, the NCC II, contains the axons of the homolateral lateral NS cells; and the third, the NCC III, contains tritocerebral NS cell axons (Gabe, 1966).

The neurohemal organs associated with the ventral ganglia have been described in only a few orthopteroid species. They are relatively small organs associated with the medial or lateral nerves arising from each ganglion. Generalizations concerning their innervation cannot yet be made (Raabe, 1965). Histological and electron microscopical evidence suggests that specialized neurohemal organs are not always required for the release of NS cell products in insects. Discharge of this material may occur from axon endings in direct contact with any one of several internal organs or from the periphery of nerves prior to the arrival of the NS product at the axon endings.

The Corpora Allata (CA)

The CA are typically paired organs, composed of a single type of secretory cell, lying near the aorta directly behind the brain. They are usually innervated by a nerve, the NCA I, from the corpora cardiaca, and in many species also receive a second nerve, the NCA II, from the subesophageal ganglion (Highnam, 1964b). Both nerves contain axons from NS and "ordinary" neurons.

The CA are known to secrete the so-called juvenile hormone (JH), and have been reported to produce a second hormone in some species. Early investigations on the chemical nature of the JH indicated a probable terpenoid compound (Schneiderman and Gilbert, 1964). Recent studies by Röller and his associates

(1967) have shown that the JH extracted from silkmoth abdomens is a terpenoid, methyl 10-epoxy-7-ethyl-3, 11-dimethyl-2, 6-tri-decadienoate. Whether or not this compound is the JH of all insects remains to be determined. In this discussion we will refer to the CA hormone as the JH, and thus imply that the compound identified by Röller's group is the hormonally active agent from the CA. The reader must bear in mind that all CA may not secrete this particular compound, and an additional hormone (s) may be secreted by these glands.

The Ecdysial Glands (EG)

These glands have been referred to as prothoracic glands, ventral glands, thoracic glands, and by some 20 other names. The collective term ecdysial glands has been accepted by the author for reasons discussed elsewhere (Herman, 1967) and will be used throughout this discussion. The EG are usually paired organs lying laterally in the head or thorax that are generally, but apparently not always, innervated from the ventral ganglia. In at least some species this innervation includes both "ordinary" and NS axons. The EG degenerate after the adult molt of almost all insects.

Karlson and his coworkers have recently described the structure of a steriod, ecdysone ($C_{27} H_{44} O_6$), that may well be the hormone produced by the EG (Karlson and Sekeris, 1966). Ecdysone duplicates in very small amounts, most of the actions of the EG hormone (EGH), but since the hormone was isolated from animals in which the EG are absent, the possibility exists that ecdysone is not normally produced by the glands. The issue is additionally clouded by the fact that other investigators have isolated and/or partially purified similar compounds with considerable EGH activity. Also, some experimental and histological evidence suggests that different EGHs may be produced in different developmental stages, or that ecdysone may not be produced in all stages. Thus, although it is generally accepted that ecdysone is the EGH, it may be prudent to reserve judgment on this issue until further evidence is available. Therefore, we will refer to the EG hormone as EGH.

Two additional insect endocrine centers, the apical cells of the testes of a coleopteran, and certain hind gut cells in a lepidopteran, have recently been described. These two centers are believed to be involved respectively in sex determination and brain NS cell regulation. The existence of additional, as yet undiscovered, endocrine organs is assumed by most insect endocrinologists.

THE CLASSICAL SCHEME

The investigations of such pioneers as Kopec, Wigglesworth, Fukuda, Piepho, and Williams have established what may be termed the "classical scheme" of molting and metamorphosis in insects. According to this basic generalization, the NS cells of the PI secrete a "brain hormone," now known as ecdysiotropin, that stimulates the EG to secrete EGH. Under the influence of this hormone, the molting process is initiated. The titer of juvenile hormone (JH) determines the type or quality of the molt. The combined action of EGH and large amounts of JH results in a larval or nymphal (immature) molt; a decrease in the amount of JH leads to the pupal molt of exopterygote insects and adult molts occur when EGH is present and JH is absent. In many adult insects, early studies by Wigglesworth and other workers established that a CA hormone, presumably JH, was required for the maturation of oöcytes (Wigglesworth, 1954).

By the early 1950's, the classical scheme had emerged and was serving as a model for the investigation of the role of neuroendocrine systems in insect growth and development. As we shall see, subsequent studies have amplified, and in some cases modified, our understanding of the classical scheme. In the following pages we will discuss what is known of the regulation of the hormones directly involved in the control of molting and metamorphosis and other major developmental events that occur during the life cycle of most insects. In some instances this knowledge is considerable and is firmly based. In others it is fragmentary, largely circumstantial, and sometimes contradictory.

EMBRYONIC MOLTING AND DIAPAUSE

The starting point of our discussion most reasonably would be that point in the insect's life cycle where hormones are first known to be produced. Unfortunately, this point has not yet been determined. The embryonic neuroendocrine system is morphologically differentiated and exhibits histological signs of secretory activity prior to eclosion in locusts and cockroaches, and substances with JH and EGH activity can be extracted from locust and moth embryos. Additionally, the embryonic NS system of the commercial silkworm *Bombyx mori* is capable of being programmed for future hormonal activity by ambient temperature and photoperiod. Based upon this information, one could postu-

late that embryonic molting, which occurs during the embryo-
genesis of most insects, is controlled by the classical brain
NS cell-CA-EG system, and early studies on embryos of
Locusta species indicated that this system was indeed functional.
However, subsequent work on embryos of related species produced contradictory results and pointed out several sources of
possible error in the earlier experiments (Mueller, 1964). These
more recent studies showed that isolated embryonic fragments
cultured in hanging drops undergo one or more molts in the
absence of both brain and EG and prompted the conclusion that
the embryonic epidermis possessed molting autonomy. Similar
studies with cultured embryos of the commercial silkworm have
also demonstrated that the brain is not required for embryonic
molting (Takami, 1963).

Therefore, the available evidence indicates that the neuroendocrine system does not control embryonic molting. When does
the system become functional and what controls the initiation of
function? When does the embryonic epidermis lose its postulated
molt-initiating autonomy? The answers to these questions are
not known.

The study of embryos provides us with an excellent example
of how hormone production in mature insects can be regulated
by conditions existing in very early development stages. Embryonic diapause, a relatively common occurrence in insects,
is known to be caused by a diapause hormone released from the
subesophageal ganglion during oögenesis in adult female *B.
mori* (Fukuda, 1962a). The temperature and photoperiod to which
the female embryo is exposed determines whether or not the
diapause hormone will be produced in the resulting female adult.
Thus, the embryonic nervous system, although not required for
embryonic molting, is capable of being programmed for future
activity. This phenomenon, i.e., the determination of hormonal
activity by events occurring in earlier developmental stages,
is relatively common in insects.

LARVAL MOLTING

According to the classical scheme, the brain NS cells, the
EG, and the CA form a tripartite system regulating larval
molting. Unfortunately, while the inhibition of precocious maturation by the CA is firmly established, conclusive evidence concerning the role of the other two components in larval molting
has been much more elusive. Thus, only single experiments
in each case have demonstrated that larval molting will not

occur in the absence of brain NS cells or EG. However, it has been shown many times that the larval brain can secrete ecdysiotropin—and the larval EG, the EGH—and insect endocrinologists are generally agreed that the brain NS cell–EG system is functional in insect larvae. Presumably, this system is operable in the first postembryonic larval instar.

Some histological studies have shown cycles of accumulation and depletion of brain NS material during larval development, and since molting is a periodic process it is believed that the release of ecdysiotropin also occurs cyclically. Unfortunately, we do not yet possess data on direct measurements of ecdysiotropin titer during these stages, so a discontinuous release has not yet been conclusively demonstrated. Additionally, in a few cases histological examinations have not disclosed cyclic NS cell activity in the PI, and the suggestion has been made that ecdysiotropin release may be continuous.

The absence of histologically demonstrable secretory cycles in the NS cells of the PI of crowded *Locusta migratoria*, and the cessation of molting after removal of the frontal ganglion, have prompted Clarke and Langley (1963) to suggest that continuous production of ecdysiotropin is stimulated by pharyngeal contraction and relaxation. Presumably, larval feeding provokes these movements early in each instar and distention of the pharynx by gut emptying and air swallowing provides the stimulus after feeding ceases. These movements are believed to generate impulses that are transmitted via proprioceptors and nerves to the frontal ganglion and thence to the brain NS cells, thus providing constant stimulation of NS cell activity. According to these authors, ecdysiotropin is used during feeding for metabolic purposes, possibly involving proteins, and with the cessation of feeding the hormone builds up in sufficient titer to stimulate the activity of the EG. Once feeding is resumed, the hormone is no longer available for EG stimulation and the process is repeated. The validity of this hypothesis is questioned by recent studies showing that removal of the frontal ganglion from adult females of the closely related desert locust *Schistocerca gregaria* results in decreased feeding and that subsequent developmental abberations result from a lack of nutrients (Hill, et al., 1966).

The role of abdominal proprioceptors in larval molting has been examined in both exopterygote and endopterygote insects, and the results indicate that abdominal stretching due to feeding will stimulate the release of ecdysiotropin. In the bug *Rhodnius prolixus*, the expansion of the abdomen caused by a blood meal stimulates receptors in each segment that continue to discharge as long as the abdomen is stretched. Impulses transmitted through the ventral nerve cord to the brain apparently provoke hormone release. Similarily, in larvae of the moth *Galleria mellonella*, pupation can be delayed or prevented by nerve cord transection or by distorting the animal in such a way as to inhibit the normal volume increase that occurs after feeding (Edwards, 1966). Presumably, in these animals the expansion of the abdomen occurring in feeding larvae would stimulate ecdysiotropin release in a manner similar to that occurring in *R. prolixus*. Since circumstantial evidence implicates abdominal stretching as a causal agent in the release of brain NS products in adults, it is reasonable to conclude that this manner of invoking ecdysiotropin release may be of widespread occurrence.

The presence or absence of food can influence the duration of the larval intermolt in many insects, presumably by influencing the timing of ecdysiotropin release. Immature stages of the cockroach *Blatella germanica* must feed for about 12 hours to initiate a molting cycle (Kunkel, 1966). As these animals increase in weight by some 80 to 100 percent, and in linear dimensions by some 26 percent, it may well be that stretch receptors similar to those discussed earlier are involved. However, since certain hemolymph levels of specific nutrients appear to be required for NS cell activity in adults, feeding may serve to bring these nutrients to the required levels. Although no other information concerning the control of ecdysiotropin release appears to be available for typical larval molts, several additional factors are known to influence this release in other developmental stages. These factors are discussed in the appropriate sections.

The control of EG activity is much more complex than was originally postulated. As mentioned earlier, it is generally believed that the brain NS cells stimulate the glands during larval molting. More recent evidence suggests that at least three additional control systems may exist for these glands (Herman, 1967).

Stainable inclusions were first reported in the nerves innervating the EG of dragonflies in 1953, and since that time similar inclusions have been reported in the EG nerves of several addtional species. Additionally, electron microscopists have recently found what appear to be elementary NS granules (small granules typically observed in NS perikaryons and axons) in the nerves innnervating the glands of cockroaches, moths, and flies—a total of five species representing three orders. The function of this NS innervation is not yet clear, but certain experimental observations suggest a role in the regulation of

EG activity. Thus, the ability of the EG to stimulate regeneration in organ cultures of cockroach legs is enhanced when the ganglion innervating the glands is added to the culture. Extracts of these same ganglia have ecdysiotropic activity and innervation is requisite for function in the EG of *Calliphora erythrocephala.* Since both morphological and experimental evidence suggest that NS innervation of these glands is of importance in glandular regulation, critical investigations of this phenomenon are certainly needed.

In *C. erythrocephala* the EG are innervated by nerves containing *two* distinct types of elementary NS granules, suggesting the possibility of a dual control system in these flies. Perhaps the two types of granules found in these nerves represent a modification of the system in other insects, where direct connection between the brain NS cells and the EG is not required. It could be that in *C. erythrocephala* one type of granule originates in the PI and represents the ecdysiotropic hormone, while the other is equivalent to the granules found in the axons innervating the glands from the ventral nerve cord in other insects. A system similar to that found by Knowles in the dogfish pars intermedia could exist. Knowles observed two types of NS granules in these animals and showed that NS axons containing one type innervated the secretory portion of the intermediate lobe cells, while axons containing the other type innervated the release area. Perhaps a similar situation exists in insects with ecdysiotropin stimulating one function and ventral cord NS another.

Considerable attention has been given recently to the possibility of EG stimulation by the JH. Several workers, primarily Schneiderman and Gilbert (1964) and their colleagues, have now shown that in certain lepidopterans—CA implants, injections of highly purified JH extracts, and injections of compounds with JH activity—all cause repupation of brainless pupae. These results have been interpreted to mean that the JH is capable of acting as both ecdysiotropin and JH and have prompted the following suggestions: (1) Ecdysiotropin and JH may be chemically similar. This is quite unlikely, for the former is probably a peptide or polypeptide, while the latter is related to the terpenoids and is definitely not proteinaceous. (2) Insects may use JH to activate EG during larval life and ecdysiotropin during later stages. This is possible, but why does the histology of the EG and the ecdysone titer (Karlson and Sekeris, 1966) indicate very low activity of the EG in larvae where JH is high? (3) Both JH and ecdysiotropin may activate the glands at all stages with the former stimulating low levels of EGH production and the latter, high levels. In this scheme, molting would occur when ecdysiotropin "superactivated" the glands, and continuous growth of the imaginal discs (known to require EGH) would occur when the JH slightly activated the glands. This possibility must be considered, but it is not in accord with the histological and electron microscopical findings that indicate periods of complete inactivity in the EG during each instar (Herman, 1967) or with the demonstration of relatively constant low levels of ecdysone in fly larvae. (4) The effect may be pharmacological. This is a strong possibility, for injections of cholesterol in amounts of 20 ng per animal (some 3 to 7 ng/g wet weight) will activate the EG, as will a "few" ng/g wet weight of highly purified JH (Kobayashi, 1963; Krishnakumaran and Schneiderman, 1965). It must be recalled that the ecdysiotropic activity of JH has only been noted in lepidopteran pupae, and attempts to duplicate these findings in other insects have failed.

Circumstantial evidence suggests that the JH may directly or indirectly inhibit EG activity. Thus, most histological studies of the EG show very low, or in some cases no activity in larval stages, and the only titer determinations available show very low titers of ecdysone during this period, although JH is known to be secreted in large amounts. Similarily, considerable and occasionally tremendous increases in EG activity have routinely been found histologically at pupation or in the early stages of adult development when JH is absent or present in very low quantities. Additionally, in the moth *Hyalophora cecropia* transplantation studies of larval CA indicate maximal activity in the last two larval instars immediately after the molt, and histological studies show no sign of EG activity at this time. Finally, the possibility exists that the JH may exert an inhibitory effect on the EG by a generalized inhibition of the NS system, for most histological studies show a low activity of this system in larval stages when the JH concentration is high and a very much more pronounced activity at pupation or in the early stages of adult development when the JH concentration is low or zero. Unfortunately, we have no data concerning the variations in ecdysiotropin levels during the various developmental stages, but the histological data suggest a low concentration in larvae as is the case with the ecdysone titer. Clearly, the relationship between the CA and the EG requires further study. Titer determinations of both hormones at carefully defined larval stages could possibly be of value, as could investigations of the possible relationship between JH and the activity of the ventral ganglia NS cells that innervate the EG.

The evidence for a fourth EG control system is based on the interpretation of certain parabiosis experiments as indicative of EGH stimulation of EG activity. These experiments, however, are compatible with alternative explanations and conclusions regarding the possible stimulation of the EG by this means and require further investigation (Gilbert, 1964).

Thus, there are at least four possible methods by which the EG may be controlled; stimulation by ecdysiotropin, some undetermined type of regulation by the ventral cord NS cells, stimulation or inhibition by the JH, and stimulation by the EGH. The role of ecdysiotropin is relatively well established for larvae, but the action of JH, ventral cord NS, and EGH is only suspected.How these factors influence the production and release of EGH is almost completely unknown (Krishnakumaran and Schneiderman, 1965). Since the production of the EGH is one of the most important events in insect development, it is hoped that future research will clarify the role of these various factors.

Early histological studies indicated cyclic activity of larval CA, and these results have been experimentally confirmed in moth and earwig larvae (Ozeki, 1965). In the former, CA activity is maximal immediately after the penultimate larval molt and then declines; in the latter, glandular activity rises to a maximum near the middle of the next to last instar and then decreases. Some authors believe that CA activity decreases progressively in successive larval stages, but no evidence for such a gradual decline has been presented.

Little data concerning the regulation of larval CA are available since most investigators have been concerned with the role of the glands in adults. In earwigs, innervation of the glands from the brain appears to normally stimulate the glands, since disconnected glands remain inactive. The reverse seems to be true in hemipterans, for detached larval glands apparently remain active for long periods. Cauterization experiments indicate that the lateral NS cells of the PI are responsible for the stimulation and the medial cells for the inhibition of the CA in larval *L. migratoria* (Girardie, 1965). As we shall see, both ordinary neurons and NS cells seem to be involved in the regulation of adult CA.

Although there is considerable information concerning the stimulation of all larval endocrine glands, little is known of how the glands are "turned off." Possibly the mechanical stimulation of brain neurosecretion by feeding is stopped when the food is digested and residues are voided. Certain experiments show that the brain is capable of secreting much more ecdysiotropin than is required for the activity of a single EG, so some factor may normally inhibit ecdysiotropin release. One would certainly suspect that a high titer of EGH may effect this shutdown. It is of interest here that EGH is known to stimulate some nerves and to depress others, suggesting that the hormone may somehow cause the electrical inhibition of brain NS cell activity (Highnam, 1964a). What causes the cyclic activity of the CA in larvae is unknown. Both the titer of JH and nutritional status may be of importance, for both these factors seem to influence cyclic activity of the adult CA.

SEX DETERMINATION

The existence of sex hormones in insects has been debated for many years, and experiments suggesting the presence or absence of such hormones have frequently been reported. Recently, however, conclusive evidence for the existence of an androgenic (male) hormone in the firefly *Lampyris noctiluca* has been presented (Naisse, 1966), and these results suggest that an examination of this phenomenon in other insects should be conducted. Sexual dimorphism of *L. noctiluca* adults is striking, the male having large wings, well-developed eyes, and poorly developed luminescent organs, while females are larger, wingless, somewhat larvoid, and have smaller eyes and larger luminescent organs. Implantation of testes from certain larval stages into young female larvae results in the development of perfect males, while the reverse operation, i.e., ovaries into males, has no effect. Additionally, the testes are only active in causing sex reversal when certain cells associated with the testes, the so-called apical cells, are present, thus implicating these cells as the site of androgen synthesis.

Control of the activity of the apical cells apparently resides in the brain NS cell-corpora cardiaca-CA system, since carefully timed extirpations of the two latter components from young male larvae will cause sex reversal, and female gonads (possessing rudimentary apical cells) implanted into castrated males will develop as normal testes. The CA are not believed to play any role in this process since their removal along with the corpora cardica is apparently necessary for technical reasons. Removal of the corpora cardiaca supposedly inhibits male development by preventing the release of a brain NS hormone.

Currently available evidence therefore suggests that the "genetic constitution" of male larvae programs the production of an NS hormone from specific cells within the PI, that stimulates the development and secretory activity of the apical cells. Since these NS cells do not become active in females, the apical cells do not develop. The hormone from these latter cells is a typical androgenic hormone and acts to promote the development of both primary and secondary male sexual characteristics.

DIAPAUSE

Diapause (Lees, 1955) is a state of arrested development that may occur in any stage of the life cycle. Two distinct types of diapause, facultative and obligatory, have generally been recognized. The former is usually induced by unfavorable, and terminated by favorable environmental conditions. It may, therefore, occur or not occur in any given generation. Insects with facultative diapause typically proceed through one or more uninterrupted generations in favorable surroundings, enter diapause at a specific stage when conditions are adverse, and then resume development when advantageous conditions return. Obligatory diapause has long been believed to invariably occur at a particular stage of the life cycle. Classically, the initiation of this type of diapause was thought to be programmed by the genetic constitution of the species and not induced by environmental conditions. Recent studies, however, have clearly demonstrated that the induction of obligatory diapause can be influenced by environmental factors. When insects with obligatory diapause are subjected to favorable conditions, the incidence of diapause is considerably reduced. Thus, it appears that the distinction between the two types of diapause is less pronounced than formerly believed, and environmental signals may be responsible for the initiation and termination of most if not all of the arrested development found in insects.

The initiation of diapause is generally regarded as being due to the failure of some component of the neuroendocrine system, usually the brain NS cells. Diapause development is the term given to the events occurring during diapause that lead to the termination of arrested development. Since diapause acts to protect the insect from adverse environmental conditions, it is not surprising that insects rely on environmental factors such as photoperiod, temperature, food supply, and available water for information with which to regulate the initiation and termination of this state. The most widely used programmer appears to be photoperiod, presumably because it is the most reliable measure of the yearly cycle.

In those facultative-diapausing insects responding to photoperiods, long days (13 to 18 hours) usually promote continuous development and act to terminate arrested development, while short days (8 to 12 hours) induce and maintain the diapause state. According to Adkisson (1966), the photoperiodic effect depends upon the relative duration of both the light and dark components of the photoperiod within a 24-hour cycle. Both components are believed to be "intimately associated in controlling the photo-chemical reactions involved in the diapause process."

How does photoperiod interact with the neuroendocrine sys-tem? Experiments with the oak silkworm *Antheraea pernyi* indicate that the brain directly receives and implements the photoperiodic signals (Williams, et al., 1965). These animals have a facultative pupal diapause that responds to photoperiod in the manner generally found in insects. Experiments subjecting only the anterior or only the posterior regions of pupae to variable photoperiods showed that photoperiodic sensitivity was localized anteriorly. Additional experiments showed that when the brain was transplanted to the rear of the animal the photoperiodic sensitivity was also transferred. Since brainless pupae do not respond to photoperiods and normal pupae are only sensitive to photoperiods during the developmental period when the brain is required for the initiation of adult development, these experi-ments have prompted the conclusion that photoperiod acts directly on the brain of *A. pernyi* to regulate the secretion of ecdysiotropin. These results have substantiated earlier specu-lations advanced from a study of the photoperiodic control of female dimorphism in aphids. In these insects the sensitivity to photoperiod was localized in the dorsum of the head, directly over the PI, suggesting that the brain might act as the primary photoreceptor.

Diapause in adult beetles is also controlled by photoperiod, perhaps by a direct effect on the brain (Wilde, 1965). In these animals a shutdown of the entire cephalic neuroendocrine system (brain NS cells, corpora cardiaca, and CA) occurs in response to short days, while long days reactivate all components. The complete diapause syndrome is apparently due to a loss of both brain NS cell and CA activity since allatectomy of nondiapausing insects, only provokes diapause-like behavior while implants of active CA into diapausing beetles do not completely eliminate developmental arrest. Since destruction of the PI results in CA inactivity, photoperiods seemingly act to regulate brain activity and thus indirectly influence the production of JH.

As mentioned earlier, the secretion of a diapause hormone from the subesophageal ganglion that provokes diapause in *B. mori* embryos is known to be controlled by the photoperiod and temperature to which the egg producing the female parent is subjected. Since eggs are only responsive during late embryo-genesis, when all organ systems are fully differentiated, it may well be that the embryonic brain directly receives and stores the photoperiodic information. The release of the diapause hormone occurs when nervous inhibition of the subesophageal ganglion by the brain is removed.

The previous discussion has strongly indicated that the brain itself may act as a primary photoreceptor. Early experiments with *Ostrinia nubilalis*, the European corn borer, indicated that in some insects photoperiod may regulate brain NS cell activity through the intervention of some other endocrine tissue. These studies showed that the long-day photoperiod normally terminating diapause in last instar larvae was not effective if diapausing larvae were ligated between the sixth and seventh abdominal segments. Since section of the nerve cord at the sixth segment did not inhibit the long-day induced termination of diapause, the production of a hormone was suspected. A search for possible hormonogenic cells in the seventh and eighth abdominal segments revealed typical secretory cells in the proctodeal epithelium, that seemed to release their secretory products into the hemolymph. The injection of extracts of these cells terminated diapause in larvae that would not normally have renewed development. Experiments involving implantation of active and inactive brains into ligated and non-ligated diapausing pupae, with and without brains, suggested that the function of the proctodeal hormone (proctodone) was to activate the inactive diapause brain (Beck et al., 1965).

Histological examinations disclosed the existence of cyclical secretory activity in the lateral NS cells of the PI and in the proctodone-producing cells. Both types of cells exhibited three complete cycles of secretory activity during each 24-hour period. The initiation of the proctodone cycle was correlated with the lights-off photoperiodic signal, while that of the lateral NS cells was related to the lights-on signal. Under short-day conditions the two cycles were asynchronous, while long-day photoperiod resulted in simultaneous maxima and minima in both cycles. Assuming that the lateral NS cells were in some manner responsible for the production of ecdysiotropin, the hypothesis was presented that short-day conditions induced diapause and retarded diapause development because the proctodone and NS cell cycles were "out of phase." Under long-day conditions the two cycles were "in phase," and diapause was either avoided or diapause development accelerated.

It was initially assumed that the proctodone-producing cells were primary photoreceptors and that photoperiods regulated the activity of the corn borer brain NS cells by regulating directly the activity of the proctodeal endocrine cells. However, more recent studies have shown that proctodone production is absent from the early larval instars when photoperiod normally act to induce diapause, and it is currently believed that some additional unknown process responds to photoperiod during larval life and in some manner programs proctodone activity in last instar larvae (Beck et al., 1965). Unfortunately, only a single group of investigators has been actively studying the proctodone phenomenon, and data confirming or extending these results have not been forthcoming. A proctodone function was not observed in *A. pernyi* pupae, and unlike in *O. nubilalis*, nerve cord section alone prevents pupation in last instar larvae of *G. mellonella* (Edwards, 1966).

What wavelengths of light are important in the photoperiod response? Light in the blue and blue-green regions of the spectrum (398 to 508 mμ in *A. pernyi*) is most effective. Any pigments involved have not been identified, although both cyclic tetrapyrroles and carotenoids have been suggested as possible photoreceptive compounds. The threshold of light intensity required to initiate photoperiodic responses ranges from 0.01 to 10 foot-candles, depending upon the individual species, and the response seems to be independent of intensity and total light energy once the threshold value has been reached (Lees, 1955).

Diapause is not the only hormonally regulated process in insects that responds to photoperiod specifically, or light generally. Color change in certain moth pupae and in locusts is known to be regulated hormonally and to respond to background colors. Photoperiod may in some manner influence caste determination in certain social insects, and in cockroaches the hormonal stimulation of activity rhythms appears to be influenced by photoperiod (Highnam, 1964a).

Thus, the brain is believed to respond directly to photoperiod in at least one species and may well be the primary photoreceptor in other species. Photoperiod may also regulate brain activity indirectly by means of proctodone-type systems or may indirectly control the production of hormones by other endocrine organs by influencing brain activity.

What cues are used by insects inhabiting equatorial regions where photoperiod is relatively constant? *S. gregaria* adults, which require the activity of the brain NS system for reproduction, remain reproductively inactive during the dry season and become active when certain plants begin to flower. In the laboratory, a single contact with any of the terpenoids derived from these plants will initiate sexual maturation and therefore NS cell activity. When these plants bloom and have the highest terpenoid content, the rainy season, a period of relatively lush vegetation, is imminent. Thus, it appears that these desert locusts have synchronized their developmental schedule to a precise indicator of the availability of food for feeding larvae (Carlisle et al., 1965).

Temperature is intimately involved with photoperiod in the induction and termination of diapause. For example, larvae of the pink bollworm *Pectinophora gossypiella* will exhibit 70 percent diapause on short days at 27°C and 100 percent diapause on short days at 20°C (Adkisson, 1966). Additionally, in some species temperature may be of more importance than photoperiod, for certain insects may exhibit up to 90 percent dispause when held on long days at low temperatures (Lees, 1955). How reduced temperatures act to induce neuroendocrine system shutdown is unknown. It may merely be a case of decreased metabolic rate. Information is available, however, on how reduced temperatures influence diapause termination. During the obligatory pupal diapause of *H. cecropia*, temperature acts to restore the ecdysiotropic activity of the brain NS cells. Diapause in this species occurs in late summer and lasts until the following spring or early summer, and it can be shown in the laboratory that diapause results from the absence of brain ecdysiotropic activity (Wigglesworth, 1954). Diapausing animals left at room temperature resume development in six months or more, but diapausing pupae subjected to reduced temperatures (6 to 15°C) for a few weeks will resume development almost immediately. Since chilled brainless animals do not resume development when inactive (diapause) brains are implanted but brains from chilled animals will cause development when implanted into unchilled brainless animals—the action of cold seems to be directly on the brain.

Early studies (see Gilbert, 1964) of the neurophysiology of brain inactivation and activation in the above species indicated that the brain became electrically silent shortly before pupation. These early studies also indicated that the cholinesterase activity of the brain dropped to almost zero, and the concentration of "cholinergic substance" (presumably acetylcholine) became very low. Chilling was reported to considerably increase the concentration of cholinergic substance. When chilled pupae were placed at room temperature, the concentration of cholinesterase was found to increase, while that of cholinergic substance decreased. From these results, it was concluded that chilling in some manner caused an increased concentration of cholinergic substance, and this increase induced the reappearance of cholinesterase. These events were postulated to be responsible for the restoration of both electrical activity in the brain and the secretory activity of the brain NS cells. This hypothesis is apparently incorrect, for recent studies using more sophisticated techniques, have demonstrated both substantial cholinesterase activity and electrical activity in diapausing pupal brains of *H. cecropia* and other lepidopteran species (Shappirio, et al., 1967).

Experiments by Schneiderman and Horwitz on certain chalcid wasps suggest that low temperature promotes diapause development by slowing down an aerobic breakdown reaction in the brain of diapausing animals, thereby permitting the synthesis of some substance necessary for brain NS cell activity. The substance involved may be the cholinergic substance found in the *H. cecropia* brain (Wigglesworth, 1964).

Histological studies of the brain of diapausing lepidopterans show that one of two situations may exist: the brain NS cells may initially be either full or empty of NS material. In the former case, secretory material appears to be progressively released as chilling proceeds; in the latter, NS material accumulates during the early stages of chilling and is released during the later stages. Since it can be shown experimentally that ecdysiotropin is released during the chilling period in at least two lepidopteran species, it would appear that the effect of chilling may be manifested in one of two ways. First, it may cause the release of hormone already accumulated. In this case diapause might be caused by a failure of the release system. Second, chilling may cause the synthesis and release of hormone by cells that were inactive. In this case, diapause would appear to be caused by a failure of only the synthetic mechanism, or by a failure of both the synthetic and release mechanisms.

Although there have been few studies on the effect of water availability on the activity of the neuroendocrine system with regard to diapause, it is well known that insect development is frequently influenced by the amount of water present. Perhaps the most striking example is found in the gall midge *Schizomyia macarangae*. Galls containing diapause last instar larvae of this species can be kept in dry conditions for many months with no sign of larval development, but prompt pupation occurs when the galls are wetted (Lees, 1955). Histologically, the brain NS cells of the diapause larvae contain very little NS material, but after wetting, the cells appear to be synthesizing and transporting large amounts of this material (K. Nayar, personal communication.)

The EG may be responsible for diapause in *Sialis lutaria*. In this species, larvae usually enter diapause in October, and tight ligatures separating the brain from the EG in early diapause larvae will not inhibit the initiation of development at a later date (Wigglesworth, 1954). Presumably, ecdysiotropin is released in October larvae, but the EG do not release EGH until a later date. These results imply that the glands are activated by ecdysiotropin in October (but they do not release EGH) and that diapause development is required to stimulate hormone release.

In some insects the activity of the brain NS cell-EG system may be inhibited during diapause by the JH. Several Japanese investigators have arrived at this conclusion after examining various lepidopteran larvae. In *Chilo suppressalis,* e.g., alla-tectomy of diapausing larvae sometimes stimulates the resumption of development, and histological studies show that the CA are active during diapause and inactive in later stages (Gilbert, 1964). Therefore, diapause is a state of arrested development typically caused by a deficiency of some component of the neuroendocrine system. Usually this deficiency is found in the NS cells of the PI, and the evidence indicates that the failure may be one of synthesis and/or release of ecdysiotropin. The brain responds, perhaps directly, to photoperiod, temperature, availability of water, certain chemicals, and probably other factors as well, and the ecdysiotropic activity can be either stimulated or inhibited by these factors. There is some evidence that a failure of the release mechanism for EGH may cause diapause in at least one species. The CA may inhibit the activity of the brain NS cell–EG system in some species. Almost no information is available concerning the exact methods by which these various agents activate or inactivate the components of the neuroendocrine system.

METAMORPHOSIS

According to the classical scheme, metamorphosis occurs in the presence of a low titer of JH in the case of pupation in endopterygote insects and in the absence of JH in the case of the adult molt of exopterygotes. The decreased activity of the CA in both groups has been repeatedly confirmed by both trans-plantation experiments and direct determination of JH titer, and the relative roles of the brain NS cells and EG are also well documented (Gilbert, 1964; Wigglesworth, 1964).

The details of the events occurring at this time are far from clear. Most histological studies have shown tremendous increases in both EG and brain NS cell activity at the meta-morphic molt, and in the social insects, molts resulting in sexually mature adults are usually associated with greatly en-larged EG. Additionally, the single determination of ecdysone titer available for both immature and mature insects shows a manyfold increase in ecdysone at the time of pupation in *C. erythrocephala* (Karlson and Sekeris, 1966). All of this evidence suggests a considerable increase in the activity of the brain NS cell–EG system at metamorphosis, and thus indicates a major alteration in the regulation of these organs. Possibly this increase is stimulated by increased food intake in a manner similar to that discussed previously, for in such animals as *H. cecropia* the final instar larva eats for a longer period and undergoes a considerable volume increase. It may also be that the observed increase in brain NS cell and EG activity merely compensates for the increased volume of the final instar larva. Since these molts occur in the presence of greatly reduced titers of JH, the apparent enhancement of both ecdysiotropin and EGH production could conceivably result from the decrease of JH, suggesting that in earlier stages the JH suppresses the activity of the brain NS cell—EG system.

What factors cause the decreased activity of the CA in the last larval instar? In cockroaches and hemipterans it seems that inhibition of the glands exists, since disconnecting the CA from the brain will result in supernumery larval instars (Highnam, 1964b). In some locusts and earwigs, where implantation of active glands into the last instar has no effect if done after the first few hours postmolt, it appears that a humoral or hormonal substance in the blood inhibits CA activity (Ozeki, 1965). Humoral or hormonal stimulation and inhibition apparently exists in larvae of the commercial silkworm, since detached or transplanted glands exhibit exactly the same activity cycles as found in normal animals (Fukuda, 1962b).

CASTE AND PHASE DETERMINATION

The neuroendocrine system plays a major role in the regulation of caste and phase differences in the social insects (Highnam, 1964a).

Volume dimorphism of the system in workers and queens (both females) of the honeybee *Apis mellifera* is well established. The CA and EG are larger and the brain NS system is apparently more active in female larvae destined to become queens. In adults, however, the brain NS system of workers is apparently more active, and the worker CA is larger (Biedermann, 1964).

Diet seems to be the factor determining the ultimate status of young larvae. Animals fed "royal jelly" become queens, while those fed "worker jelly" (a diet low in protein and high in carbohydrate) develop into workers. The more nutritious diet of queen larvae is thus considered to stimulate the development of the neuroendocrine system, and this enhanced activity results in queen development (Liu and Dixon, 1965). Which dietary components are responsible, how these components influence the neuroendocrine system, why enhanced activity of the system is necessary for queen development, and whether the increased size of the various components in queen larvae actually indicates enhanced activity are all unanswered questions.

The regulation of the colony depends upon the presence of a queen. When adult queens are present, adult workers feed larvae only worker jelly and the worker ovaries remain un- developed (Wilson, 1965). In the absence of queens, the workers build special queen-rearing cells, begin to feed royal jelly to the larvae, and their ovaries initiate development. These events are controlled by pheromones (substances produced by one member of a species that influence another member) produced by the queen. These pheromones lead to worker jelly feeding and ovarian inhibition. One of these compounds, *trans*-9-keto- 2-decenoic acid, inhibits ovarian development when injected into workers reared in the absence of queens, but it does not influence queen-rearing behavior. Since the CA of worker adults are much larger than those of queens and therefore are believed to be storing JH, it would seem that this acid somehow inhibits hormone release. What controls pheromone production in queens is unknown.

Nothing is known of the neuroendocrine control of develop- ment in the other social bees, i.e., the bumblebees (*Bombus* species) and the "stingless bees" (Meliponinae). Perhaps the factors regulating the more advanced honeybee societies could be more easily studied in these more primitive societies.

Relationships comparable to those in the honeybee seem to be present in some ants, for histological studies have demon- strated caste associated differences in brain NS cell activity and CA and EG volume in two species (Schmidt, 1964) while other studies have shown that the queen is the source of pheromones influencing worker feeding behavior and ovarian maturation (Wilson, 1965). Since few detailed examinations have been made, and these only in the relatively specialized ants Myrnecinae and Formicinae, the developmentally oriented in- vestigation of ant societies would seem to present unlimited research opportunities.

Early investigations presented histological evidence for a role of both EG and CA in caste determination in termites. This work showed that the EG of sexual larvae, i.e., larvae destined to develop into functional reproductives, were much larger than those of other castes and that the EG of soldiers, unlike those of all other castes, persisted after the terminal molt. These results led to the conclusion that relative titers of

JH and EGH were responsible for caste determination. Experimental investigations of this hypothesis have not been forthcoming, and information is not available concerning the possibility of concentration differences and the factors regulating these differences in the various castes.

More recent investigations have been concerned with the role of pheromones and the CA, especially with regard to the relatively primitive termite *Kalotermes flavicollis* (Lüscher, 1962, 1963; Highnam, 1964a). In this species, there are three fixed castes: sexually mature adults, supplementary reproductives, and soldiers. Development proceeds through a series of typical larval molts to a mature larval stage, the pseudergate, and subsequent developmental pathways are determined by the above mentioned factors with the possible involvement of annual cycles, diet, and brain NS products. Circumstantial evidence indicates that direct development of pseudergates into first- and second-stage nymphs and then into sexually mature adults results from a more nutritious diet that in some manner inhibits the activity of the CA during a pseudergate molt. In the presence of a decrease in JH titer, development apparently follows the classical scheme of molting and metamorphosis.

The development of supplementary reproductives is normally inhibited by sex specific pheromones produced by sexually mature male and female adults. Early investigations suggested that these pheromones inhibited brain NS cell activity, while later results indicated an influence on CA activity. Since feeding JH extracts and substances with JH activity inhibits supplementary reproductive development, and since the presence of large and presumably active CA in pseudergates decreases the number of developing supplementaries, a reasonable action for the pheromone would seem to be stimulation of CA activity. However, a stimulatory action is difficult to postulate since removal of the source of the pheromones results in an increased volume of the CA in developing supplementaries. Could the pheromones act by stimulating the release of JH? The enlargement of the glands in developing supplementary reproductives could then be interpreted as storage of hormone, as appears to be the case with the large and swollen CA of worker bees. Additionally, the presence of pheromone would stimulate release of JH in pseudergates and thereby effectively inhibit progressive development of these animals.

Implantation of CA from stages other than pseudergates and young nymphs into pseudergates will initiate soldier development. Injections of compounds with JH activity or implantation of glands from young nymphs or pseudergates are ineffective. These results have prompted the suggestion that a hormone from the CA, but not the JH, is responsible for soldier differentiation. On the other hand, Wigglesworth (1964) has suggested that the differences observed may be due to dissimilarities in the activity of the implants since pseudergate and young nymph glands may be less active. Information concerning the factors controlling the synthesis and release of this other hormone, if it exists, is totally lacking.

Clearly, the problems presented by caste determination in termites are far from solved. Information concerning the details of regulation is almost totally lacking, as are data concerning the control of pheromone production, the number of pheromones produced and the chemistry of the pheromones. Studies on the relative titers of JH, EGH, and ecdysiotropin at specific intervals during all stages of caste development would be of considerable value, as would detailed histophysiological studies of all neuroendocrine components in all developmental stages. Nothing is known concerning the neuroendocrine control of the more highly specialized termite families Rhinotermitidae and Termitidae.

Pheromones, CA, EG, and brain neurosecretions all seem to influence phase polymorphism in locusts (Highnam, 1962 and 1964a). In animals such as *L. migratoria* and *S. gregaria* there are prominent differences between solitary and crowded (gregarious) individuals, with crowded animals being easily recognizable by their darker pigmentation. Additionally, unlike crowded animals, solitary adults exhibit depressed motor activity and seem to be less responsive to stimuli. Differences in reproductive activity between the two forms also exist, with gregarious females exhibiting quantitatively lower ovarian activity. Finally, solitary individuals have larger CA, do not lose their EG after the adult molt, and have less active NS systems.

The differences in pigmentation seem to be due to a higher titer of JH and possibly EGH in the solitary forms (Carlisle and Ellis, 1963; Highnam, 1964a). Implants of CA will cause solitary pigmentation in crowded animals, while allatectomy of isolated insects results in gregarious coloration. Similarily, partial extirpation of the EG of isolated *S. gregaria* also results in gregarious pigmentation, but the procedure is much less effective in *L. migratoria*. Presumably, the larger glands of solitary individuals are normally more active, and this hyperactivity invokes light pigmentation. What controls the enhanced activity of these two components is not yet known.

In both these species the adults are immature immediately after the adult molt. The presence of mature males accelerates, and that of immature males inhibits the sexual maturation and CA activity of immature members of each species (Norris and Pener, 1965). The net result of these actions is that populations mature at about the same time, since the presence of the first mature males hastens the maturation of other animals. The accelerating influence of mature *S. gregaria* males is due to a pheromone produced by the epidermal cells. Pheromones are also believed to be responsible for the accelerating or inhibiting action of other males. The presence of an active CA is required for accelerating pheromone production in mature *S. gregaria* males, while the inhibiting pheromones produced during periods of CA inactivity or in allatectomized mature males seem to require the absence of CA activity for their production. Why the CA are inactive for a relatively short period after the adult molt, how CA activity influences pheromone production, and how pheromones activate or suppress these glands are questions not yet answered. It has been suggested that the pheromone may act directly upon the CA. In view of the results obtained from studies of the effect of pheromones upon females, this mode of action seems unlikely.

The brains of immature and isolated *S. gregaria* females contain more NS material than those of mature crowded forms (Highnam, 1964a). In the presence of mature males this material is rapidly released, and CA activity and oöcyte maturation ensues. It has been suggested that the pheromone acts by lowering the thresholds of sensory receptors, thereby promoting enhanced motor activity and copulation, both of which are known to enhance brain NS cell activity. This conclusion is based on several experiments showing that forced hyperactivity or electrical stimulation of isolated females induces changes in the brain NS cells very similar to those found in females reared with mature males.

The relative inactivity of isolated *S. gregaria* may be related to the fact that these animals retain their EG after the adult molt. Experiments showing that EG implants result in a lessening of activity in crowded animals and that blood from molting locusts or injections of ecdysone reduce the activity of nerves innervating certain leg muscles have been interpreted in this fashion (Highnam, 1964a). Why the glands are larger in solitary nymphs and why they persist in solitary adults are as yet unanswered questions.

ADULTS

Investigations concerning the endocrinology of adult insects have been concerned primarily with the hormonal regulation of oöcyte maturation. These studies have shown that in most insects the CA are required for this process, and more recent studies have demonstrated that brain NS products are also required for the complete development of oöcytes in many species (Highnam, 1964b; Wigglesworth, 1964; Gilbert, 1964).

The activity of the NS cells in adult insects has been reported to be influenced by a variety of factors, including feeding and dietary constituents, nervous impulses, JH titers, pheromones, ovarian hormones, and, as discussed previously, photoperiod. Several studies show that feeding may regulate NS cell activity by mechanically provoking stimulatory nervous impulses from sensory receptors responsive to volume alterations in whole insects or in certain internal organs. Abdominal distention after feeding of *R. prolixus* results in the release of a diuretic NS hormone, and severance of certain abdominal nerves eliminates this response (Maddrell, 1965). In the tsetse fly, where a brain NS hormone is presumably responsible for the production of gut protease, the size of the blood meal and therefore the degree of crop distention is known to be directly related to the amount of gut protease produced (Langley, 1966). Starvation of *S. gregaria*, the desert locust, causes accumulation of brain NS material, while feeding of starved animals results in such a rapid depletion of this material that nervous impulses are believed to be involved (Hill, et al., 1966). In all of these examples, sensory receptors seem to respond to mechanical distortions caused by feeding by stimulating the production of NS hormones, presumably in a manner comparable if not identical to that by which feeding and abdominal distention stimulates the release of ecdysiotropin in certain immature insects.

The involvement of external sensory receptors in the regulation of NS cell activity is illustrated by the control of the release of bursicon, the hormone responsible for cuticular tanning in adult flies and possibly other insects (Fraenkel and Hsiao, 1965). This hormone is apparently produced by both brain and ventral ganglia NS cells, and its release is regulated by sensory receptors in the thoracic and abdominal cuticle. These receptors respond to confinement within the puparium prior to adult emergence by sending inhibitory impulses to the brain, thereby preventing bursicon release. After adult emergence from the puparium is accomplished and wing expansion begins, these receptors respond to the termination of confinement by sending out stimulatory impulses that promote hormone release. This situation is similar to that found in many other insects where the ''feel of the surroundings'' has been reported to stimulate or inhibit various developmental events now known to be controlled by NS hormones.

Brain NS hormones are known to regulate oviposition in at least some insects (Wigglesworth, 1964). Since injections of ripe ovarian extracts result in both the discharge of NS material and oviposition in nearly gravid females of the hemipteran *Iphita limbata*, it has been suggested that a hormone produced by mature ovaries stimulates the production of the oviposition hormone. In the beetle *Dermestes maculatus*, the production of a similar NS hormone is apparently promoted by a spermathecal factor produced when active sperm are in the spermathecae. Since it is well known that the presence of certain odors or particular foods will also stimulate oviposition in many insects, such stimuli can presumably effect NS hormone release.

Several authors have reported an interaction between the brain NS cells and the activity of the CA. In *C. erythrocephala* adult females, active CA may stimulate the medial NS cells (Highnam, 1964b). Implants of active glands result in increased size and presumably increased activity of the medial NS cells, while implants of inactive glands do not. Similar results have been observed in *Tenebrio molitor* and in the desert locust, but in the cockroach *Periplaneta americana*, injections of JH extracts cause accumulation of NS material in the brain and therefore are believed to inhibit NS activity (Nayar, 1962).

Specific dietary ingredients may normally be required for NS cell activity. Feeding on senescent *Brassica* species leaves retards sexual development in the desert locust, a species known to be dependent upon brain NS material for maturity, while feeding on fresh green leaves promotes rapid development (Ellis et al., 1965). The former leaves apparently have very low levels of gibberellin A3, and the addition of this compound to a diet of senescent leaves results in prompt sexual maturation. This phenomenon may be of considerably adaptive significance for the species, for the initial appearance of fresh leaves in the environment signals the beginning of the rainy season and the presence of numerous food plants.

The brain NS system of adult insects therefore can be either stimulated or inhibited by several types of intrinsic and extrinsic mechanical stimuli. It can also respond to hormones produced by other endocrine organs and may be activated by specific dietary components. As previously discussed, photoperiod and pheromones are also important regulators of the system. Exactly how these factors act, i.e., precisely what points in the production, transport, and release of NS products they influence, is unknown. Those factors regulating the system via the nervous system may provide information to the NS cells by altering the temporal patterns of nervous impulses. Highnam (1962) has shown that low frequencies of direct electrical stimulation to *S. gregaria* females results in accumulation of brain NS material, while stimulation at higher frequencies leads to depletion.

The most thoroughly studied and least understood endocrine regulatory system in insects is that controlling the activity of the adult CA (Highnam, 1964b; Highnam et al., 1966). Although studies on the control of these glands have been conducted for over 20 years, Berta Scharrer recently surveyed the field and concluded that the problem of CA control was unresolvable with presently available data. Most investigators in the area would heartily agree. The goal of research in this field is to understand how the cyclic secretory activity of the CA necessary for the intermittent maturation of eggs in long-lived female adults is accomplished. Several possible mechanisms have been proposed.

First, the glands may be directly stimulated by NS innervation from the brain (Highnam, 1964b). Work with *L. migratoria, S. gregaria, T. molitor,* and *Dytiscus marginalis* has shown that severing the nerves from the corpora cardiaca to the CA in these species prevents glandular activity. In the first three species, cauterization of the PI NS cells results in CA inactivity. Since brain NS is required for glandular activity, and the NS material must reach the glands for activation to occur, direct NS stimulation is indicated. Additionally, isolated inactive CA of *S. gregaria* never become active, and isolated active glands become and remain inactive. Finally, histological studies on several species have shown that NS material is present in the NCA I or in the glands themselves during periods of activity and is absent during periods of inactivity. Therefore, there is good evidence that in at least some species, direct innervation of the CA by brain NS cells stimulates glandular activity.

The second possibility is that the NS activity of the brain stimulates the glands indirectly (Highnam, 1964b). The best example of this situation is found in the fly *C. erythrocephala,* where the medial NS cells are required for CA activity but innervation is not. How do NS hormones act in such a system? In several insects it is known that brain neurosecretion regulates hemolymph protein concentrations, and Strangeways-Dixon has suggested that the medial NS cells may control CA activity in C. *erythrocephala* by regulating hemolymph protein levels. This author finds that in normal animals the volume of the glands varies directly with the amount of protein ingested and that denervated glands remain small in sugar-fed animals and become larger in animals consuming protein. Additionally, CA volume usually decreases during yolk deposition in normal females when proteins are taken up by the oöcytes, but force feeding of protein during this period will stop the volume decrease. The fact that protein is somehow required for CA activity is shown by the absence of ovarian development in flies fed protein-free diets and its presence in flies fed diets containing proteins. A direct effect of hemolymph protein concentration on CA activity has also been proposed from similar studies on the cockroach *Leucophaea maderae* (Engelmann, 1965), and studies on the fly *Phormia regina* suggest the existence of the same mechanism. Protein levels do not influence CA activity in certain other insects, such as *S. gregaria,* where operations resulting in alterations of hemolymph protein concentrations are without effect on glandular activity.

Unlike *S. gregaria,* the isolated CA of some insects continue to function normally during several developmental stages. This situation is found in *B. mori,* where implants of adult CA into allatectomized penultimate instar larvae promote perfectly normal molting and metamorphosis, i.e., the larvae undergo a normal molt to the last larval instar and subsequently pupate and develop as normal adults (Fukuda, 1962b). These isolated glands therefore must have periods of activity and inactivity identical to those of normal animals, thus suggesting either the existence of a blood-born regulator (protein levels? NS hormones?) or of some precise regulating mechanism within the glands. Isolated cockroach CA are also capable of cyclic activity, but the glands are not synchronously active with those of the host, suggesting the necessity of anatomical attachments for normal activity (Engelmann, 1962).

Which NS cells are involved in corpora allata regulation? In most insects the medial NS cells as a group appear to be responsible for stimulation, and in *Oncopeltus fasciatus* certain large medial ''A'' cells seem to fulfill this function (Highnam, 1964b). In locusts, however, the lateral NS cells are believed to be the stimulatory elements (Girardie, 1965). How NS material may act to directly stimulate CA activity is unknown (Highnam, 1964b). Wigglesworth has suggested that the material may act as a precursor of the JH, and some histological studies have noted a decrease in NS material in or near the glands during activity, but in view of the probable chemical dissimilarities between the two hormones this suggestion seems highly improbable. Alterations in RNA and ribosomes reported for activated glands suggest that this area might be profitably explored.

A third possible method of CA control, that of "ordinary" nervous inhibition by PI neurons, is suggested by studies on the cockroaches *L. maderae* and *Diploptera punctata* and on the hemipteran *O. fasciatus*. Unlike those animals discussed previously, cutting the nerve to the CA in these insects results in activation of inactive glands (Engelmann, 1965). The source of this inhibition in *L. maderae* appears to be certain neurons lying laterally to the medial NS cells in each hemisphere of the brain. Since in both *L. maderae* and *O. fasciatus* the activity of the CA requires the presence of medial NS cells, it appears that in these animals stimulation is under NS control and inhibition is under nervous control. Unlike *L. maderae,* protein levels do not appear to effect the glands in *O. fasciatus* since cutting the nerve to the glands in starved animals, where protein levels are very low, will result in glandular activation.

It may be that several regulatory systems normally influence the CA. Studies on such insects as *O. fasciatus,* L. *migratoria,* and *T. molitor* have indicated that growth of the glands and hormone production by the glands may be controlled by different factors (Highnam, 1964). The hypertrophied CA of the fes mutant of *Drosophila melanogaster,* a mutant that cannot mature oocytes, is returned to normal morphology when a wild-type ovary is implanted (King et al., 1966), suggesting that the presence of an abnormal ovary somehow inhibits JH release although growth and hormone synthesis proceeds normally. As we have seen earlier, there is also reason to believe that the glands may contain but not release hormones in other developmental stages. These observations suggest the possibility of separate factors controlling gland size, hormone production, and hormone release, and it is certainly conceivable that more than one of these factors may be present in any given species. Could it be that both the CA and the EG are controlled by multiple factors? Since the two glands arise from adjacent embryological positions and are structurally similar, and since both glands apparently cyclically secrete chemically similar compounds, it would not be surprising to find comparable regulatory systems for both glands.

Numerous factors are known to influence the activity of the adult CA, presumably by some action on the control systems of the brain. Several authors have observed that implants of active CA into intact hosts will result in decreased activity of the host gland. However, this compensatory relationship is not universally observed. Starvation generally inhibits, and feeding stimulates both CA activity and oöcyte maturation. In both locusts and cockroaches, a pheromone is released by mature males and females that stimulates the activity of the CA in immature adults. In both groups, active CA are required for pheromone production.

In cockroaches, where the brain is believed to inhibit the CA, this inhibition, mediated through the ventral nerve cord, is apparently removed by the act of mating, and subsequent CA activity leads to the maturation of oöcytes. The act of mating may be of secondary importance because in some cockroaches the presence of a spermatophore in the bursa copulatrix mechanically activates the ventral cord and thereby acts to remove CA inhibition. The CA generally decline in activity when mature oöcytes are present. In *S. gregaria* the brain begins to accumulate NS material when the terminal oöcytes reach a certain size and the activity of the CA declines as the NS material accumulates. Sensory impulses from receptors promote inhibition of the CA when egg cases are present in pregnant cockroaches (Highnam, 1964b).

Thus, the brain may control the CA of adults by at least four methods: direct NS stimulation, indirect NS stimulation, NS inhibition, and direct nervous inhibition. Currently, the most reasonable working hypothesis seems to be that the brain usually stimulates by means of NS hormones, either directly or indirectly, and inhibits by direct innervation (Highnam, 1964b). It may be that in some insects only one of the above are operable, while in others any or all of the above are found. The remote possibility exists that in certain insects the glands somehow regulate themselves. It may also be that individual control systems regulate CA growth, JH synthesis, and JH release.

The factors controlling the degeneration of the EG in adult insects are not clear and certainly deserve further attention. Wigglesworth has shown that in *R. prolixus* two requirements must be met for degeneration (Gilbert, 1964). First, the glands must undergo a molt in the absence of JH, i.e., the adult molt. Second, some "other factor" must be present. The identity of this additional factor is currently unknown. Why the glands do not degenerate in certain castes of social insects is also conjectural. It has been suggested that such castes are neotenic and that they do not undergo a terminal molt in the complete absence of JH.

CONCLUDING REMARKS

The author has attempted to summarize the available information concerning the regulation of neuroendocrine system activity during the development of insects and to point out where additional information is required. It is hoped that this discussion will serve to stimulate the developmentally oriented reader to undertake individual research in this fascinating field. Certainly the opportunities for investigations at all levels of refinement are limitless, and biologists of many interests could well devote their energies to the developmental problems posed by the Insecta.

REFERENCES

Adkisson, P. L. 1966. Internal clocks and insect diapause. Science, 154:234–241.

Beck, S. D., J. L. Shane, and I. B. Colvin. 1965. Proctodone production in the european corn borer, *Ostrinia nubilalis*. J. Insect Physiol., 11:297–304.

Biedermann, M. 1964. Neurosekretion bei Arbeiterinnen und Königinnen von *Apis mellifica* L. unter natürlichen und experimentellen Bedingungen. Z. Wiss. Zool., 170:255–308.

Carlisle, D. B., and P. E. Ellis. 1963. Endocrine glands and phase in locusts. Sympos. Gen. Biol. Ital., 10:219–224.

———, and E. Betts. 1965. The influence of aromatic shrubs on sexual maturation in the desert locust *Schistocerca gregaria*. J. Insect Physiol., 11:1541–1558.

Clarke, K. U., and P. A. Langley. 1963. Studies on the initiation of growth and moulting in *Locusta migratoria migratorioides* R. and F. IV. The relationship between the stomatogastric nervous system and neurosecretion. J. Insect Physiol., 9:423–430.

Edwards, J. S. 1966. Neural control of metamorphosis in *Galleria mellonella* (Lepidoptera). J. Insect Physiol., 12:1423–1434.

Ellis, P. E., D. B. Carlisle, and D. J. Osborne. 1965. Desert locusts: Sexual maturation delayed by feeding on senescent vegetation. Science, 149:546–547.

Engelmann, F. 1962. Further experiments on the regulation of the sexual cycle in females of *Leucophaea maderae* (Blattaria). Gen. Comp. Endocr., 2:183–192.

_____. 1965. The mode of regulation of the corpus allatum in adult insects. Arch. Anat. Micr. Morph. Exp., 54:387–404.

Fraenkel, G., and C. Hsiao. 1965. Bursicon, a hormone which mediates tanning of the cuticle in the adult fly and other insects. J. Insect Physiol., 11:513–556.

Fukuda, S. 1962a. Hormonal control of diapause in the silkworm. Gen. Comp. Endocr., 1:337–340.

_____. 1962b. Secretion of juvenile hormone by the corpora allata in pupae and moths of the silkworm, *Bombyx mori*. Annot. Zool. Jap., 35:199–212.

Gabe, M. 1966. Neurosecretion. New York, Pergamon Press.

Gilbert, L. I. 1964. Physiology of growth and development: Endocrine aspects. *In* Rockstein, M., ed., The Physiology of Insecta, vol. 1, 149–225, New York, Academic Press.

Girardie, A. 1965. Contribution a l'étude du contrôle de l'activité des corpora allata par la pars intercerebralis chez *Locusta migratoria* (L.). C. R. Soc. Biol. (Paris), 261:4876–4878.

Herman, W. S. 1967. The ecdysial glands of arthropods. *In* Bourne, G. H., and J. F. Danielli, eds., International Review of Cytology, Vol. 22, 269–347, New York, Academic Press.

Highnam, K. C. 1962. Neurosecretory control of ovarian development in *Schistocerca gregaria* and its relation to phase differences. Coll. Intern. Centre Nat. Rech. Sci. Paris, No. 114:107–121.

_____. 1964a. Hormones and behaviour in insects. Viewpoints Biol., 3:219–255.

_____. 1964b. Endocrine relationships in insect reproduction. *In* Highnam, K. C., ed., Insect Reproduction, pp. 26–42, London, Royal Entomology Society.

_____, L. Hill, and W. Mordue. 1966. The endocrine system and oöcyte growth in *Schistocerca* in relation to starvation and frontal ganglionectomy. J. Insect Physiol., 12:977–994.

Hill, L., W. Mordue, and K. C. Highnam. 1966. The endocrine system, frontal ganglion, and feeding during maturation in the female desert locust. J. Insect. Physiol., 12:1197–1208.

Karlson, P., and C. E. Sekeris, 1966. Ecdysone, an insect steriod hormone, and its mode of action. *In* Pincus, G., ed., Recent Progress in Hormone Research, vol. 22, 473–493, New York, Academic Press.

King, R. C., S. K. Aggarwal, and D. Bodenstein. 1966. The comparative submicroscopic cytology of the corpus allatum-corpus cardiacum complex of wild type and *fes* adult female *Drosophila melanogaster*. J. Exp. Zool., 161:151–176.

Kobayashi, M. 1963. The chemistry and physiology of the brain hormone. Proc. XVI Intern. Congr. Zool. Wash. 4:226–233.

Krishnakumaran, A., and H. A. Schneiderman. 1965. Prothoracotrophic activity of compounds that mimic juvenile hormone. J. Insect Physiol., 11:1517–1532.

Kunkel, J. G. 1966. Development and the availability of food in the German cockroach *Blatella germanica*. J. Insect Physiol., 12:227–236.

Langley, P. A. 1966. The control of digestion in the tsete fly, *Glossina morsitans*. Enzyme activity in relation to the size and nature of the meal. J. Insect Physiol., 12:439–448.

Lees, A. D. 1955. The Physiology of Diapause in Arthropods, Cambridge, England, Cambridge University Press.

Liu, T. P., and S. E. Dixon. 1965. Studies on the mode of action of royal jelly in honeybee development. VI. Haemolymph protein changes during caste development. Can. J. Zool., 43:873–879.

Lüscher, M. 1962. Hormonal regulation of development in termites. Sympos. Gen. Biol. Ital., 10:1–11.

——. 1963. Functions of the corpora allata in the development of termites. Proc. XVI Intern. Congr. Zool. Wash., 4:244–249.

Maddrell, S. H. P. 1964. Excretion in the blood-sucking bug, *Rhodnius prolixus* Stal., III. The control of the release of the diuretic hormone. J. Exp. Biol., 41:459–472.

Mueller, N. 1964. An experimental analysis of molting in embryos of *Melanoplus differentialis*. Develop. Biol., 8:222–240.

Naisse, J. 1966. Contrôle endocrinien de la différenciation sexuelle chez *Lâmpyris noctiluca* (Coléoptère Lâmpyride). III. Influence des hormones de la pârs ıntercerebralis. Gen. Comp. Endocr., 7:85–104.

Nayar, K. K. 1962. Effects of injecting juvenile hormone extracts on the neurosecretory system of adult male cockroaches *(Periplaneta americana)*. *In* H. Heller and R. B. Clark, eds., Neurosecretion, Vol. 12, 371–378, New York, Academic Press.

Norris, M. J., and M. P. Pener. 1965. An inhibitory effect of allatectomized males and females on the sexual maturation of young male adults of *Schistocerca gregaria* (Forsk.) (Orthoptera: Acrididae). Nature, 208:1122.

Ozeki, K. 1965. Control of the secretion of juvenile hormone in the earwig. Zool. Jb. Physiol., 71:641–646.

Raabe, M. 1965. Etude des phénomènes de neurosécrétion au niveau de la chaine nerveuse ventrale des phasmides. Bull. Soc. Zool. Fr., 40:631–654.

Röller, H., K. H. Dahm, C. C. Sweely, and B. M. Trost. 1967. The structure of the juvenile hormone. Ang. Chemie (English Ed.) 6:179–180.

Schmidt, G. H. 1964. Aktivitätsphasen bekannter Hormondrüsen wahrend der Metamorphose von *Formica polytena* Foerst. (Hym. Ins.) Insectes Sociaux, 10:41–58.

Schneiderman, H. A., and L. I. Gilbert. 1964. Control of growth and development in insects. Science, 143:325–333.

Shappirio, D. G., D. M. Eichenbaum, and B. R. Locke. 1967. Cholinesterase in the brain of the cecropia silkmoth during metamorphosis and pupal diapause. Biol. Bull. 132:108–125.

Takami, T. 1963. In vitro culture of embryos of the silkworm, *Bombyx mori* L. III. Moult of brainless embryos in culture. J. Exp. Biol., 40:735–739.

Wigglesworth, V. B. 1954. The Physiology of Insect Metamorphosis. Cambridge, England, Cambridge University Press.

———. 1964. The hormonal regulation of growth and reproduction in insects. *In* Beament, J. W. L., J. E. Treherne, and V. B. Wigglesworth, eds., Advances in Insect Physiology, vol. 2, 247–336, New York, Academic Press.

de Wilde, J. 1965. Photoperiodic control of endocrines in insects. Arch. Anat. Micr. Morph. Exp., 54:547–564.

Williams, C. M., P. L. Adkisson, and C. Walcott. 1965. Physiology of insect diapause. XV. The transmission of photoperiod signals to the brain of the oak silkworm, *Antheraea pernyi*. Biol. Bull., 128:497–507.

Wilson, E. O. 1965. Chemical communication in the social insects. Science, 149:1064–1071.

four

BIOCHEMISTRY OF
INSECT METAMORPHOSIS

Gerard R. Wyatt

Department of Biology
Yale University
New Haven, Connecticut

INTRODUCTION

The metamorphosis of the higher insects embodies the most profound reorganization of a grown animal that is known (see Chapter 2). It represents advanced polymorphism, for a single genome determines the development of a differentiated free-living organism which, when fully grown, is largely destroyed and reconstituted in a new form adapted for a totally different life. Such a phenomenon, under the control of hormones, should provide prime material for the study of the regulation of genetic expression and its role in morphogenesis.

This challenge has inspired biochemical study of insect metamorphosis for many years. However, since all organ systems of the insect are to a greater or lesser extent modified in structure and function during metamorphosis, some change may be expected in almost any biochemical feature that is examined. Accordingly, the literature of the subject is extensive and diffuse, and reviews of it have tended to give weight to each author's own predilections (Gilbert and Schneiderman, 1961; Karlson and Sekeris, 1964; Agrell, 1964). The contemporary emphasis on molecular genetics and nucleic acid and protein synthesis seems most likely to yield understanding of the fundamental mechanisms in metamorphosis, but investigation of these fields has not yet progressed far with insects. The earlier attention to nutrient reserves and pathways of energy conversion now seems less close to the central question. Nevertheless, these studies have contributed to knowledge of the milieu in which the genes are working and of the nature of the biochemical systems for which they are responsible, and we are not yet in a position to say confidently what is essential and what is not. Therefore, I shall attempt to summarize the present state of understanding in several biochemical areas where enough work has been done to permit some coherent discussion. Other subjects will be arbitrarily omitted; among the more important of these are the development and functions of the silk gland and the ovaries, although much work has been done on both. References to the literature will necessarily be selective, and most examples will be drawn from two insect groups which have received a great share of research attention. The higher Diptera undergo the most complete metamorphosis among insects, replacing most of their organ systems (see Chapter 2). Some are easy to raise in the laboratory with a short generation time, but they have the disadvantage of small size which has discouraged biochemical work with discrete tissues (except to some extent flight muscle). In the Lepidoptera, there is far less abandonment of larval cellular structure, but this order includes many species with the experimental advantage of large size, and more work has been done with discrete tissues. Biochemically, there is probably unity in the underlying mechanisms of histolysis and of histogenesis in all insect groups. Processes which are not strictly part of metamorphosis may be relevant—e.g., the degeneration and reconstruction of muscles in the larval molting cycle of the bug *Rhodnius* or in the adult diapause of the Colorado potato beetle. Metamorphosis is not wholly confined to the transformation from larva to adult, as there is often a small degree of change in form at each larval molt.

USE AND INTERCONVERSION OF RESERVES

During their last larval stage, in preparation for metamorphosis, holometabolous insects accumulate substantial nutrient reserves. These are chiefly deposited as fat and glycogen in the fat body, a cellular tissue which is a center both for storage and for intermediary metabolism and which proliferates greatly during the last larval instar (Kilby, 1963). In the larva of the wax moth, *Galleria mellonella*, this preparation for metamorphosis can be detected early in the last instar, which differs metabolically from the preceding larval stages (Janda et al., 1966). Peak values for glycogen content are often in the neighborhood of 10 percent (but sometimes as high as 30 percent) of total body dry weight, and the lipid reserves are generally greater, values of 20 to 50 percent of dry weight before metamorphosis being common.

Analytical studies on changes and conversions in the insect pupa have been stimulated by the fact that it is a closed system which exchanges only gases with the environment. A body of the early work is summarized and discussed in an admirable review by Needham (1929), but few conclusions can be drawn from it because of inadequacies in the analyses. In particular, trehalose was not recognized as an ubiquitous sugar in insects until 1957, and the extent to which the chitin and protein of the cuticle are resorbed in the molt and reutilized was generally underestimated or ignored. References to more recent studies can be found in several reviews (Wigglesworth, 1965; Gilbert, 1967; Wyatt, 1967a).

Among the most comprehensive data on a single species are those recently obtained by Birt and colleagues on the sheep blowfly, *Lucilia cuprina* (Fig. 1). Several conclusions may be drawn. The principal source of energy is fat, the content of

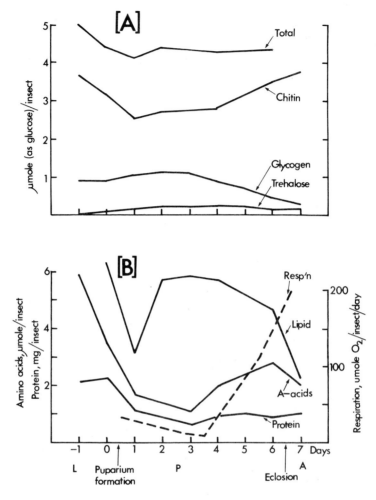

FIG. 1. Changes in composition and respiration of the blowfly, *Lucilia cuprina*, during metamorphosis. A: Carbohydrates (after Crompton and Birt, 1967). B: Respiration, neutral lipid, free amino acids, and soluble protein (after Howells and Birt, 1964, and D'Costa and Birt, 1966). The scale for protein has been corrected according to personal communication from Dr. Howells. Developmental stages: L, larva; P, pupa and pharate adult; A, adult.

which at adult emergence is about one third of that in the mature larva. The rate of fat oxidation is more rapid at the beginning and the end of metamorphosis than in the middle, in accord with the changing rate of respiration. At the beginning of metamorphosis before the pupal molt, there is a fall in total protein and in free amino acids, which are partly oxidized and partly converted to carbohydrate and fat. The utilization of protein leads to accumulation of much uric acid in the early fly pupa (Russo-Caia, 1960). There is also a fall, before the pupal molt, in chitin as the inner layers of the larval cuticle are digested and resorbed; some of this is apparently deposited as glycogen, which is later reconverted to chitin in the growing adult cuticle. Thus, when chitin is included, the total carbohydrate content undergoes only a slight net fall throughout metamorphosis. Since flies depend upon carbohydrate for flight energy, its conservation during their development is advantageous. A slight temporary rise in total carbohydrate which is observed just after pupation is attributable to glyconeogenesis from amino acids. These conclusions differ in several respects from those from earlier, less complete analyses on related species, which had suggested synthesis of glycogen at the expense of fat, followed by substantial oxidation of carbohydrate during metamorphosis. The net conversion of fat to carbohydrate is not known to be possible in insects or vertebrate animals.

Analyses on metamorphosing Lepidoptera, such as the oriental silkworm, *Bombyx mori* (Niemierko et al., 1956; Zaluska, 1959), and the American saturniid silk moth, *Hyalophora cecropia* (Gilbert and Schneiderman, 1961; Bade and Wyatt, 1962; Domroese and Gilbert, 1964), present a generally similar picture. Again, fat is an important energy source. However, the extent of net oxidation of carbohydrate in passing from caterpillar to moth is greater than in the case of the fly, perhaps because moths use fat as their fuel for flight and so its conservation, rather than that of glygogen, is advantageous. There is a further adaptive difference between the sexes in that male moths, which are more ambitious in flight, conserve more lipid than do the relatively sedentary females of a species. As in the blowflies, there is a phase of glycogen deposition about the time of pupation, which is attributable to synthesis from chitin and protein. A large proportion of the cuticle is resorbed and reutilized in each molt; thus, in the larval-pupal and pupal-adult molts of the Cecropia silk moth, the resorbed fraction is more than 80 percent of the cuticular chitin.

Evidence concerning the balance of metabolism in insects also often has been sought by measurement of respiratory quotients. Such measurements, especially with pupae, however, are subject to a number of pitfalls (e.g., release of CO_2 in bursts, trapping of CO_2 in nongaseous forms, disturbance of metabolism by accumulated CO_2), and in general more direct methods of study are preferable. The more reliable estimates of respiratory quotients are in reasonable agreement with analytical results.

Along with the quantitative changes in body composition are certain cases of apparently qualitative change (Wyatt, 1967a). In blowflies, e.g., trehalose cannot be detected in the feeding larva, but makes its first appearance just before pupation and then increases (Fig. 1) to play an important role in the flight metabolism of the adult. In pupae of the Cecropia silkworm, which pass the winter in diapause, most of the glycogen is converted to glycerol, and part of this is reconverted to glycogen at the beginning of adult development in the spring. But this is an adaptation to survival in cold weather rather than a process characteristic of metamorphosis, for glycerol is accumulated by many insects which survive cold winters, and the life-cycle stage in which it appears is always that which passes the winter, be this the embryo, larva, pupa, or adult. In short, the use and interconversions of reserves in the metamorphosis of different species is variously adapted to their respective needs.

Little is known about the regulation of these conversions. A recent review on metabolic control mechanisms in insects cited much evidence for the existence of control but few instances where enough is known to justify designation as a mechanism (Harvey and Haskell, 1966). Fat and carbohydrate metabolism, like other aspects of insect development, must be more or less directly under control by hormones, and cases can be cited in which metabolic change follows change in hormonal state (Wyatt, 1967a). Certain rapid adaptive changes can result from hormonally released activation of preexisting enzymes, such as glycogen phosphorylase. The longer term changes in metamorphosis are presumably associated with changing enzyme levels, but there exists little satisfactory biochemical evidence on this point. One example is the elevation of chitinase, a participant in digestion of the cuticle, at each molt in the silkworm, *Bombyx mori* (Jeuniaux, 1961).

RESPIRATORY METABOLISM

Respiration and Energy Supply During Metamorphosis

One of the earliest and most frequently recorded metabolic observations concerning insect metamorphosis is that the rate of respiration changes in a manner that can be described as a U-shaped curve (Fig. 1, 3, see also Agrell, 1964, Wigglesworth, 1965, p. 574). In the earlier papers, the significance of this general course of respiration was much discussed. The first suggestion was that it reflected successive histolysis and histogenesis, the rate of respiration changing in accord with the amount of organized tissue present at any time, but it then became clear that the histological picture often did not support this simple view. When the activities of respiratory enzymes, such as cytochrome oxidase and dehydrogenases, were measured, a somewhat better correlation with respiratory rate was found (Agrell, 1949; Sacktor, 1951). No more than a rough agreement between respiratory rate and activites can be expected from such measurements, however, for the course of change during metamorphosis varies for different enzymes and different tissues.

In any case, it is now clear that tissue respiration is generally not limited by the levels of respiratory enzymes. The capacity for respiration depends on the content of mitochondria and their electron transport system, which is relatively low in tissues such as fat body and high in others such as muscles. But the actual respiration is generally substantially less than this capacity, as a result of respiratory control by the coupled phosphorylating system, which is subject to the levels of ADP, ATP, and inorganic phosphate in the cell (Harvey and Haskell, 1966). Thus, the rate of respiration adjusts itself to supply the demand, in the form of high-energy phosphate, of the work done by the tissue, which includes biosynthesis, active transport, muscular activity, and so on. In the pupa and the pharate adult insect, where there is little muscular activity, one may expect protein synthesis to be a major energy user, and indeed the rates of respiration often show some correlation with those of protein synthesis.

Some evidence on the balance of energy metabolism in insect metamorphosis can be obtained by analysis of metabolite and coenzyme levels. It was suggested as early as 1893 by Bataillon, on the basis of crude carbohydrate analyses, that the metabolism of the silkworm pupa might somehow be anaerobic, and similar ideas have recurred in various forms (Wyatt, 1963). Several compounds are now recognized as products of experimentally induced anaerobic glycolysis in insects: lactate, alanine, pyruvate, and glycerol-1-phosphate (Gilmour, 1965), but recent analyses show none of these accumulating during metamorphosis of the blowfly (Crompton and Birt, 1967). There is, in fact, much more lactate in the actively respiring larva than in the pupa. In addition, analyses of pyridine nucleotide coenzymes show that the ratio NADH/NAD is somewhat lower in midpupal life than in the active larval and adult stages, whereas anaerobic mechanisms would be expected to lead, on

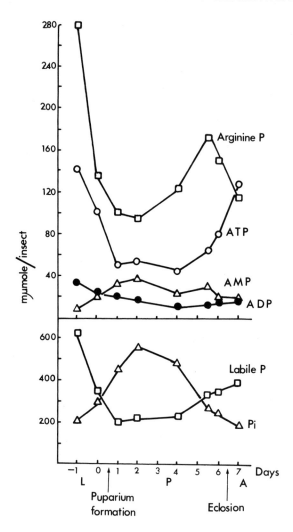

FIG. 2. Acid-soluble phosphorus compounds during metamorphosis of the blowfly, *Lucilia cuprina*. The adenine nucleotides were estimated by enzymic assays. Labile phosphate is that released in 10 min by 1 N H_2SO_4 at 100°. After Crompton and Birt, 1967.

the contrary, to accumulation of the reduced form (Birt, 1966). Thus, there is no evidence for anaerobic processes in the blowfly pupa. Indeed, it would be surprising to find them, for the supply of oxygen is ample to support the depressed rate of metabolism, and aerobic processes give more efficient use of reserves which the pupa needs to conserve for the construction and initial activity of the imago.

The levels of "high-energy" and related phosphate compounds are also of interest. In the blowfly, ATP and the phosphagen, arginine phosphate, show a decrease in the midpupa, and inorganic phosphate shows an almost reciprocal increase (Fig. 2). This doubtless corresponds to changes in the body content of tissues which are characteristically rich in high-energy phosphate, notably muscle. The rise in AMP presumably represents degradation of ATP and ADP from such tissues. That the ATP/ADP ratio remains high through metamorphosis, and that phosphagen is never exhausted, show that the ATP-generating processes in the pupa are at all times fully able to keep up with the energy demand.

Respiratory Metabolism and Diapause

When the pupal stage enters the resting state of diapause, the depression of metabolism is extreme and prolonged. This is the case with *Hyalophora cecropia* and some related saturniid moths (Fig. 3), which have received much attention directed toward testing the relationships between respiration, respiratory enzymes, tissue growth, and hormone action (reviewed by Shappirio, 1960; Harvey, 1962; Wyatt, 1963; Harvey and Haskell, 1966). Since diapause is terminated and adult development is initiated by the prothoracic gland hormone, ecdysone (see Chapter 3), this system has been used for analyzing its action. A provocative observation was that respiration of pupae in diapause is highly resistant to the cytochrome oxidase inhibitors carbon monoxide and cyanide, a fact previously noted for the embryonic diapause of the grasshopper, *Melanoplus differentialis*. In spectroscopic and enzymic assays, the cytochrome content of tissues in diapause was found to be much reduced—cytochrome oxidase is present at low levels, but cytochromes b and c could not be detected at all. Accordingly, it appeared possible that terminal electron transport in diapause might proceed by some pathway other than the usual cytochrome system and that resumption of growth might depend upon the resynthesis of cytochromes which in turn might be closely linked to the action of the hormone. Further experiments showed, however, that when appropriately tested, diapause respiration is indeed sensitive to cyanide and carbon monoxide and since the latter inhibition can be reversed by light, participation of cytochrome oxidase is indicated. Apparently, the tissues contain substantially

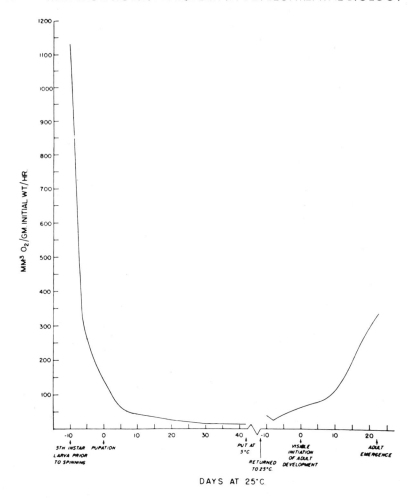

FIG. 3. Respiratory rate in the silkmoth, *Hyalophora cecropia*, in the mature larva, the pupal diapause, and the developing adult. From Schneiderman and Williams, 1953.

more cytochrome oxidase than is needed to support the normal rate of electron transport, so that the oxidase can be largely inhibited with no effect on net pupal respiration. When the demand upon this enzyme is increased, however, either by lowering the oxygen tension or by enhancing the rate of respiration (e.g., with 2, 4-dinitrophenol), inhibition of the pathway becomes demonstrable.

    This conclusion raises the question: How is diapause respiration held to its low rate? Since cytochromes b and c were not detected spectroscopically, it seemed at first that a limiting step might exist here. Oxygen uptake by the pupae, however, is strongly stimulated by dinitrophenol, which shows that the capacity of the electron transport enzymes exceeds their normal load and indicates respiratory control via the coupled phosphorylation system, as is usual in active tissues. In addition, analyses of adenine nucleotides in diapause and developing tissues show that the ATP/ADP ratio changes little, even though the turnover rate is much higher in development, so that a nice coordination between phosphorylation and dephosphorylation is indicated, just as in the nondiapausing blowfly pupa discussed above. The ATP level in diapause tissues is high enough so that deficiency of metabolic energy can scarcely be responsible for restraint of growth.

The suggestion has also arisen that diapause pupae possess partially anaerobic metabolism as a consequence of restricted electron transport. This seemed to be supported by the gradual conversion of glycogen to glycerol in the Cecropia pupa. It now appears, however, that the characteristic glycolytic products glycerol-1-phosphate, lactate, and pyruvate are not elevated in the normal diapause pupa, though they are produced in experimental anaerobiosis. In addition, the NADH/NAD ratio is not elevated in diapause. The production of glycerol, therefore, is probably subject to special regulatory mechanisms as an adaptation to cold, and the diapause silkmoth pupa is no more anaerobic than is the blowfly pupa.

The present indication from these extended studies on the extremely suppressed metabolism of diapause is that the pathways do not differ qualitatively from those of other tissues, but there is a coordinated decrease in activities. The breakdown of the cytochrome system is impressive, yet the actual rate of respiration appears to be limited by energy demand which, in the pupa, must largely represent biosynthesis of protein and other tissue constituents. Furthermore, resynthesis of cytochromes, though necessary, is not sufficient to release resumption of development, for injury to diapause pupae is followed by the former but not the latter. Certain problems remain: e.g., cytochromes b and c have not been detected in tissues other than muscle of the diapausing Cecropia pupa, and the evidence for their participation in electron transport remains indirect. The measurements of respiration all have been made with whole pupae, and it is not known how much is contributed by muscle, epidermis, fat body, and other tissues whose activities and enzyme complements are quite distinct.

Respiration and the Corpus Allatum Hormone

In addition to the effect of ecdysone in increasing respiration when diapause is broken, enhanced respiration is often attendant upon the action of the hormone of the corpora allata (see Chapter 3). Increased respiration has been noted both during the "juvenile" action of this hormone, when corpora allata are implanted into larval insects, and during its gonadotrophic action in the adult. When corpora allata were implanted into *Galleria* larvae of different ages, however, and development was modified to various extents, the effect on respiration was always correlated with the degree of morphogenetic change. It appears that this hormone, like ecdysone, may influence respiratory metabolism indirectly by inducing growth and structural change in the tissues (Sehnal and Slama, 1966).

DEVELOPMENT OF FLIGHT MUSCLE

A picture of the coordinated synthesis of enzymes in the construction of a specialized tissue has been gained from studies on the biochemical development of flight muscle. The indirect flight muscles of insects are of the fibrillar type. Between the bundles of large fibrils are packed rows of giant mitochondria ("sarcosomes") which may be 1 to 3 μ in diameter and make up 30 to 40 percent of the weight of the tissue. These are directly supplied with oxygen by tracheoles. The flight muscle has almost no lactate dehydrogenase and in its normal activity is totally aerobic. The contents of soluble NAD-linked α-glycerophosphate dehydrogenase and of mitochondrial flavoprotein α-glycerophosphate oxidase are usually high and provide a shuttle for the oxidation of extramitochondrial NADH by passage of glycerol-1-phosphate and dihydroxyacetone phosphate in and out of the mitochondria (Sacktor, 1965). Flight muscle is thus constructed for sustained aerobic activity with exceptionally high energy output. Insect leg muscle, such as the jumping muscles of the locust, on the other hand, has a smaller content of mitochondria and possesses lactate dehydrogenase in adaptation for sporadic violent activity followed by rest.

The most comprehensive picture of the structural and biochemical development of flight muscle is that due to the work of Bücher and his colleagues on the locust, *Locusta migratoria* (Bücher, 1965). The muscle develops during a period of rather more than two weeks starting from a small *anlage*, or precursor muscle, that is present just after the fourth

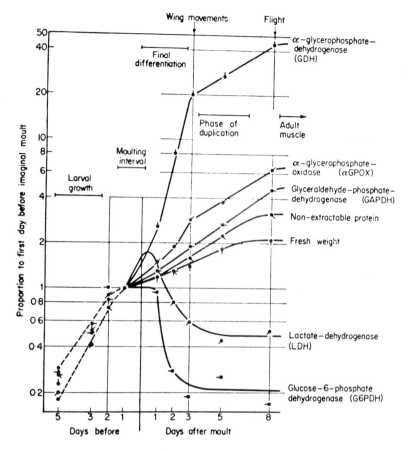

FIG. 4. Biochemical development of the flight muscle in *Locusta migratoria*. From Bücher, 1965.

molt. Even this precursor muscle resembles flight muscle in having only a low content of lactate dehydrogenase. Four phases of growth are described (Fig. 4): (1) larval growth, with increase in size (but not number of nuclei) with little differentiation; (2) a phase about the time of the final molt when the larval tracheal supply breaks down and new tracheoles penetrate into the muscle and a transient elevation of lactate dehydrogenase may indicate some temporary anaerobiosis; (3) a phase of differentiation, during the first days of adult life, in which the characteristic enzyme pattern of flight muscle is established by elevation of mitochondrial enzymes and degeneration of lactate dehydrogenase and glucose-6-phosphate dehydrogenase; (4) finally, further growth, with approximate doubling of all components. Thus, most of the growth of the mitochondria and synthesis of the eventual enzymes takes place after emergence of the adult insect, and the locust cannot fly until this maturation is completed. There are "constant-proportion groups" of enzymes, so that the mitochondrial oxidative enzymes (represented by α-glycerophosphate dehydrogenase) increase coordinately with one another and, similarly, a group of soluble glycolytic enzymes (represented by glyceraldehyde phosphate dehydrogenase) retain an approximately constant mutual relationship. The existence of such constant proportionality within groups of enzymes, despite wide variations in absolute levels, extends to other tissues than flight muscle and presumably indicates some common regulation of their synthesis (Harvey and Haskell, 1966).

Although the flight muscle of the locust is somewhat less specialized than that of holometabolous insects such as flies and bees, the biochemical development of the latter is probably essentially similar. A greater proportion of the enzyme synthesis may occur before eclosion than in the locust, but there is always a period of maturation, involving further mitochondrial growth and enzyme synthesis, in the emerged adult. In saturniid silk moths, cytochrome c first appears in measurable amounts in the flight muscle on about the sixteenth day of the 21-day period of adult development, and its synthesis thereafter is very rapid (Chan and Margoliash, 1966). In the blowfly, *Phormia*, the cytochrome content rises about fourfold during the first week of adult life, which reflects an increase in the size of the mitochondria while their number remains constant (Levenbook and Williams, 1956). Growth of the flight muscle mitochondria is also reflected in a 50 percent increase in phospholipid content of the thorax of *Lucilia* during the week after emergence (D'Costa and Birt, 1966). In *Lucilia*, the distribution of enzymes and protein in particles of various sizes has been determined, and inasmuch as the specific activities of several respiratory enzymes relative to mitochondrial protein change greatly during development of the fly, it is proposed that the respiratory enzymes and the nonrespiratory, structural protein follow different courses of synthesis (Lennie and Birt, 1967). This is quite likely, since it appears that the nonextractable, structural protein of mitochondria may be synthesized within them, whereas synthesis of the extractable enzymes is a function of extramitochondrial ribosomes.

In the honeybee, the mean volume of a flight-muscle sarcosome increases from 0.015 μ^3 in the 10-day pupa (pharate adult) to 0.041 μ^3 on the day of emergence and to 0.52 μ^3 in the 20-day-old adult. The increase in content of several cytochromes,

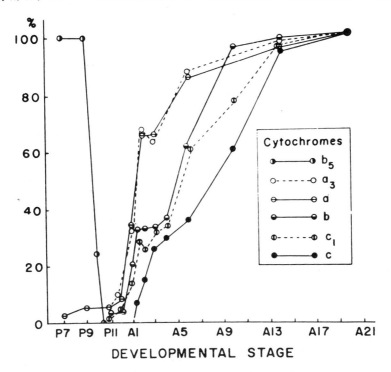

FIG. 5. Changes in concentrations of cytochrome components during development of flight muscle in the honeybee. For each cytochrome, the maximum concentration achieved is put equal to 100 percent. From Herold and Borei, 1963.

determined by the sensitive technique of spectroscopy at the temperature of liquid nitrogen, is shown in Fig. 5 (Herold and Borei, 1963). It is evident that their synthesis is by no means synchronous. Cytochrome b_5, which occurs in the microsomal fraction and is believed to participate in biosyntheses, is found in the pupa and declines sharply in adult development. Among the mitochondrial cytochromes, although the general pattern is similar, there are distinct differences in time of first detectability and course of synthesis, so it is clear that constant mutual proportionality is not a universal rule among these electron carriers.

SCLEROTIZATION OF THE CUTICLE

A characteristic feature of insects is their tough external cuticle. This is secreted at each molt by the epidermis and consists chiefly of protein and chitin, plus smaller amounts of

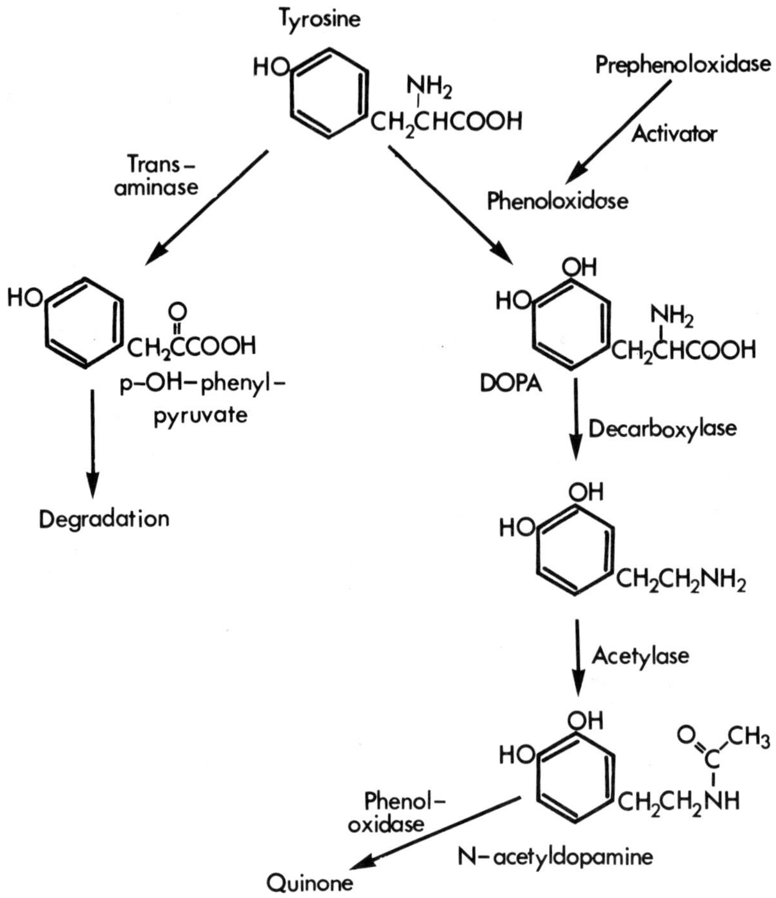

FIG. 6. The metabolism of tyrosine in the tanning of the blowfly puparium, according to the work of Karlson, Sekeris, and colleagues.

specialized lipoidal substances. Unlike the cuticle of Crustacea, which contains inorganic deposits, it is hardened by organic tanning or cross-linking of the protein in a process known as sclerotization. It has been accepted for many years that sclerotization involves quinones derived from tyrosine, but the chemical nature of the tanning agent was established only recently, and the details of its reactions with the protein are still obscure. The biochemistry of sclerotization of the blowfly puparium has recently been intensively studied by Karlson, Sekeris, and coworkers because of its connection with the

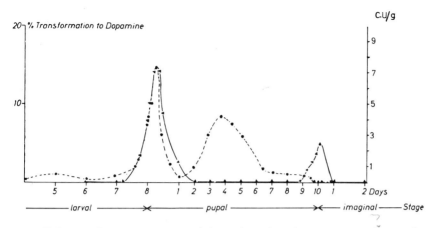

FIG. 7. Ecdysone titer and dopa decarboxylase activity during development of the blowfly *Calliphora erythrocephala*. Ecdysone titer (-----) is expressed Calliphora-units per gram, and enzyme activity (——) as percent transformation of dopa to dopamine. From Shaaya and Sekeris, 1965.

action of the hormone, ecdysone. This subject is reviewed by Cottrell (1964), Brunet (1965), and Sekeris and Karlson (1966).

When the blowfly maggot is full grown and ready to pupate, its soft, white cuticle is inflated into a barrel shape and then becomes hard and dark brown, as the puparium, before the insect molts to a pupa within it. The principal tanning agent has been identified as N-acetyldopamine (Fig. 6); its acetylation has the chemical role of preventing cyclization into an indole, and when the phenolic ring is further oxidized to an o-quinone, it is reactive with protein amino groups. In the early third-instar larva, metabolism of tyrosine is largely by a degradative pathway that starts with transamination. During the instar, the level of tyrosine mounts until it is one of the most abundant free amino acids in the hemolymph Then, at the time of puparium formation, it is largely used in the production of N-acetyldopamine by the enzyme-catalyzed steps shown. The switch in metabolic fate of tyrosine is the result of changed enzyme activities: tyrosine transaminase apparently decreases, prephenol oxidase accumulates in the hemolymph and its activator protein builds up in the integument, and a specific dopa decarboxylase is synthesized. The acetylase, on the other hand, is present throughout the instar. The decarboxylase, whose activity shows the greatest changes, is believed to be the controlling enzyme (Fig. 7). The whole process is set off by the increasing level of ecdysone at this stage of the life cycle: it can be prevented by ligation and induced by injection of the hormone, and this forms the basis of the usual assay for ecdysone. Because of the close correlation between production of dopa decarboxylase and ecdysone titer, and other evidence to be discussed below, it has been proposed that the hormone "induces" this enzyme by an effect on nucleic acid metabolism (Karlson and Sekeris, 1966).

The tanning of the dipteran puparium just before the pupal molt is a special case in insect ontogeny, as sclerotization commonly affects newly deposited cuticle just after ecdysis. In several such cases recently examined in Karlson's laboratory (the blowfly adult, the locust, and the mealworm, *Tenebrio molitor*) the mechanism appeared to be similar, for dopa decarboxylase was active, and tyrosine was converted to N-acetyldopamine, close to times of sclerotization. In the blowfly adult, a further source of tanning agent is apparently the hydrolysis of N-acetyldopamine-4-0-β-glucoside, in which form excess N-acetyldopamine is conserved after puparium formation. After the adult molt, ecdysone titer is low, but there is now recognized another hormone specifically associated with cuticular hardening and designated bursicon (Cottrell, 1964; Fraenkel, Hsiao, and Seligman, 1966). It is required for sclerotization of the cuticles of newly emerged flies and newly molted cockroaches and will effect the darkening of discs of colorless integument from the latter in vitro. Little is known about the biochemistry of its action; it has a molecular weight of about 40,000 and possibly may be itself an enzyme. It appears to act at a later stage than the production of N-acetyldopamine. Thus, ecdysone and bursicon could have complementary roles in stimulating the production and use, respectively, of the tanning quinones.

PIGMENT PRODUCTION

Insects possess many kinds of pigment, including the ubiquitous and refractory melanin, and creation of the characteristic adult color pattern is often one of the most striking features of metamorphosis. In the pierid butterflies, the wing patterns are due chiefly to pteridines, and the several pteridines of *Colias eurytheme* wings follow characteristic courses of synthesis, beginning on the third day of pupal life (Watt, 1967). But little is yet known about the regulation of such processes.

One instance in which there is a relation to hormone action involves certain ommochromes. These are phenoxazone compounds derived from tryptophan via kynurenine, which occur widely in the eyes, integument, and internal organs of insects. They are of historic interest because it was experiments with certain eye-color mutants of *Drosophila* and *Ephestia* blocked in tryptophan metabolism that some 30 years ago first demonstrated the association of specific genes with successive steps in a metabolic sequence. The structure and distribution of ommochromes was worked out in a monumental series of investigations in Butenandt's laboratory (see Brunet, 1965). In the hawk moth, *Dicranura vinula*, the green caterpillar develops a characteristic red-brown pattern six days before pupation as a result of the deposition of xanthommatin and rhodommatin. Ligation prevents this change in the abdomen, and it can then be induced by injection of small doses of ecdysone. The enzymic basis of the change has not been established, but the hemolymph levels of tryptophan and 3-hydroxykynurenine rise sharply at the time of pigment synthesis, and it is proposed that ommochrome formation may serve in the removal of tryptophan liberated by proteolysis (Bückmann, Willig, and Linzen, 1966).

BIOSYNTHESIS AND DEGRADATION OF MACROMOLECULES

The Proteins of Larval and Adult Insects

A question of fundamental importance is to what extent the protein constitution of an adult insect differs from that of a larva of the same species. No all-out attack on this problem has been described, but there has recently been a good deal of skirmishing with it.

Most attention has been given to insect blood (hemolymph), because this protein solution is easy to obtain and it undergoes large quantitative changes during ontogeny (Wyatt, 1961). The usual pattern with respect to protein is a relatively low level (often 1 to 2 percent) during the earlier larval stages, then a rapid rise just before pupation (often 6 to 8 percent, but 18 and 20 percent have been recorded), then there is some decline in the pupa and a further fall during the later part of adult development. Qualitatively, a number of analyses by electrophoresis on filter paper (summarized by Wyatt, 1961) gave too little resolution to be of much significance. More recently, starch gel and acrylamide gel electrophoresis have been applied to the hemolymph of a number of species, and between

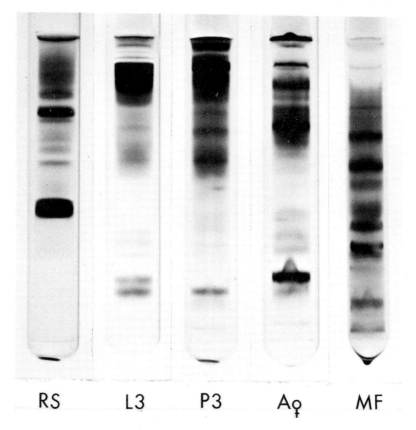

RS   L3   P3   A♀   MF

FIG. 8. Acrylamide gel electrophoretic patterns of proteins from the blowfly, *Phormia regina*. RS, rat serum (for comparison); L3; hemolymph of 3-day-old larva; P3, hemolymph of 3-day-old "pupa" (pharate adult); A♀, hemolymph of adult female; MF, molting fluid. Courtesy Dr. P. S. Chen and Dr. L. Levenbook; in part from Chen and Levenbook, 1966.

10 and 20 bands can generally be recognized. These have no correspondence with the components of mammalian serum (Fig. 8) and differ characteristically with the species. There is often a yellow or green chromoprotein band and a dense band of low mobility which may represent the major hemolymph component of very high molecular weight (more than 500,000) which has been detected in several insects by other methods. In the transformation from larva to adult, most of the electrophoretic components generally persist, but there are certain qualitative differences. Thus, in the tent caterpillar *Malacosoma americanum*, out of 17 bands detected in the full-grown

larva and early pupa, two to five were apparently missing in young larvae and in adult moths, and the adult did not possess any obvious new components (Loughton and West, 1965). When blood from fourth-instar tomato hornworms was concentrated fourfold before electrophoresis, several otherwise undetected components were revealed, and in this insect the adults apparently lack some components characteristic of larvae and contain several fresh ones (Hudson, 1966). A study on the blowfly, *Phormia regina*, in which polyacrylamide gel was used with equal amounts of protein from each developmental stage, led to the conclusion that "the newly emerged adult fly has an entirely different picture" from the larva and pupa (Chen and Levenbook, 1966a), though inspection of the published diagrams suggests that about the half of the bands in the adult pattern may correspond to larval components (Fig. 8).

Bands observed in zone electrophoresis are, of course, rarely pure proteins, nor is their mobility an adequate criterion of identity. The technique of immunodiffusion, in which antigen and antibody diffuse toward one another in an agar gel, can assist with establishing identity, although when applied to whole hemolymph, it has generally revealed fewer components than has electrophoresis. In an immunological study on Cecropia silkworm hemolymph, Telfer and Williams (1953) observed nine distinct antigens and followed six of them quantitatively from the fifth-instar larva to the adult. Each followed its own course of variation, which shows that their levels are individually regulated. One protein found in female pharate adults was passed into the ovaries and their contained eggs, and was present only as traces in the male (Telfer, 1954). But the appearance of uniquely adult antigens, distinct from those of the larva, is not reported. By a technique of immunoelectrophoresis, which should combine high resolution with definitive identification, Terando and Feir (1967) detected 11 antigens in hemolymph of the milkweed bug, *Oncopeltus fasciatus*, and, finding no evidence for stage-specific antigens, arrived at the conclusion that nymphs and adults of both sexes showed only quantitative differences; but it should be noted that this concerns a hemimetabolous insect. Laufer (1963) has applied both electrophoretic and immunological methods to the examination of hemolymph and tissue protein of the Cynthia silk moth and several other species and concludes that there exist both stage-specific and tissue-specific antigens. Enzyme activity (esterases and dehydrogenases) was found associated with a number of the protein zones, but as the enzyme assay is very sensitive it may reveal proteins other than those made visible by staining.

Extracts of the cellular tissues would be expected to be more representative than hemolymph of the overall protein makeup of an insect. Butler and Leone (1966) have prepared whole-insect extracts of several developmental stages of the beetle (mealworm) *Tenebrio molitor* and examined these by several types of electrophoretic and serological test. By immunoelectrophoresis, 10 precipitin zones were obtained; in several zones, larval and adult protein were distinguished serologically despite similar electrophoretic mobility. These authors conclude that during ontogeny there are gradual and sequential qualitative and quantitative changes in protein complement.

The electrophoretic pattern of basic proteins extracted from an acetone powder with acid also changes during blowfly metamorphosis (Agrell and Lindh, 1966).

From these various studies, it is very difficult to feel confident in any conclusions as to the extent of changeover from a larval set of proteins to an adult set in metamorphosis. For the enzymic requirements for their metabolism, insect cells, like other cells, must contain at least several hundreds of distinct proteins. Yet the methods that have been used have detected at most 20. These are no doubt the most abundant or the most antigenic components but are not necessarily the most significant in ontogeny. In only a few studies has there been any attempt at quantitation, and in view of the limited sensitivity of the detection methods, it is very difficult to distinguish a qualitative from a quantitative change. There is suggestive evidence (with respect to hemolymph proteins) that, as might be expected, some correlation exists between the completeness of metamorphosis in an insect group and the extent of change in its proteins. Thus, a bug shows no qualitative change, a moth changes a small proportion of its complement, and flies exhibit extensive change. In all cases, however, a proportion of the demonstrable protein components are found at all stages of development.

A quite different, and more demanding, approach to the question of identity of larval and adult proteins is to isolate homologous proteins from each stage and compare them chemically. This has been done with tropomyosin, which was obtained crystalline and apparently pure from both larvae and adults of the blowfly, *Phormia regina* (Kominz et al., 1962). The two preparations were very similar but showed slight differences in amino acid and peptide composition and physical properties. These small differences could conceivably result from impurity or secondary modifications of the protein rather than genetic difference, and thus the question of genetic identity is unfortunately unresolved. Another indication of similarity of larval and adult proteins, though not conclusive evidence of identity, comes from low-temperature spectra of mitochondria from larvae and adult thoraces of *Drosophila;* the two show no significant differences, while both differ characteristically from mammalian mitochondria (Goldin and Farnsworth, 1966).

Free Amino Acids and Peptides

A peculiar feature of insects that always has to be taken into account in a discussion of their protein metabolism is their high level of free amino acids. This is highest in the blood, and the tissue pool is generally somewhat less concentrated and differently constituted with respect to individual amino acids. In the more advanced insects, the hemolymph amino acid level is commonly in the range 5 to 20 mg/ml—many times that of mammalian plasma. In addition to the amino acids of proteins, some less usual ones have been identified from certain insects, including β-alanine, tyrosine-0-phosphate, methionine sulfoxide, D-alanine, D-serine and others. The literature of this subject, as well as other aspects of amino acid and protein metabolism in insect development, is reviewed by Chen (1966). The significance of the high amino acid level is not well understood, although it provides a pool for protein synthesis and appears to have an osmotic role. During metamorphosis, while individual amino acids change in concentration, the variation in total free amino acid pool is remarkably small when one considers the extent of tissue reconstruction that is taking place (Levenbook and Dinamarca, 1966).

Along with free amino acids, insects also exhibit a variable content of peptides. In *Drosophila* larvae, intensive chromatographic analysis led to the conclusion that more than 600 peptides were present, and these incorporated injected C^{14}-glutamate much more rapidly than did the total body protein (Mitchell and Simmons, 1962). In *Phormia,* a group of peptides is transiently abundant during the early third instar; these are mostly composed of only two amino acids one of which, in each that was analyzed, was either lysine or histidine (Levenbook, 1966). Their metabolism and significance is unknown.

The Biochemistry of Histolysis

It repeatedly has been observed since the early histological studies on insect metamorphosis that at certain developmental stages the fat body, and to a lesser extent other tissues, become loaded with protein granules or "albuminoid spheres" (Kilby, 1963; Wigglesworth, 1965).   These have been regarded as a form of protein reserve and appeared to constitute an exception to the generalization from mammalian biochemistry that anima: tissues have no specifically storage proteins. Their probable nature is now becoming apparent with the use of the electron microscope and with growing understanding of the nature and functions of lysosomes (de Duve and Wattiaux, 1966). In Lepidoptera, such as the skipper *Calpodes ethlius*, protein granules appear in the fat body about one day before pupation, at the time when the larval cuticle is being resorbed. Since injected radioactive amino acid showed little incorporation into these granules, whereas injected plant peroxidase (detectable histochemically) appeared specifically in them, it was inferred that they contain protein sequestered from the hemolymph and not newly synthesized (Locke and Collins, 1966 and 1967). Similar uptake occurs in other tissues, particularly the epidermis and especially at times in the molting cycle when there is active protein synthesis.   The granules are surrounded by membranes and are believed to transform into multivesicular bodies in which digestion takes place, presumably by addition of lysosomal enzymes, as a source of amino acids for new protein synthesis. Cell organelles, such as mitochondria due for destruction, are believed to be isolated in a similar way. The uptake of hemolymph proteins into fat body, gut, and to some extent other tissues of Lepidoptera is independently demonstrated by immunodiffusion tests, which show several blood antigens to be present in them during the prepupal and early pupal stages (Loughton and West, 1965).

As an example of programmed histolysis, Lockshin and Williams (1965) have studied the breakdown of the abdominal intersegmental muscles of saturniid silk moths, whose function is to pump blood into the wings of the newly emerged moth and which lyse when this role is completed. The trigger for lysis is apparently the cessation of nervous motor stimuli to the muscle. Lysosomelike bodies are observed to undergo change at this time. Proteolytic activity of a catheptic type (pH optimum 4.0) builds up in these muscles at first gradually, then rapidly, during the 3 weeks of pharate adult development, and is associated with lysosomelike particles. It can be activated and partially released from the particles by detergent treatment, but in the emerged moth the activity and the proportion of soluble enzyme are naturally enhanced. Similar catheptic activity is found also in the fat body, but not in thoracic muscle (which, of course, is not destined for dissolution). The intersegmental muscles and fat body also contain an acid phosphatase which shows greatest activity in advanced adult development. These enzymes are considered to be directly responsible for the destruction of the intersegmental muscles.

It is remarkable that, despite the dominant place of histolysis in insect metamorphosis, there is almost no other information on the enzymic basis of the process. Not much can be concluded from several reports of hydrolytic activities without evidence as to their source in tissues or cytological fractions.

Rates of Protein Synthesis and Turnover

Linked to the question of changing protein composition of an insect during metamorphosis is that of the rates and extent of protein degradation and synthesis. A number of measurements have been reported of the incorporation of injected amino acids into the proteins of hemolymph or tissues of insects at selected stages (see Chen and Levenbook, 1966b). It is found that incorporation rates rise sharply when adult development is initiated in diapausing silk moth pupae, and that fat body qualifies kinetically as a source of hemolymph proteins. Similar results have been obtained with isolated insect tissues incubated in vitro, a technique which avoids complications due to the blood amino acid pool. But the systematic quantitative study of protein metabolism during metamorphosis seems to be confined to the recent work of two laboratories.

Using *Drosophila melanogaster*, Boyd and Mitchell (1966) fed C^{14}-amino acids to larvae, then after appropriate times for incorporation, extracted body fluid (chiefly hemolymph), and separated radioactive protein fractions from it by acrylamide gel electrophoresis. Then, their turnover was measured by reinjecting into larvae or pupae the isolated radioactive protein fractions and, after incubation, subjecting hemolymph samples to the same kind of analysis. The redistribution of activity was extensive and varied in different fractions: One was stable in the larva, but after pupation had a half-life of 13 hours; another was too stable for the half-life to be measured. Specificity is also indicated by the fact that injected mammalian hemoglobin did not turn over. When enough nonradioactive valine was injected to increase the blood valine pool about thirty-fivefold, the redistribution of activity from valine-labeled protein during 42 hours was cut from 56 to 39 percent, which suggests that free valine, but not the valine of the hemolymph, may be an intermediate in the interconversion of hemolymph proteins. The authors conclude that hemolymph proteins "may be an important channel through which the massive protein turnover of the metamorphosing insect passes.''

Levenbook and colleagues have examined the question of protein synthesis and turnover in *Phormia regina*. The hemolymph protein is shown to be synthesized chiefly in the larva; at pupation there is a rapid fall in blood protein content, and there is little synthesis from injected amino acids or change in level thereafter (Chen and Levenbook, 1966b). Radioactive hemolymph protein was prepared from C^{14}-labeled larvae, and after injection into larvae, pupae, and pharate adults, its fate was followed. Very little was converted to $C^{14}O_2$, although injected free amino acids were rapidly oxidized, and conversion of hemolymph protein to free amino acids was also slow. It is inferred, in contrast to the conclusions of Boyd and Mitchell, that the hemolymph proteins are relatively stable. When mature larvae were injected with labeled hemolymph protein and kept until they emerged as flies, however, about three quarters of the recovered radioactivity was found in protein in the tissues. Since the blood free amino acids clearly cannot be intermediates, some form of direct transformation of blood proteins into tissue proteins is suggested. The data seem only to rule out *hemolymph* free amino acids as intermediates and do not oppose degradation to free amino acids which remain within the tissues and are rapidly used in resynthesis.

In a related study, Dinamarca and Levenbook (1966) examined the dynamic state of the free amino acid pool and the rate of protein synthesis from it in *Phormia regina* at different developmental stages. C^{14}-alanine and C^{14}-lysine were injected, and their conversion to $C^{14}O_2$, total disappearance from the pool, and incorporation into protein were measured, as well as the pool size for each amino acid in each insect used. Corrected values for the rate of incorporation into protein could then be calculated and were found to follow a U-shaped curve, closely similar for the two amino acids, except in the adult (Fig. 9). The importance of the procedure became clear, for lysine always yielded more of the injected dose into protein than did alanine, but this was a consequence of the more rapid turnover of alanine. With the assumption of a single homogeneous pool of each amino acid in the insect, the further calculation could be made of the total amount of new protein synthesis during metamorphosis, and this came out at the surprisingly small value of 0.16 mg, or about 2 percent of the total protein of the insect.* As Dinamarca and Levenbook recognize, the

---

*A recalculation from the data has given values about twice these (Levenbook, personal communication), but this does not modify the conclusions from this study.

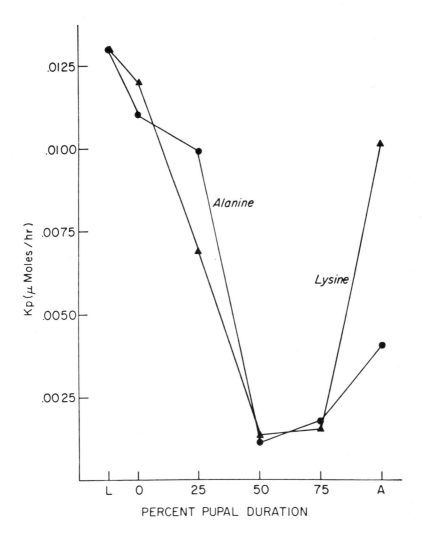

FIG. 9. Rates of incorporation of alanine and lysine into protein during metamorphosis of *Phormia regina*. K_p is calculated from the incorporation of radioactive amino acids into protein, their total rate of utilization in the insect, and the pool size. From Dinamarca and Levenbook, 1966.

assumption is a great oversimplification; nevertheless, they suggest that the total amount of new protein synthesis during metamorphosis is less than has been generally assumed.

The chief conclusions from these studies are, perhaps, to confirm that the hemolymph amino acids (which make up more than half of the total pool) are not in free exchange with those in the tissues and to indicate that the greater part of the protein turnover involves only local intracellular pools. This would be in accord with the cytological evidence that proteins are engulfed from the blood and digested within various tissues that are also synthesizing protein. Calculations based on the total pool of the animal might then fail to give any indication of the true amount of protein synthesis. It seems that still more refined techniques, perhaps involving isolation of specific proteins from individual tissues, are required.

Enzymes Associated with Protein Synthesis

The amino acid activating enzymes, responsible for the first step in protein synthesis, have been assayed and to some extent characterized in different developmental stages of the blowfly, *Lucilia cuprina*, and the fat body of *Sarcophaga bullata* (Howells and Birt, 1964; Allen and Newburgh, 1966). Activity was found for almost all of the protein amino acids, and where it was not found, this may have been due to inactivation. The total soluble enzyme activity in both series of experiments was minimal in midpupal life and rose to a maximum just before emergence of the adult fly, thus paralleling the changes in rate of protein synthesis in a blowfly pupa (Fig. 9). In *Lucilia*, during the early pupal stage, some amino acid activating enzymes, particularly for tyrosine, are bound to a class of cell particle, and it has been suggested that these may have some role in storage of tyrosine for use in cuticular synthesis and tanning.

The activity of glutamate-aspartate transaminase in the housefly declines from a high value at pupation to a minimum just before adult emergence and then rises steeply (McAllan and Chefurka, 1961). A relation to protein synthesis is suggested, but the curve appears more closely correlated with that to be expected of protein degradation. In the Cecropia silk moth, however, this enzyme rises strikingly in thoracic muscle during late adult development, which is certainly an active site of protein synthesis.

Ribonucleic Acid and the Machinery of Protein Synthesis

Increasing attention has been directed recently to the nucleic acids as determinants in the specificity and possible regulators in the rate of protein synthesis, but there is not yet a great deal of information relevant to insect metamorphosis. Measurements of total RNA during metamorphosis of several insect species reveal little change, which is consistent with the histological observation that histolysis and histogenesis are concurrent rather than consecutive, so that the total amount of cellular tissue does not change much (see Wyatt, 1959, for a review of the earlier work, and Lang et al., 1965, for data on the mosquito). Some changes reported in RNA fractions differing in extractability with phenol from *Calliphora erythrocephala* are very difficult to interpret (Agrell, 1964).

When a single tissue is examined, more significant changes may be seen. Thus, in the fat body of the saturniid silkworm, *Samia cynthia ricini*, during pupation there is a great decrease in cytoplasmic RNA, which is shown by P^{32} incorporation to have been synthesized early in the fifth larval instar (Takahashi, 1966). In the Cecropia silk moth, when adult development begins after the pupal diapause there is no discernible net increase in fat body RNA, but there is an increase in turnover, associated with renewed activity in protein synthesis (Wyatt and Linzen, 1965).

Other recent studies on RNA in insect metamorphosis have concentrated on particular developmental processes related to hormone action. Karlson, Sekeris, and colleagues have examined changes in fully grown *Calliphora* larvae, at the stage when formation and tanning of the puparium follow upon the increasing titer of ecdysone. After injection of ecdysone into larvae taken about two days before pupation, the incorporation of P^{32} into RNA is elevated. With 1.5-hour pulse incorporation, the maximal stimulation of 80 percent over controls was observed at 4 to 7 hours after giving the hormone (Karlson and Peters, 1965). A greater effect was observed in RNA from the epidermis, a target tissue for ecdysone, and in RNA prepared with hot phenol from epidermal nuclei there was some stimulation within 1 hour of giving the hormone. The nuclear RNA stimulated amino acid incorporation in microsomal preparations from rat liver or *Calliphora* epidermis (Sekeris et al., 1965). It has been reported from the same laboratory that ecdysone added to isolated epidermal nuclei stimulates their incorporation of C^{14}-uracil into RNA and that RNA prepared from pupating larvae when added to rat liver microsomal preparations acts as a template in the synthesis of dopa decarboxylase, but fuller data are required before one can interpret these observations with confidence. The results obtained with this system have been presented in support of the view that ecdysone and other hormones act by directly causing derepression of DNA in the cell nucleus and release of specific messengers (Karlson and Sekeris, 1966). The evidence, however, does not eliminate the presence of further links in the chain of hormone action (Chapter 5; Tata, 1966).

The synthesis of RNA under the stimulus of ecdysone has also been investigated in the pupal wing epidermis of *Hyalophora cecropia*, during the initiation of adult development after diapause (Linzen and Wyatt, 1964; Wyatt and Linzen, 1965; Wyatt, 1967b). During natural development, in pupae incubated after a period of chilling, the synthesis of RNA begins well before morphological change, and by the second day of visible adult development the content of RNA in the wing tissue is about fourfold that in diapause. After initiation of development by injection of ecdysone into pupae whose endogenous endocrine sequence is blocked by removal of the brain, stimulation of RNA synthesis is detectable at 8 to 10 hours, intense (about sixfold) at 24 hours, and falls off thereafter (Fig. 10). Some effect on protein synthesis begins to appear at about the same time, but the rise is more gradual and more prolonged. The RNA produced under the influence of ecdysone has been characterized in several ways. Its base com-

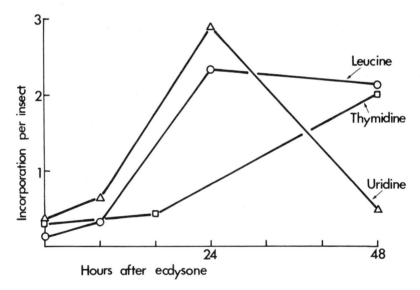

FIG. 10. The effects of ecdysone on macromolecular synthesis in wing tissue of Cecropia silk moth pupae. Into pupae from which the brains had been removed, sufficient ecdysone was injected to cause visible initiation of development. Then, at the intervals shown, radioactive leucine was injected as a precursor of protein uridine as a precursor of RNA, and thymidine as a precursor of DNA. After 4 hours for incorporation, the pupal wings were removed and prepared for counting. Results are given in arbitrary units per insect. Wyatt, unpublished.

position (by pulse labeling with P^{32}) is intermediate between the bulk RNA and the DNA of the species and could be accounted for by synthesis of a mixture of ribosomal RNA and DNA-like RNA. Fractionation of the RNA, after pulse labeling with uridine, showed incorporation in the 4s, 17s, and approximately 30s regions (corresponding to transfer, ribosomal, and ribosomal precursor RNA, respectively) and also in the residue from cold phenol extraction, which would contain nuclear RNA. The extent of stimulation by ecdysone was rather similar in each of these fractions. When assayed for stimulation of amino acid incorporation in an *E. coli* ribosomal system, the RNA produced early in Cecropia wing development was found to be highly active, but there are reasons for believing that such stimulation in a heterologous system may not signify true template activity. Polysomes, of which few are detectable in the epidermis in diapause, become abundant early in development. It is concluded from this work that new RNA synthesis forms an important early part of the action of ecdysone and contributes to building the stage for increased protein synthesis. But the connection between hormone action and RNA synthesis, and the question of specificity in template RNA production, require further study. The picture in a tissue being awakened from diapause may, of course, differ from that in a tissue which, when already metabolically active, is influenced by ecdysone. But the observations on the Cecropia wing epidermis are consistent with those on the actions of various developmental hormones in vertebrate material (Tata, 1966).

The juvenile hormone of the corpora allata, acting in the presence of ecdysone, permits growth and molting in insects but modifies their course, so that the characteristics of immature stages are retained. A plausible basis for this would be a regulatory effect upon RNA synthesis so that larval-specific templates are produced and adult templates repressed (Wigglesworth, 1964), but there is as yet no biochemical evidence for this. When juvenile hormone is injected into *Antheraea polyphemus* pupae at the beginning of adult development, the rate of RNA synthesis is increased, but this may be a result of stimulated output of ecdysone from the prothoracic gland rather than a direct effect on other tissues (Oberlander and Schneiderman, 1966).

A provocative observation for which no interpretation can be offered concerns RNA-methylating enzymes (Baliga et al., 1965). In *Tenebrio molitor*, the enzymes active in adding methyl groups to *E. coli* tRNA are more active (with a characteristic day-to-day pattern) in the early pupa than in the larva or pharate adult, thus portraying the approximate reverse of the U-shaped curve seen in various other metabolic activities.

Another intriguing observation concerns the composition of insect ribosomal RNA. Analyses of ribosomal RNA from bacteria, yeast, and vertebrates invariably have found guanine as the most abundant base and the ratio of guanylic plus cytidylic acids to adenylic plus uridylic $(G + C/A + U)$ to be greater than 1.0. Insect ribosomal RNA, however, varies widely, the $G + C/A + U$ ratio ranging, in several species examined, from 0.70 to 1.20 or higher (Gumilevskaya and Sisakyan, 1963; Hastings and Kirby, 1966). A correlation was noted between ribosomal RNA composition and the rate of growth and development in a number of species, and it was suggested that these may be related because of differences in heat stability of the RNA (Mednikov, 1965). Inspection of the data, however, suggests that there is also a correlation with phylogeny. The more primitive insects (Orthoptera) tend to have high $G + C$, Coleoptera and Lepidoptera are intermediate, and the most specialized group (Diptera) have RNA distinguished by low $G + C$ content. Studies on the properties of ribosomes with such differently constituted RNA would be of interest.

Understanding of the control mechanisms of rate and specificity of protein synthesis in insect metamorphosis will undoubtedly depend on the development and study of cell-free amino acid incorporating systems of insect origin (Fox et al., 1965; Ilan and Lipmann, 1966). In such a system for *Tenebrio molitor*, the ratio of incorporation of tyrosine to that of leucine rises greatly during the last two days of adult development, which is believed to reflect the high tyrosine content of the cuticular proteins then being synthesized.

Deoxyribonucleic Acid

When one considers the pivotal position of DNA in determining the characters of organisms, and the wealth of recent critical and ingenious research on this nucleic acid in various living systems, the paucity of information on DNA in insect metamorphosis is remarkable. For very few insect species do we even have reliable estimates of the changing quantity of DNA during development. Nucleic acid determinations with insect material require special attention to technique because of various complications that may arise, e.g., difficulty in securing quantitative extraction, the presence of compounds which interfere in colorimetric reactions, and uric acid which interferes in the ultraviolet range (Linzen and Wyatt, 1964). In *Lucilia cuprina*, the total body DNA falls to about one half just before pupation and then rises rather steadily during the pupal stage and adult development, presumably reflecting

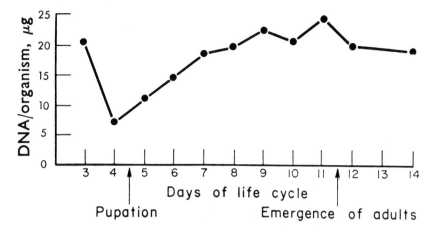

FIG. 11. The content of DNA in *Lucilia cuprina* during metamorphosis. From Howells and Birt, 1964. The scale has been corrected according to personal communication from Dr. Howells.

breakdown of larval cells, followed by cell multiplication in the imaginal *anlagen* (Fig. 11). In the mosquito, on the other hand, there is apparently little change in DNA during metamorphosis, although in larvae there is the unusual situation that up to 30 percent of the total DNA is found in the soluble supernatant fraction of homogenates (Lang et al., 1965).

Patterns of DNA synthesis in different tissues are readily surveyed by autoradiography after incorporation of H^3-thymidine, and this technique has been applied to the development of saturniid silk moths (Bowers and Williams, 1964; Krishnakumaran et al., 1967). In the larval molting cycle, there is a burst of synthesis in most tissues centered about 3 days before the molt, but in the hemocytes and midgut, synthesis continues at a reduced rate at other times, and in the imaginal wing buds synthesis is apparently unrelated to the molt cycle. Shortly after pupation, in diapausing species such as *Hyalophora cecropia*, DNA synthesis stops in all tissues except the hemocytes and spermatogonia, in which a significant rate of incorporation continues. In a species without diapause (*Samia cynthia ricini*), incorporation in most tissues comes almost to a stop at the time of pupation, but then resumes within a day with the onset of adult development. At the conclusion of a pupal diapause, DNA synthesis appears to be correlated with the stimulation of growth by ecdysone. Adult development of moths is blocked by mitomycin C, an inhibitor of DNA synthesis, and it is clear that DNA replication is an essential part of ecdysone-stimulated development.

The Cecropia wing epidermis developing after the pupal diapause has also been examined by biochemical methods (Wyatt, 1967b). When incorporation of thymidine is measured at intervals after injection of ecdysone, clear stimulation of DNA synthesis is not detected until about 48 hours—much later than the effect upon RNA (Fig. 10). Thus, the stimulation of DNA synthesis seems to be separated from the earliest effects of the hormone. During the 21-day period of natural development to the moth, two cycles of DNA replication centered at about the second and sixth days can be detected in the wing tissue.

In a quest for the enzymic basis of the cessation of DNA synthesis in diapause, the crucial enzymes thymidine kinase and thymidylate kinase were assayed in silk moth pupal wing epidermis (Brookes and Williams, 1965). Both increased manyfold at the initiation of adult development, yet diapause tissue did contain appreciable activity, so that the lack of these enzymes could not be responsible for the total cessation of synthesis.

INORGANIC IONS

One further subject which must be mentioned is the remarkable inorganic ion content of many insects (Duchateau et al., 1953; Wyatt, 1961). In contrast to the usual composition of body fluids of vertebrates and most other animals, the higher insects, particularly phytophagous species, contain much potassium and little sodium, so that the $Na^+:K^+$ ratio is far below unity. Further, the level of magnesium is often extraordinarily high (often up to 30 mM and occasionally to 100 mM, though part of this is chemically complexed). This situation is regarded as an adaptation to a vegetarian diet high in potassium and magnesium. Normal ion levels are maintained with the aid of active transport mechanisms, including the transport of K^+ through the gut wall (Harvey and Haskell, 1966).

In metamorphosis, the inorganic levels may be changed. Thus, in the silkworm, *Bombyx mori*, falls in sodium and magnesium at pupation have been reported, though the data of different authors are not consistent (Bialaszewicz and Landau, 1937; Tobias, 1948). Since the ionic proportions found in different insect species vary greatly, their having an important role in metabolic regulation is perhaps unlikely. Little is known, however, about the distribution of ions between hemolymph and intracellular fluids in insects, and it is interesting that an effect of ion levels on protein production by blowfly larval fat body in vitro recently has been reported (Price, 1966). The matter deserves further attention, in view of the indications that potassium can have roles in the regulation of gene activity in insects (Chapter 5) and in protein synthesis in various living systems.

CONCLUSIONS

Body form and function are determined by the genes, operating under various influences. In the holometabolous insect, the totally different selective pressures upon larva and adult have led to their independent evolution, and it is an interesting question to what extent they have become genetically distinct. In view of the gross differences between larva and adult, and the many mutations that affect only one stage, it is generally assumed that metamorphosis involves a major switchover from one battery of genes to another. But the biochemical evidence, while still quite inconclusive, suggests tentatively that the difference in terms of proteins may be less complete than morphological grounds would lead one to suppose.

The central metabolic pathways, with their numerous enzymes, are possessed by larva and adult in common, and mutations in these would presumably be lethal and escape detection. Differences between larva, pupa, and adult in respiratory and carbohydrate metabolism appear mostly to reflect quantitative rather than qualitative changes in enzymes. Certain changes indicate new enzymes, e.g., the appearance of dopa decarboxylase at the conclusion of larval life in the blowfly and the appearance of trehalose (implying the enzymes of its synthesis) at about the same time. But the question of new enzyme appearance has never been attacked in a rigorously quantitative manner, as was done some years ago in the case of enzyme induction in bacteria. The profiles of protein from insect blood and tissues, distributed by electrophoresis or similar means, suggest that some components persist while others disappear and appear newly during development, but these methods have detected only a small proportion of the most abundant proteins and have only rarely given conclusive evidence of identity. The eventual answer to this question will bear on the general problem of the role of proteins in determining animal development. The metamorphosing insect should provide uniquely favorable material for this study, for proteins not essential to the differences between larva and adult will presumably be identical in them.

Cytological and biochemical evidence indicates that protein degradation in metamorphosis takes place in intracellular vesicles embodying lysosomes, and the turnover involved in the synthesis of adult proteins from the material of larval proteins occurs locally without extensive passage through the blood amino acid pool. The pathway of protein synthesis resembles that in other organisms, the control mechanisms still being obscure.

In addition to the qualitative changes during insect metamorphosis, there are profound differences in rates of metabolic processes. Many of these, in respiration, carbohydrate metabolism, protein synthesis, pigment metabolism, and other areas have been documented, and in a few cases they have been tentatively assigned to the activities of certain enzymes. But analysis of metabolic regulation in insects, and the respective roles of enzyme synthesis and degradation, and enzyme activation and inhibition, which are active current fields of research in bacterial and mammalian systems, has scarcely begun.

With regard to the actions of insect hormones, what is known biochemically is fully consistent with knowledge of developmental hormones in other organisms. The action of ecdysone, like the actions of estrogens or thyroxine, involves stimulation of the protein-synthesizing system, including synthesis of all kinds of ribonucleic acid, but the nature of the hormones' primary action, and the basis of their specificity, are still quite obscure. In the further study of these matters, the juvenile hormone will be of outstanding interest because of the exceptional degree to which it appears to control the selective expression of alternative sets of genes.

I wish to acknowledge the support, during the preparation of this chapter, of the Whitehall Foundation and the National Institutes of Health, U.S. Public Health Service (grant HD-02176). Mr. M. Crompton and Dr. L. M. Birt kindly made their paper available to me before its publication. I am also especially grateful for assistance from the staff of the National Institute for Medical Research, London, where this chapter was written.

REFERENCES

Agrell, I. P. S. 1949. The variation in activity of apodehydrogenases during insect metamorphosis. Acta Physiol. Scand., 18:355–360.

———. 1964. Physiological and biochemical changes during insect development. *In* Rockstein, M., ed., Physiology of Insecta, vol. 1, 91–148, New York, Academic Press.

_____, and T. N. O. Lindh. 1966. Changes in basic proteins during the metamorphosis of the fly *Calliphora erythrocephala*. Comp. Biochem. Physiol., 19:691–698.

Allen, R. R., and R. W. Newburgh. 1966. Amino acid activating enzymes in *Sarcophaga bullata*. Comp. Biochem. Physiol., 17:309–317.

Bade, M. L., and G. R. Wyatt. 1962. Metabolic conversions during pupation of the cecropia silkworm. 1. Deposition and utilization of nutrient reserves. Biochem. J., 83:470–478.

Baliga, B. S., P. R. Srinivasan, and E. Borek. 1965. Changes in the t-RNA methylating enzymes during insect metamorphosis. Nature, 208:555–557.

Bialaszewicz, K., and C. Landau. 1937. Sur la composition minérale de l'hémolymphe des vers à soie. Acta Biol. Exp., Lodz, 12:307–

Birt, L. M. 1966. The distribution of nicotinamide nucleotides during the life cycle of the blowfly, *Lucilia cuprina*. Biochem. J.. 101:429–434.

Bowers, B., and C. M. Williams. 1964. Physiology of insect diapause. XIII. DNA synthesis during the metamorphosis of the Cecropia silkworm. Biol. Bull., 126:205–219.

Boyd, J. B., and H. K. Mitchell. 1966. Turnover of the hemolymph proteins in *Drosophila melanogaster*. Arch. Biochem. Biophys., 117:310–319.

Brookes, V. J., and C. M. Williams. 1965. Thymidine kinase and thymidylate kinase in relation to the endocrine control of insect diapause and development. Proc. Nat. Acad. Sci. USA, 53:770–777.

Brunet, P. C. J. 1965. The metabolism of aromatic compounds. *In* Goodwin, T. W., ed., Aspects of Insect Biochemistry, pp. 49–77. Biochemical Society Symposium No. 25. London and New York, Academic Press.

Bücher, T. 1965. Formation of the specific structural and enzymic pattern of the insect flight muscle. *In* Goodwin, T. W., ed., Aspects of Insect Biochemistry, pp. 15–28, Biochemical Society Symposium No. 25, London and New York, Academic Press.

Bückmann, D., A. Willig, and B. Linzen. 1966. Veränderungen der Hämolymphe vor der Verpuppung von *Cerura virula:* der Gehalt an Eiweiss, Ommochrom-Vorstufen und Ommochromen. Z. Naturforsch., 21b:1184-1195.

Butler, J. E., and C. A. Leone. 1966. Antigenic changes during the life cycle of the beetle, *Tenebrio molitor*. Comp. Biochem. Physiol., 19:699–711.

Chan, S. K., and E. Margoliash. 1966. Biosynthesis of cytochrome *c* in developing pupae of *Samia cynthia*. J. Biol. Chem., 241:2252–2255.

Chen, P. S. 1966. Amino acid and protein metabolism in insect development. Advances Insect Physiol., 3:53–132.

———, and L. Levenbook. 1966a. Studies on the hemolymph proteins of the blowfly, *Phormia regina*. I. Changes in ontogenetic patterns. J. Insect Physiol., 12:1595–1609.

———, and L. Levenbook. 1966b. Studies on the hemolymph proteins of the blowfly, *Phormia regina*. II. Synthesis and breakdown as revealed by isotopic labelling. J. Insect Physiol., 12:1611–1627.

Cottrell, C. B. 1964. Insect ecdysis with particular emphasis on cuticular hardening and darkening. Advances Insect Physiol., 2:175–218.

Crompton, M., and L. M. Birt. 1967. Changes in the amounts of carbohydrates, phosphagen and related compounds during the metamorphosis of the blowfly, *Lucilia cuprina*. J. Insect Physiol., 13:1575–1592.

D'Costa, M. A., and L. M. Birt. 1966. Changes in the lipid content during the metamorphosis of the blowfly, *Lucilia*. J. Insect Physiol., 12:1377–1394.

Dinamarca, M. L., and L. Levenbook. 1966. Oxidation, utilization and incorporation into protein of alanine and lysine during metamorphosis of the blowfly, *Phormia regina*. Arch. Biochem. Biophys., 117:110–119.

Domroese, K. A., and L. I. Gilbert. 1964. The role of lipid in adult development and flight-muscle metabolism in *Hyalophora cecropia*. J. Exp. Biol., 41:573–590.

Duchateau, G., M. Florkin, and J. Leclercq. 1953. Concentrations de bases fixes et types de composition de la base totale de l'hémolymphe des insectes. Arch. Int. Physiol., 61:518–549.

de Duve, C., and R. Wattiaux. 1966. Functions of lysosomes. Ann. Rev. Physiol., 28:435–492.

Fox, A. S., J. Kan, S. H. Kang, and B. Wallis. 1965. Protein synthesis in cell-free preparations from *Drosophila melanogaster*, J. Biol. Chem., 240:2059–2065.

Fraenkel, G., C. Hsiao, and M. Seligman. 1966. Properties of bursicon, an insect protein hormone that controls cuticular tanning. Science, 151:91–93.

Gilbert, L. I. 1967. Lipid metabolism and function in insects. Advances Insect Physiol., 4:69–211.

———, and H. A. Schneiderman. 1961. Some biochemical aspects of insect metamorphosis. Amer. Zoologist, 1:11–51.

Gilmour, D. 1965. The Metabolism of Insects. San Francisco, W. H. Freeman.

Goldin, H. H., and M. W. Farnsworth. 1966. Low temperature spectra of the cytochromes of *Drosophila melanogaster*. J. Biol. Chem., 241:3590–3594.

Gumilevskaya, N. A., and N. M. Sisakyan. 1963. Comparative study of the nucleotide composition of microsomal and soluble RNA of insects. Dokl. Akad. Nauk SSSR, 149:198–201.

Harvey, W. R. 1962. Metabolic aspects of insect diapause. Ann. Rev. Entomol., 7:57–80.

_____, and J. A. Haskell. 1966. Metabolic control mechanisms in insects. Advances Insect Physiol., 3:133–205.

Hastings, J. R. B., and K. S. Kirby. 1966. The nucleic acids of *Drosophila melanogaster*. Biochem. J., 100:532–539.

Herold, R. C., and H. Borei. 1963. Cytochrome changes during honeybee flight muscle development. Develop. Biol., 8:67–79.

Howells, A. J., and L. M. Birt. 1964. Amino acid-dependent pyrophosphate exchange during the life cycle of the blowfly *Lucilia cuprina*. Comp. Biochem. Physiol., 11:61–83.

Hudson, A. 1966. Proteins in the hemolymph and other tissues of the developing tobacco hornworm, *Protoparce quinquemaculata*. Canad. J. Zool., 44:541–555.

Ilan, J., and F. Lipmann. 1966. A cell-free protein synthesis system from pupae of *Tenebrio molitor* Acta Biochem. Polon., 13:329–335.

Janda, V., F. Sehnal, and V. Simek. 1966. Changes in some chemical constituents of *Galleria mellonella* larvae in relation to growth and morphogenesis. Acta Biochem. Polon., 13:329–335.

Jeuniaux, C. 1961. Biochimie de la mue chez les arthropodes. Bull. Soc. Zool. Fr., 86:590–599

Karlson, P., and H. Peters. 1965. Zum Wirkungsmechanismus der Hormone—IV. Der Einfluss des Ecdysons auf den Nucleinsaeurestoffwechsel von Calliphora Larven. Gen. Comp. Endocr., 5:252–259.

_____, and C. E. Sekeris. 1964. Biochemistry of insect metamorphosis. *In* Florkin, M., and H. Mason, eds., Comparative Biochemistry, vol. 6, Chap. 4, New York, Academic Press.

_____, and C. E. Sekeris. 1966. Ecdysone, an insect steroid hormone, and its mode of action. Recent Progr. Hormone Res., 22:473–502.

Kilby, B. A. 1963. The biochemistry of the insect fat body. Advances Insect Physiol., 1:111–174.

Kominz, D. R., K. Maruyama, L. Levenbook, and M. Lewis. 1962. Tropomyosin, myosin and actin from the blowfly, *Phormia regina*. Biochim. Biophys. Acta, 63:106–116.

Krishnakumaran, A., S. J. Berry, H. Oberlander, and H. A. Schneiderman. 1967. Nucleic acid synthesis during insect development. II. Control of DNA synthesis in the Cecropia silkworm and other saturniid moths. J. Insect Physiol., 13:1–58.

Lang, C. A., H. Y. Lau, and D. J. Jefferson. 1965. Protein and nucleic acid changes during growth and aging in the mosquito. Biochem. J., 95:372–377.

Laufer, H. 1963. Antigens in insect development. Ann. N.Y. Acad. Sci., 103:1137–1154.

Lennie, R. W., and L. M. Birt. 1967. Aspects of the development of flight-muscle sarcosomes in the sheep blowfly *Lucilia cuprina*, in relation to changes in the distribution of protein and some respiratory enzymes during metamorphosis. Biochem. J., 102:338–350.

Levenbook, L. 1966. Hemolymph amino acids and peptides during larval growth of the blowfly, *Phormia regina*. Comp. Biochem. Physiol., 18:341–351.

_____, and M. L. Dinamarca. 1966. Free amino acids and related compounds during metamorphosis of the blowfly *Phormia regina*. J. Insect. Physiol., 12:1343–1362.

_____, and C. M. Williams. 1956. Mitochondria in the flight muscle of insects. III. Mitochondrial cytochrome *c* in relation to the aging and wing beat frequency of flies. J. Gen. Physiol., 39:497–512.

Linzen, B., and G. R. Wyatt. 1964. The nucleic acid content of tissues of cecropia silkmoth pupae. Relations to body size and development. Biochim. Biophys. Acta, 87:188–198.

Locke, M., and J. V. Collins. 1966. Sequestration of protein by the fat body of an insect. Nature, 210:552–553.

_____, and J. V. Collins. 1967. Protein uptake in multivesicular bodies in the molt-intermolt cycle of an insect. Science, 155:467–469.

Lockshin, R. A., and C. M. Williams. 1965. Programmed cell death. V. Cytolytic enzymes in relation to the breakdown of the intersegmental muscles of silkmoths. J. Insect Physiol., 11:831–844.

Loughton, B. G., and A. S. West. 1965. The development and distribution of haemolymph proteins in Lepidoptera. J. Insect Physiol., 11:919–932.

McAllan, J. W., and W. Chefurka. 1961. Some physiological aspects of glutamate-aspartate transamination in insects. Comp. Biochem. Physiol., 2:290–299.

Mednikov, B. M. 1965. Correlation between rate of development of insects and nucleotide composition of their ribosomal RNA. Dokl. Akad. Nauk SSSR, 161:721–723.

Mitchell, H. K., and J. R. Simmons. 1962. Amino acids and derivatives in *Drosophila*. *In* Holden, J. T., ed., Amino Acid Pools, pp. 136–146. Amsterdam, Elsevier.

Needham, D. M. 1929. The chemical changes during the metamorphosis of insects. Biol. Rev., 4:307–326.

Niemierko, S., P. Wlodawer, and A. F. Wojtczak. 1955. Lipid and phosphorus metabolism during growth of the silkworm, *Bombyx mori*, Acta Biol. Exp., Lodz, 17:255–276.

Oberlander, H., and H. A. Schneiderman. 1966. Juvenile hormone and RNA synthesis in pupal tissues of saturniid moths. J. Insect Physiol., 12:37–41.

Price, G. M. 1967 The effect of different ions on the incorporation of [U–^{14}C]-valine into fat body protein of the larva of the blowfly, *Calliphora erythrocephala*. J. Insect Physiol., 13:69–80.

Russo-Caia, S. 1960. Aspetti biochimici della metamorfosi degli insetti. Ric. Sci., 30:1861–1907.

Sacktor, B. 1951. Some aspects of respiratory metabolism during metamorphosis of normal and DDT-resistant houseflies, *Musca domestica*. Biol. Bull., 100:229–243.

———. 1965. Energetics and respiratory metabolism of muscular contraction. *In* Rockstein, M., ed., Physiology of Insecta, vol. 2, Chap. 10, New York, Academic Press.

Schneiderman, H. A., and C. M. Williams. 1953. The physiology of insect diapause. VII. The respiratory metabolism of the Cecropia silkworm during diapause and development. Biol. Bull., 105:320–334.

Sehnal, F., and K. Slama. 1966. The effect of corpus allatum hormone on respiratory metabolism during larval development and metamorphosis of *Galleria mellonella*. J. Insect Physiol., 12:1333–1342.

Sekeris, C. E., and P. Karlson. 1966. Biosynthesis of catecholamines in insects. Pharmacol. Rev., 18:89–94.

———, N. Lang, and P. Karlson. 1965. Zum Wirkungsmechanismus der Hormone. V. Der Einfluss von Ecdyson auf der RNA-Stoffwechsel in der Epidermis der Schmeissfliege, *Calliphora erythrocephala*. Hoppe-Seyler's Z. Physiol. Chem., 341:36–43.

Shaaya, E., and C. E. Sekeris. Ecdysone during insect development. III. Activities of some enzymes of tyrosine metabolism in comparison with ecdysone titer during the development of the blowfly, *Calliphora erythrocephala*. Gen. Comp. Endocr., 5:35–39.

Shappirio, D. G. 1960. Oxidative enzymes and the injury metabolism of diapausing Cecropia silkworms. Ann. N.Y. Acad. Sci., 89:537–548.

Takahashi, S. 1966. RNA in the fat body of *Philosamia cynthia* during development. J. Insect Physiol., 12:789–801.

Tata, J. R. 1966. Hormones and the synthesis and utilization of ribonucleic acids. Progr. Nucleic Acid Res. Molec. Biol., 5:191–250.

Telfer, W. H. 1954. Immunological studies of insect metamorphosis. II. The role of a sex-linked protein in egg formation by the cecropia silkworm. J. Gen. Physiol., 37:539–558.

_____, and C. M. Williams. 1953. Immunological studies of insect metamorphosis. I. Qualitative and quantitative description of the blood antigens of the cecropia silkworm. J. Gen. Physiol., 36:389–413.

Terando, M. L., and D. Feir. 1967. Immunoelectrophoresis of proteins in the hemolymph of the large milkweed bug, *Oncopeltus fasciatus*. Comp. Biochem. Physiol., 21:31–38.

Tobias, J. M. 1948. The high potassium and low sodium in the body fluid of a phytophagous insect, the silkworm, *Bombyx mori*, and the change before pupation. J. Cell. Comp. Physiol., 31:143–148.

Watt, W. B. 1967. Pteridine biosynthesis in the butterfly, *Colias eurytheme*. J. Biol. Chem., 242:565–572.

Wigglesworth, V. B. 1964. The hormonal regulation of growth and reproduction in insects. Advances Insect Physiol., 2:243–332.

_____. 1965. The Principles of Insect Physiology, 6th ed., London, Methuen.

Wyatt, G. R. 1959. Phosphorus compounds in insect development. Proc., 4th Int. Congr. Biochem., Vienna, 1958, 12:161–184.

_____. 1961. The biochemistry of insect hemolymph. Ann. Rev. Entomol., 6:75–102.

_____. 1963. Metabolic regulation in the development of insects. *In* Wright. B. ed., Control Mechanisms in Respiration and Fermentation, pp. 179–188. New York, Ronald Press.

_____. 1967a. The biochemistry of sugars and polysaccharides in insects. Advances Insect Physiol., 4:281–354.

_____. 1967b. Hormone action and macromolecule biosynthesis in silkmoth pupae. *In* Novak, V., and K. Slama , ed. The Insect Endocrines. London, Academic Press. In press.

_____, and B. Linzen. 1965. The metabolism of ribonucleic acid in cecropia silkmoth pupae in diapause, during development, and after injury. Biochim. Biophys. Acta, 103:588–600.

Zaluska, H. 1959. Glycogen and chitin metabolism during development of silkworm (*Bombyx mori* L.). Acta Biol. Exp., Lodz, 19:339–351.

five

GENE ACTIVITIES DURING
INSECT METAMORPHOSIS
AND THEIR CONTROL
BY HORMONES

Heinrich Kroeger

Zoologisches Institut
Eidgenössische Technische Hochschule
Zürich, Switzerland

INTRODUCTION

The information for every detail of an organism is stored in the genome of the zygote from which it developed. In animals that undergo metamorphosis, the genome must contain information for the development of *more than one form* (e.g., caterpillar, pupa, butterfly). It would appear that in the genome of such organisms *different sets of information* exist for the development of either form. Can this be demonstrated? How are these sets distinguished? How is the transition from the use of one set to the use of another instigated concurrently in all cells of an organism? We know that insect metamorphosis is set into motion and controlled by the relative titers of two hormones: ecdysone and juvenile hormone (see Chapter 3, this volume). Do these hormones exert their effects partly or wholly by intervening with the pattern of information retrieval from the genome? Do they do so directly or indirectly? By what mechanism do the relatively small and simple molecules exert such a complicated and fundamental effect?

GENE ACTIVITIES DURING METAMORPHOSIS

Today it is assumed that most if not all features of a cell are determined by its population of protein molecules. Any fundamental changes in a cell therefore might be expected to involve alterations in the composition or activity of its protein pool. In view of the process of DNA → RNA → protein information transfer, the protein complement of a given cell should reflect that set of cistrons in the genome whose code message is being transliterated. Can it be shown that at different stages of metamorphosis cells retrieve different sets of information from their genome?

Recognition of Genomic Activities: The Puff

If only part of the information stored in the genome is used at a given time, a "physiological sieve" must exist that allows one set of informational units to be expressed while others are kept from doing so. In principle, such discrimination could operate at any level or, in fact, at several levels concurrently. In terms of cellular economy, the most efficient way would be to allow some cistrons to form mRNA while others are kept "mute." In autoradiographic experiments this *should manifest itself as a discontinuity of RNA precursor incorporation along the axis of chromosomes.*

Unfortunately, most somatic cells of higher organisms are too small for such an analysis. In addition, in most cells chromosome individuality can unambiguously be recognized only in metaphase, a state in which the chromosomes display little or no synthetic activity. However, in some tissues of most dipteran larvae (and in some dipteran pupae) there exists an unusual type of chromosome that has neither of these disadvantages. These so-called "giant chromosomes" (1) are 10 to 100 times longer than average-sized chromosomes, (2) do not have any visible mitotic or endomitotic multiplication cycles, and (3) display a banding pattern that makes all their parts easily identifiable in simple squash preparations. They are polytene in nature, i.e., they actually consist of bundles of many tightly aligned chromosomes and are usually found in tissues with some type of secretory function (see Chapter 2, this volume). All aspects of these chromosomes have been reviewed extensively in a monograph by Beermann (1962).

If one explants a dipteran larval organ whose cells carry giant chromosomes (for instance, a salivary gland, a Malpighian tubule, a piece of gut) into a medium containing H^3-labeled RNA precursor molecules, and subsequently subjects the organ to autoradiography, an examination of the incorporation pattern in the chromosomes shows *that some regions incorporate more labeled precursors than do others* (Fig. 1). For the same organ taken from animals at the same developmental stage *this pattern is constant.* Ultraviolet absorption measurements combined with RNA digestion studies support the contention that the material synthesized is RNA (Rudkin, 1962). It seems, therefore, that *RNA synthesis is discontinuous along giant chromosomes.*

Chromosomes that have been treated for autoradiography are largely destroyed and very little detail remains. However, if one examines giant chromosomes in ordinary squash preparations and compares these to autoradiographs, an additional phenomenon becomes apparent. Chromosome segments that show high RNA synthetic activity also exhibit characteristic modifications of their structure. As compared to "inactive" regions, these segments are swollen, their bands are dispersed, and their internal arrangement is looser and less ordered (Fig. 2). *Such regions are called puffs.* Particularly large modifications of the chromosome structure, which appear to surround the chromosomes like rings, are called Balbiani rings after the scientist who first described them in 1881.

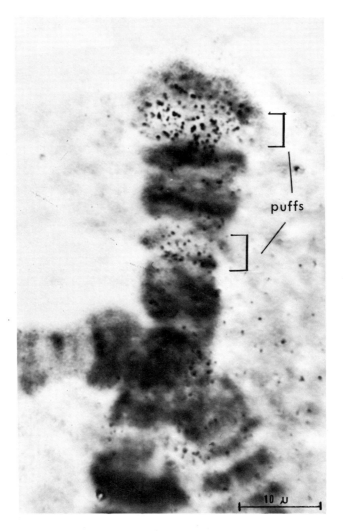

FIG. 1. Autoradiograph demonstrating discontinuous incorporation of H^3-guanosine into giant chromosomes from *Chironomus thummi* salivary gland cells. Focus on silver grains, therefore the chromosome is out of focus. Areas with high activity coincide with puffed chromosome regions. Courtesy of Dr. M. Lezzi.

Because of the direct correlation of these structural modifications with high activity in autoradiographic experiments (see Pelling, 1964), puffs and Balbiani rings can be considered signs of high RNA synthetic activity in a particular chromosome region. In view of the ease with which squash preparations of giant

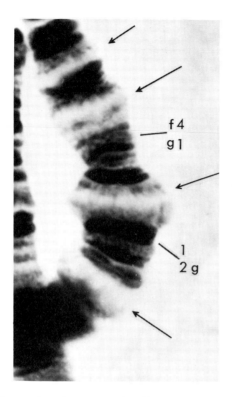

FIG. 2. Typical appearance of puffs in squash preparation. Giant chromosomes from salivary gland of *Chironomus thummi*. Orcein, acetic acid stain. (Original.)

chromosomes can be prepared, the recording of puffing patterns has become an invaluable tool for (1) the determination of genomic activities and their patterns, (2) the evaluation of the effects hormones and other chemical or physical agents might have on these activities, and (3) a direct attack on the mechanism by which gene activities are controlled in a cell. The literature pertaining to "puffing" has been reviewed extensively by Kroeger and Lezzi (1966).

The chemical composition, morphology, and physiology of puffs have been studied in great detail. Puffs are composed of DNA, RNA, and protein. When a chromosome region forms a puff, its DNA becomes considerably less tightly coiled but does not appear to change in amount. Exceptions are a few puffs in sciarid tissues and the foot pads of some higher cyclorrhaphous flies, which in addition to RNA also synthesize DNA (see Breuer and Pavan, 1955; Rudkin and Corlette, 1957). In the foot pads, this DNA is released from the puffs in granules (Whitten, 1965), but some of it seems to be retained at the site when the puff regresses. This DNA is a marker for a chromosome region that has previously been in a puffed state (Breuer and Pavan, 1955). It is not known whether the additionally synthesized DNA serves as a template for the production of RNA, either in the nucleus or in the cytoplasm, or possesses another function. However, the vast majority of puffs studied do not display this special phenomenon.

RNA produced in puffs has a high turnover rate. In *Drosophila busckii* for example, pulse labeling for only 30 sec results in some radioactivity in the RNA (Ritossa, 1962). The A/U:G/C base ratios have been determined by an ultramicro method. For some large Balbiani rings they were found to be highly asymmetric, indicating that the RNA produced was a copy of only one strand of the chromosomal DNA (Edström and Beermann, 1962). The RNA synthetic activity of puffs can be blocked almost entirely by treatment with actinomycin D at a concentration of 0.1 μg/ml medium. It is of interest to note that concurrently with the suppression of RNA synthesis the puffs regress and eventually disappear (Beermann, 1963). This is further support for the view that puffing of a chromosome region is a dependable marker of RNA synthesis. Occasional deviations from this rule (Pelling, 1964) do not significantly alter its general value. At excessive doses (20 μg/ml) of actinomycin D, RNA synthesis ceases without disappearance of the puff, possibly because at this dose the antibiotic interferes with the mechanical properties of the DNA in such a way that it becomes unable to return to the coiled state (Beermann, 1963).

When a puff is formed, proteins accumulate at the site. Some of these (but possibly only a very small fraction) can be synthesized in the puff itself (Lezzi, 1967), but the major part seem to aggregate from the nuclear sap. The functional significance of the accumulation of large amounts of protein is presently still a matter of speculation (see Lezzi, 1967).

The RNA synthesized in puffs appears to migrate through the nuclear sap and into the cytoplasm in the form of ribonucleoprotein granules. These granules can readily be observed under the electron microscope and range from 100 to 1,000 Å in diameter (Swift, 1963). The larger particles seem to be composed of smaller subunits (Schurin, 1959), which have recently been interpreted to be ribosomes (Lezzi, 1967).

The puffing phenomenon supports the contention that at the level of the synthesis of RNA on the chromosomal DNA template, discriminatory mechanisms exist that favor the transcription of some information present in the DNA of the chromosome. Of course this does not exclude the possibility of additional discrimination during subsequent steps in the expression of genomic information. However, no methods presently exist that allow the direct observation of such a phenomenon.

Dynamics of Genomic Activity During Metamorphosis

Screening of giant chromosomes for their puffing activity affords a rapid and simple method for determining parts of the chromosome set engaged in RNA synthesis. By comparing puffing patterns from different stages of development and from different tissues, one can determine whether genomic activity patterns change during development and whether they are tissue specific. This allows an insight into the participation of the genetic material in the events of metamorphosis.

A comparison of puffing activities from different individuals shows that puffs are highly dynamic. They appear, they disappear, and the maximal size they attain (characteristic for every puff) ranges from barely discernible modifications of one band to the large Balbiani rings that can comprise more than 20 bands. Puffs regularly begin to form at a single band (Beerman and Clever, 1964), but as they enlarge they incorporate more and more neighboring bands. This suggests that during puff development more and more cistrons are incited to deliver their information . The sequence in which the cistrons become activated would be determined by their position relative to the starting point of the puff. Although this may well be a true picture, it must be viewed with caution. Perhaps part of the DNA is *passively* drawn into the puff without actually participating in its synthetic activity. In fact, it is not known whether part of the DNA serves a function other than that of a matrix for RNA synthesis.

If one follows the puffing activity of giant chromosomes from a specific tissue from the beginning of the last larval instar to pupation in a chironomid, it appears that the pattern of activity remains rather constant. However, shortly before the first signs of preparations for the molt can be detected in the larva, *drastic changes occur in the pattern of activity.* New puffs appear, others disappear, while still others change in size (see Fig. 3). While all workers engaged in these studies agree on this fact, differences do exist between dipteran species regarding the *total* puffing activity during this period. Becker (1959) reports that in *Drosophila melanogaster* salivary glands

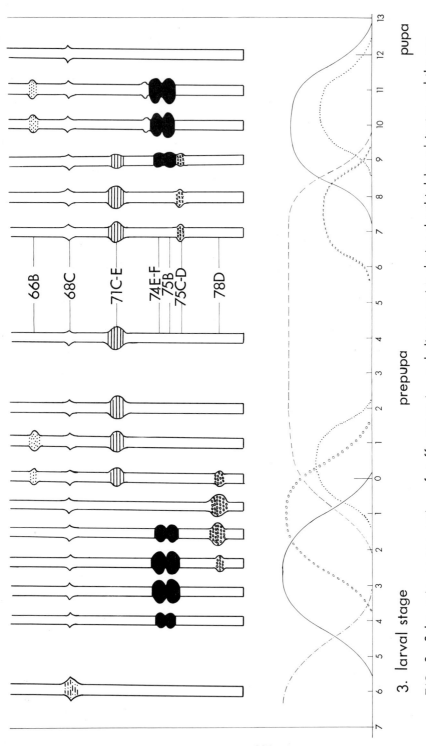

FIG. 3. Schematic representation of puffs appearing and disappearing during the third larval instar and the pre-pupal stage at the base of chromosome arm III L of *D. melanogaster* salivary glands. Numbers indicate hours before or after puparium formation. From Becker (1959) by permission of Springer-Verlag, Berlin-Göttingen-Heidelberg.

66B

68C

71C-E

74E-F
75B
75C-D

78D

3. larval stage   prepupa   pupa

an actual "puffing period" precedes puparium formation; i.e., more and larger puffs appear. In contradistinction, a study of *Chironomus tentans* indicates only a shift in the pattern of activity, the overall number and size of puffs remaining approximately constant (Clever, 1962).

The number of puffs that disappear entirely or appear de novo is small. The majority of puffs undergo changes in size only. In fact, the size of only a few puffs are unaffected during the preparation and execution of the pupal molt. For example, in a study of 143 puffs in the salivary gland of *D. hydei*, Berendes (1965) found only 9 to appear de novo or to disappear, while 110 changed in size during puparium formation and the subsequent pupal molt. Although the groups of puffs studied by individual investigators are selected to some extent in that they contain disproportionately more puffs that change during metamorphosis, it nevertheless is justifiable to state that the pattern of RNA synthesis changes not only quantitatively, but to some extent qualitatively as well during preparation for the pupal molt.

In an exhaustive study, Pelling (1964) found approximately 275 puffs in the chromosomes of the salivary glands of last larval instar *C. tentans*. Of the 1900 bands that are discernible, about 10 percent seem to be in a puffed state at a given time, and about 15 percent are part of a puffed region *at some time* during the last larval instar.

No comparable data exist for other tissues that carry giant chromosomes, but the general puffing activity of these other tissues does resemble that of the salivary glands. Thus, we can postulate that only about 15 percent of a tissue's DNA partakes in the biochemical events that occur during the last larval instar.

Comparisons of the puffing patterns of different tissues usually reveal that tissues differ in only a small number of puffs. Berendes (1966) has specifically investigated this phenomenon in *D. hydei* where 76 (equals 69 percent) of 110 puffs studied are present in the Malpighian tubules, the stomach, and the salivary glands at one time or another during the midlarval instar and late last larval instar. A small number of puffs were tissue specific; three were restricted to the Malpighian tubules, four to the stomach, and seven to the salivary glands. A number of puffs were absent in only one of the tissues investigated during this entire period. However, puffs common to more than one tissue do not necessarily appear or reach maximal size simultaneously.

Puffing and Cell Biochemistry

The cuticle, imaginal discs, and so forth are usually considered to undergo metamorphosis (see Chapter 2, this volume) but those cell types that carry giant chromosomes do not show many outward signs of partaking in the metamorphic events. However, recent investigations show that they undergo considerable biochemical changes correlated with the alterations observed in genomic activity.

As puparium formation approaches, a number of alterations can be seen under the light or electron microscope in the salivary glands of *D. hydei*. The distal cells of the gland acquire a reticulated structure and contain mucoprotein inclusions not previously visible, along with numerous other changes. Parallel with this, the cells stop secreting digestive enzymes and initiate production of a glue substance that is stored in the glandular lumen (Berendes, 1965). The chemical composition of these products differs from one lobe of a chironomid salivary gland to the next (Baudisch, 1963). Laufer (1963) demonstrated that the secretory product of *C. thummi* salivary gland cells, as well as the secretory cells themselves, change in a regular pattern as the pupal molt approaches. Partly, these changes seem to consist of an altered pattern of enzyme synthesis, but they also appear to reflect the ability of the cells to sequester specific protein fractions from the hemolymph and to incorporate these into the secretory product, possibly via the synthesis of specific "permeases" (Laufer and Nakase, 1965). Shortly after the pupal molt, the larval salivary glands undergo histolysis as a result of the liberation of hydrolytic enzymes from previously manufactured lysosomes (Schin and Clever, 1965). This process, too, should require specific mRNA.

While these investigations demonstrate a *parallelism* between changes in genomic activities and changes in morphological and biochemical patterns of cells, they do not demonstrate *causal relationships*. That such relationships exist is seen from the work of Laufer, Nakase, and Vanderberg (1965) who showed that enzyme activity in the salivary secretion (which, as mentioned above, shows a typical change during preparation of the pupal molt) is depressed in cells where RNA synthesis is inhibited by actinomycin D. Therefore, it appears that normal enzyme activities are dependent upon an uninterrupted flow of information from the genome.

It has also been possible to show that the intermediate link between the events at the genomic level and the subsequent appearance of one identifiable enzyme in the cell cytoplasm is probably mRNA. RNA from *Calliphora* larvae was prepared that exhibits characteristics typical of the messenger fraction. Depending on the developmental stage of the larvae this mRNA could or could not direct the synthesis of DOPA decarboxylase (see Fig. 4) in an in vitro system (Sekeris and Lang, 1964). The

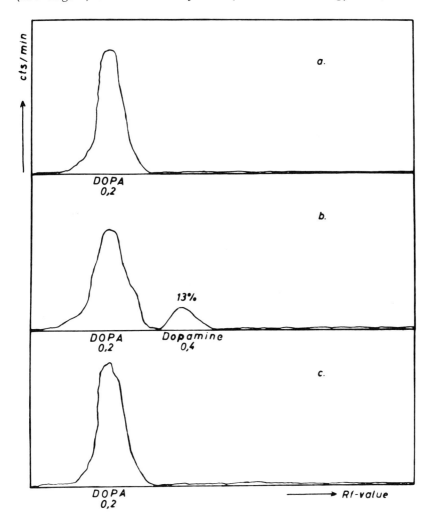

FIG. 4. DOPA-decarboxylase activity of (a) rat liver microsomes and (b) rat liver microsomes plus mRNA from epidermal cells of *Calliphora* with high ecdysone titer and (c) rat liver microsomes plus mRNA from epidermal cells of *Calliphora* in which ecdysone secretion has not yet begun. From Sekeris and Lang (1964) by permission of Pergamon Press, Oxford.

appearance of this enzyme is a typical and well-delineated step in the preparation of the pupal molt.

In view of these findings it appears that at least some of the RNA produced in the puffs is operative in directing cellular biochemical events. In all likelihood it acts by coding for amino acid sequences in proteins. In other words, puffs seem to be production sites of mRNA.

What kinds of proteins are coded for by the mRNA synthesized in the puffs? It can be assumed that those puffs present at all times that change their activity little if at all during metamorphosis and that are shared by many or all tissues are involved in cellular functions common to all cells (i.e., respiration, carbohydrate metabolism, and so forth). These form by far the larger group of puffs. In contrast, the smaller group of puffs that appear or disappear in the preparation of a molt may mediate the less-common chemical reactions characteristic of a specific step in metamorphosis. In summary, it seems that the genome exerts a permanent control over the chemical and morphological events that occur in the cytoplasm during metamorphosis.

Mutation and Puffing

It would be of interest to investigate the consequences of mutations on puffing in giant chromosomes. However, such an approach must surmount an experimental obstacle. Only mutations with a phenotypic expression in one of the tissues carrying, giant chromosomes can be investigated by this method. In addition, the mutation in question has to affect one of these tissues during the late last larval instar since puffs can be analyzed only during this period. Even the large number of mutations known in *Drosophila* includes few with an expression in the larva, and almost none of these affect internal organs during this period.

Two cases have been described where mutations affect the puffing activity at a specific chromosomal site: (1) In certain chironomid species one lobe of the salivary gland includes granules in its secretory product (the function of which is unknown). In interspecies crosses the ability to form these granules behaves as a simple Mendelian recessive that is situated at a specific region of the fourth chromosome. Cytological examination revealed that all cells forming granules show a Balbiani ring in this region; all cells that do not form granules lack this structure. Heterozygotes produce a reduced number of granules and exhibit the Balbiani ring in a heterozygous form, i.e., the puff stretches only over one half of the tightly paired homologous chromosomes (Beermann, 1961). (2) Slizynski (1964) has reported a similar case in *D. melanogaster*. Here, the appearance of large vacuoles in salivary gland cells of larvae homozygous for the mutation fat (ft) is linked to the presence or absence of a puff at precisely that chromosome area where crossing-over analysis places the mutation.

In both cases a clearly delineated functional capacity of a cell depends on the existence of one specific puff and is further support for the premise that puffs indeed produce mRNA. In addition, the absence of a puff or its de novo appearance at a mutated site is surprising. "Point mutations" are considered to represent alterations in the nucleotide sequence of a cistron, which result in the production of a protein with an altered amino acid sequence. The disappearance of a puff as a consequence of a mutation, on the other hand, infers that this chromosomal segment has stopped producing *any* RNA, at least during the period investigated. In wild populations of chironomids, "heterozygous puffs" are not infrequent. Therefore, the presence and absence of a puff due to differences in the genotype are not uncommon and the two cases described are not exceptional. The most plausible interpretation for this finding is that a situation prevails similar to that found in bacteria (see Jacob and Monod, 1961). The element responsible for the activation of a chromosomal segment is not identical with the elements containing the information for amino acid sequences in proteins. In bacteria these elements are called "operator" and "structural genes," respectively. In a chromosome, the mutation of an "operator" element would lead to the disappearance or de novo appearance of a puff.

Support for the notion of a separate "activation receptor site" comes from an observation made by M. Ashburner (personal communication), which shows a situation somewhat different from that reported by Beermann in chironomids (see above). Ashburner found that two stocks of *D. melanogaster*, vg6 and Oregon, are distinguished by the presence in the former stock of a puff in chromosome section 64 C of the third chromosome. Unexpectedly, vg6/Oregon heterozygotes display a puff at this location that is not restricted to one member of the closely synapsed giant chromosomes but stretches across the whole width of the chromosome. Whenever the homologous chromosomes are accidentally not synapsed in vg6/Oregon heterozygotes, only one of the homologues displays the puff. It appears that in this case an activating stimulus received by the "operator" site in one chromosome can activate "structural genes'' in the other homologue, provided they are paired.

If this view should be further substantiated, it will have important implications for students of evolution. If the decision as to when and where in a developing organism a group of genes becomes active is cast by a determinant separate from that specifying amino acid sequences, a higher degree of freedom should exist for evolutionary mechanisms. By altering the ''operator'' element they may rearrange the appearance of a group of enzymes in time and place of a developing organism while the structure and specificity of these enzymes could be manipulated independently by mutations in the ''structural'' elements. The mere reorganization of identical elements into different patterns, which plays such an important role in evolution, could be accounted for by mutations of the operator elements (or of other genetic units that might determine their reactivity), while the functional efficiency of enzymes could be improved by an independent line of evolution.

HORMONAL CONTROL OF GENE ACTIVITIES

What causes the observed changes in genomic activity during metamorphosis and the differences in activity patterns between tissues? A large body of evidence makes it clear that most events of metamorphosis are set into motion and controlled by *hormones*. Some form intermediate links in the overall hormonal system and serve specifically to stimulate the synthesis or release of other hormones (see Chapter 3, this volume). Two hormones, however, *ecdysone* and *juvenile hormone*, are responsible for the many transformations that occur during metamorphosis, and the following discussion will be devoted entirely to these two hormones.

Previously, the role of the genome as an important control center for cellular biochemistry and for its alterations during metamorphosis was discussed. Do ecdysone and juvenile hormone exert their effects partly or entirely via intervention with the patterns of information retrieval? If so, can insight be gained into the means by which they exert such effects?

Effects on Puffing Pattern

In several instances it has been demonstrated that the puffing pattern reflects the hormonal milieu. Panitz (1964) found that different puffing patterns occurred in excised salivary glands when they were incubated for 6 hours in hemolymph that was (1) larval in origin, (2) prepupal mixed with pupal hemolymph, (3) larval supplemented with brain complex and adhering endocrine structures. Becker (1962) ligated *Drosophila* larvae in such a way that one compartment contained half of the salivary glands plus all those endocrine components located in the anterior half of the larva, while the other compartment contained half of the gland but no endocrine components. Within a few hours after the ligation, the two parts of the salivary gland exhibited different puffing patterns. The halves in the anterior compartment exhibited all changes in puffing activity typical of the period shortly before puparium formation, while the portions in the posterior compartment showed no such activity. Furthermore, by transplanting salivary glands into hosts of different ages Becker showed that the transplanted giant chromosomes displayed a puffing pattern similar or identical to that of the host's salivary gland. While these experiments demonstrate a general endocrine control of puffing patterns, it has also been possible to elucidate the specific contributions of ecdysone and, in a less clear way, of juvenile hormone in this overall effect.

Ecdysone. Panitz (1964) found, that the addition of brain complex to an otherwise inactive hemolymph induces changes in the puffing pattern. Furthermore, Panitz (1964) incubated various parts of the brain complex with salivary glands. In this way he traced the origin of the active principle to Weismann's ring and specifically to that portion which is a homologue of the prothoracic (ecdysial) glands of other insects. Since these are the glands that produce ecdysone, this hormone seemed to be responsible for the observed effects on the puffing pattern.

Ecdysone has been prepared in crystalline form and has recently been synthesized (see Chapter 3, this volume). Its effect on puffing patterns therefore can be directly tested by injection of the pure hormone into larvae followed by an examination of the puffing patterns. Such experiments have been conducted by Clever (1961 and 1963b), and his results can be summarized as follows: 15 to 30 min after an injection of 45 Calliphora Units (CU) ecdysone into a larva of *C. tentans*, one chromosome segment (I-18-C) starts to puff; shortly afterward (within 30 to 60 min after injection), another segment (IV-2-B) is transformed to the puffed state. These puffs may be termed the "primary set" of puffs. Further experiments showed that at any given time the size of both these puffs is dependent upon the ecdysone titer in the hemolymph, demonstrating that the hormone not only triggers their appearance but exerts a continuous and quantitative control over their existence and size.

If a smaller amount (10 to 15 CU) is injected, the "primary set" of puffs also appears, but both puffs soon regress and disappear entirely within 24 to 48 hours. Their disappearance probably signals a decrease in the ecdysone titer of the hemolymph. In contrast, the injection of 45 CU serves to maintain a higher titer of ecdysone over an extended period and leads to the appearance of a series of other puffs within 5 to 72 hours. During normal development these same puffs appear following activation of the "primary set" and, in contrast to these, may be called the "secondary set" of puffs. Their size is *not* correlated with the ecdysone titer. A normal molt ensues in animals that receive 45 CU and develop the "secondary" as well as the "primary set" of puffs. Animals that receive 10 to 15 CU do not molt and show only a temporary activation of the "primary set."

On the other hand, Berendes (personal communication) in a study of *D. hydei,* found 31 puffs to respond to an injection of ecdysone within 1 hour. Some puffs appeared de novo, others disappeared, and still others changed in size in a regular manner. It appears that in this organism the primary impact of ecdysone affects many more chromosome segments than in *Chironomus.*

Juvenile Hormone. Thus far it has not been possible to induce changes in the puffing pattern of dipteran salivary glands by injection of lepidopteran juvenile hormone preparations. However, this negative result does not exclude a direct effect of juvenile hormone on puffing patterns since lepidopteran juvenile hormone preparations do not influence metamorphosis in Diptera.

While no direct evidence of the effect of juvenile hormone on genomic activity is available, Clever (1963a) has presented some indirect evidence. Comparing genomic events during a larval molt with those during a pupal molt, he observed that the "primary set" of puffs in the salivary glands is similar in both molts while the "secondary set" differs considerably. Most puffs comprising the "secondary set" during the pupal molt are not seen during the preparation of a larval molt, while one puff is specific for the pupal molt. Since both molts are initiated by ecdysone, any differences in puffing activity should be a result of changes in the juvenile hormone titer. Changes in the genomic activity patterns therefore seem to form a link somewhere in the causal chain between the primary effect of juvenile hormone and its ultimate morphogenetic consequences.

Mechanisms of Action

By what mechanisms do ecdysone and juvenile hormone cause shifts in information retrieval patterns in the genome? This question is of unusual interest, since both hormones are characterized by a diversity of effects and tissues react differently and in a complex manner to both hormones. An understanding of the way in which the hormone molecules intervene with the previously existing pattern of RNA synthesis as well as the reasons for the differential reactivity of the tissues may elucidate the means by which hormones invoke concerted and integrated effects.

Ecdysone. When the ecdysone titer reaches a critical level, a number of events occur: (1) within 1 min post ecdysone application the electric potential difference across the nuclear and cell membranes starts to rise and continues to do so for about 12 min, until it has risen by about 15 mv (Kroeger 1966b); (2) within 15 min, isolated nuclei from blowfly epidermis cells show a general increase in RNA synthetic activity (Sekeris, Dukes, and Schmid, 1965); (3) within 15 to 30 min, the "primary set" of puffs mentioned above appears; (4) within 60 min, the resistance of the nuclear membrane has risen to about twice its value (Ito and Loewenstein, 1965); (5) within 5 to 72 hours, the "secondary set" of puffs appears; (6) followed by a series of events such as enlargement of nucleoli, swelling of mitochondria, and stimulation of mitosis that precede the actual molt (for literature concerning these effects see Kroeger, 1967a).

The time sequence of these events can serve only as a preliminary guide since differences in the speed of reaction between species and differences in the recording sensitivities and in the mode of hormone application might easily obscure a true temporal sequence.

The first observable effect of ecdysone is the increase in electric potential found in explanted salivary gland cells. It has been postulated that this effect signals an ecdysone induced accumulation of K^+ by the cell (Kroeger, 1966b). Furthermore, it has been determined that the typical effect of ecdysone on the puffing pattern—the induction of the "primary set of puffs"—can be invoked without addition of ecdysone by increasing the intracellular or intranuclear concentration of K^+ (Fig. 5; Kroeger, 1963a; Lezzi, 1966)! Taken together these data strongly suggest that the primary effect of ecdysone is a stimulation of the K^+ uptake of the cell and nucleus and that it is the resulting elevated K^+ titer that causes the observed alterations in the puffing pattern (Fig. 6).

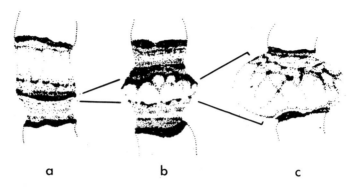

a   b   c

FIG. 5. The most ecdysone sensitive chromosome section in giant chromosomes of *Chironomus thummi* salivary glands. a: Puff (between lines) absent; b: puff present in approximately maximal size attained during normal development or after ecdysone injection; c: puff present in abnormal size induced by K^+ — by varying K^+ concentration and period of exposure to this ion any size between a and c can be induced. In a, a puff is seen upward from the region that forms the ecdysone sensitive puff; this puff is absent in b and belongs to those which reappear during rollback of puffing patterns induced by Na^+. (Original.)

The appearance of the "primary set of puffs" is the first easily demonstrated morphological effect of ecydysone on the giant chromosomes. However, during normal development this event is preceded by the *disappearance of a number of puffs* in a specific sequence (Kroeger, 1963b and 1964). Usually, animals used for ecdysone experiments have passed the stage of puff disappearance, but in all likelihood the diappearance of these puffs is the result of a very low ecdysone titer that prevails during the first phases of ecdysial gland activity. These puffs, whose disappearance precedes the induction of the "primary set" by ecdysone, can be made to reappear by an increase in the Na^+ titer of a salivary gland cell (Kroeger, 1963b and 1964; Rey 1963; Lezzi and Kroeger, 1966). It appears that the disappearance of these puffs during normal development is caused by a lowering of the intracellular Na^+ titer and that this lowering is another effect of ecdysone at very low concentrations. (Fig. 5).

As mentioned above, a consequence of the activation of the "primary set" of puffs is the appearance of the "secondary set," and it seems that the latter event is caused by the former. How this is achieved remains unclear, although some clues exist as to the possible mechanisms involved: (1) Clever (1964) found that previous administration of puromycin, a potent inhibitor of protein synthesis, does not inhibit the induction of the "primary

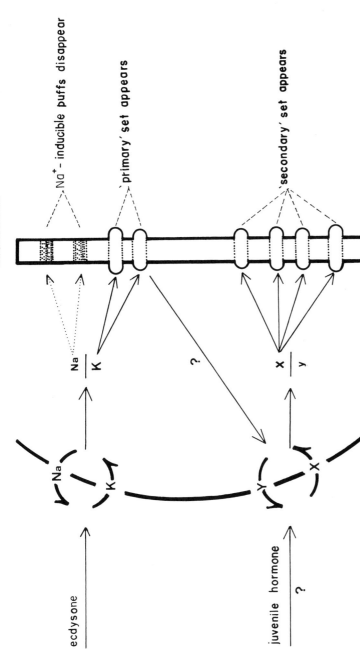

FIG. 6. Schematic representation summarizing probable ecdysone and possible juvenile hormone action. See text for details. Although some of the events pictured to occur at the cell membrane may actually occur at the nuclear membrane, the nuclear membrane is omitted for simplicity. Arrows pointing to transport systems indicate that effectiveness of these systems is modified; this might also be achieved by changes in membrane permeability, leaving the transport systems themselves uneffected. (Original.)

set'' of puffs by ecdysone but does inhibit the appearance of the
''secondary set.'' This demonstrates that protein synthesis is
an obligatory link in the induction of the ''secondary set'' by
the ''primary'' one, but not in the induction of the ''primary
set'' by ecdysone. (2) Damage to cell membranes, which leads
to a mixing of the intracellular solute with the extracellular
one, results in characteristic alterations in the ''secondary set''
of puffs. The kinetics of this process suggest that the puffs of
the ''secondary set'' are dependent on an intracellular titer of
some small as yet unidentified molecules that leach out from a
damaged cell (Fig. 6). Thus, it would seem that the mRNA synthesized in the puffs of the ''primary set'' direct the synthesis
of proteins that alter the permeability and transport functions
of the cell in such a way that the intracellular solute undergoes
further alterations. These then cause the loci of the ''secondary
set'' to become puffed. However, in the absence of direct proof,
these assumptions can only be considered guidelines to further
experiments.

Juvenile Hormone. No data comparable to those discussed
above on the action of ecdysone are available concerning juvenile
hormone. As described above, the puffing patterns during the
preparation of the larval and pupal molts differ considerably
in their ''secondary'' but not in their ''primary'' set of puffs,
suggesting that the juvenile hormone intervenes in an unknown
fashion with the pattern of chromosomal sites that become
activated by the ''primary set.'' However, as long as no direct
effect of purified juvenile hormone on genomic activity patterns
can be demonstrated, it is possible that these changes are only
indirect consequences of other more fundamental changes induced
by the juvenile hormone.

Molecular Events During Hormone Action

The hormonal message acts at two sites. (1) At the cell
membrane the hormonal impact is converted into an alteration
of the intracellular and intranuclear electrolyte milieu. (2) At
the chromosomal level this shift in the milieu is translated
into a differential pattern of mRNA synthesis. What is the molecular mechanism that operates at each of these sites?

Hormones and Transport. Practically all cell types so far
investigated exhibit active transport systems that allow them to
transport various inorganic and organic molecules against con-

centration gradients. In view of the above findings regarding the exquisite sensitivity of genomic activity patterns to variations in the intracellular solute, the mechanism by which cells are segregated from their surroundings as well as the ways by which hormones may influence this segregation gain new significance. Recent work summarized by Skou (1965) has described a delicate homeostatic mechanism that keeps the Na^+/K^+ concentration in the cell at a certain level and buffers it against various factors. The Na^+ secretion (and the concomitant K^+ accumulation) of most cells gains its energy from specific "pump-ATPases" which are fixed constituents of the membranes and are stimulated by intracellular Na^+ (and to some extent by extracellular K^+). If, due to an interference with active transport or with the integrity of cell membranes, the intracellular Na^+ titer increases, Na^+ is excreted until the intracellular Na^+ titer has been lowered to the original value. As a rule, transport systems for other molecules are energetically linked to the Na^+/K^+ transport system. If this system ceases to function, they also come to a standstill.

As described above, the first effect of ecdysone seems to be a lowering of the Na^+ titer and an increase in the K^+ titer of the cell. It appears that ecdysone produces this effect by increasing the effectiveness of the Na^+/K^+ transport system. How this increase is achieved is presently unknown. Perhaps the hormone directly stimulates transport functions by "setting" the Na^+ sensitivity of the transport ATPases to a higher level or reducing the passive back leakage of extruded Na^+ through the membrane by altering its permeability. In this context it is interesting to note that many vertebrate hormones, notably the neurohypophyseal peptides and the mineralocorticoids, also have drastic effects upon the electrolyte content of cells (see Kroeger, 1967b). However, as with ecdysone, the mechanism by which these hormones influence the composition of the intracellular solute is unknown.

Ecdysone *increases* the asymmetry of ion distribution between the interior of a cell and its surroundings and possibly between the nucleus and cytoplasm of a cell. A reduction of these differences should be easy to produce (for instance, by damage to the cell membranes) and would be expected to have effects on the puffing pattern opposite to those elicited by ecdysone. Such phenomena have indeed been observed by several authors. In some species, the mere excision of a salivary gland from a larva seems to upset the ionic distribution and results in a remarkable reaction of the giant chromosomes; their puffing pattern shifts back toward a state typical of a lower ecdysone titer. In developmental terms this is a more "juvenile pattern", and is why this reaction has been called "rollback" (Becker, 1959) or "rejuvenation" (Kroeger, 1963b) of the puffing pattern. Some dipteran species do not show this effect (Clever, 1965), presumably because their cells have more stable membranes.

The main impetus for this reaction of the giant chromosomes may be an influx of Na^+ into the cells, and this actually has been measured using Na^{22+} (Lezzi and Kroeger, 1966). This influx leads to a reactivation of Na^+-sensitive chromosome segments. However, other molecular species are also exchanged with the surrounding medium at this time. In summary, rollback or rejuvenation of puffing patterns may consist of a mixing of the solute in the interior of the cell with that outside of the cell and leads to alterations in the genomic activity pattern. It is possible that a similar mixing of the intranuclear milieu with that of the cytoplasm also takes place, but this has not yet been demonstrated.

Effects of wounding have been observed in insect tissues that are probably reflections of such a "genomic rejuvenation": First, wounding provokes an "injury metabolism" in diapausing saturniid pupae characterized by a steep increase in respiratory rate and in several biosynthetic activities. Although they do not lead to developmental progress, these metabolic events closely resemble those occurring when diapause is terminated by ecdysone (Shappirio and Harvey, 1965). Perhaps wounding causes an influx of Na^+ into cells of various tissues and the subsequent activation of genetic loci causes the "injury metabolism." Under this view, wounding and ecdysone treatment would both alter the composition of the intracellular solutes. The former would be expected to raise the Na^+ and the latter the K^+ titer in the cell, which may explain the difference between both agents in terms of developmental progress. Second, wounding specifically alters the synthetic activity of cuticle cells. If a larva is wounded, during the next molt the cells surrounding and covering the wound form a more juvenile type of cuticle (see Fig. 7). The two types of cuticle that form the body of a caterpillar—a hard, brown cuticle at the head and over some body areas and, a thinner, more flexible type that covers the rest of the body— appear in a typical pattern because the epidermal cells in these areas differ in their sensitivity to juvenile hormone (Heims, 1956). The interconversion of the two types of cuticle as a result of wounding may be explained again by a wound-induced equalization between intracellular and extracellular concentrations of those molecular species responsible for the activation of genetic loci.

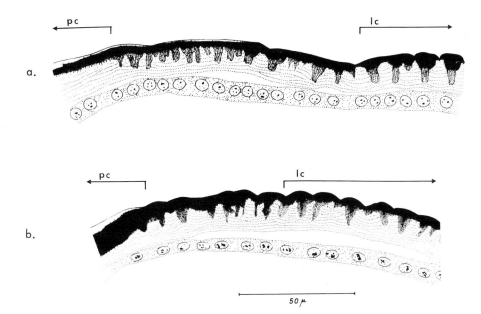

FIG. 7. Juvenile hormone mimicking effect of wounding: a: Transition from hard brown cuticle (pc) at pronotum of *Galleria mellonella*, which is of same type as pupal cuticle, to thin, flexible, typically larval cuticle (lc); b: transition from hard, brown pupal cuticle to thin, flexible cuticle induced by wounding. From Heims (1956) by permission of München, Bergmann, Berlin-Göttingen-Heidelberg, Springer-Verlag.

Besides those at the cell membrane, there also exist intracellular transport systems that can move molecules from one cellular compartment to another. Contrary to earlier views that considered the nuclear envelope a sieve, recent investigations by Loewenstein and Kanno (1963) reveal that it forms a distinct ion barrier that can sustain active transport functions (Allfrey et al., 1961). This means that the nucleoplasm is separated to some extent from the cytoplasm. Furthermore, mitochondria have transport systems that allow them to obtain and release certain ions from and into the cellular solute and this can be influenced by certain hormones (Rasmussen and Deluca, 1963). Finally, it is well known that the cytoplasm and apparently the nucleus as well (Siebert and Humphrey, 1965) can selectively bind and release ions. They have what may be termed an ''ion exchange function.'' All of these mechanisms, although not well elucidated, are of significance for the study of the control of gene activities since they allow a cell to alter the distribution of ions in its interior without exchanging materials with the surroundings.

Molecular Events at the Gene Locus. The second site for the hormonal message occurs at the chromosomes, where changes in ion concentrations are translated into patterns of RNA synthesis. How is this achieved?

During the last decade it has become increasingly clear that the larger part of the DNA found in metazoan chromosomes is in a "repressed" state, i.e., cannot serve as a template for RNA synthesis. It is possible that the agents keeping the DNA in this repressed state are histone molecules to which most or all DNA of a somatic cell is bound (for a general reference, see Busch, 1965). Therefore, "activation of a gene" should be an act of derepression.

Evidence exists that puffing involves an alteration of the molecular configuration of histones. Trypsin injected into chironomid salivary gland cell nuclei causes a three-fold increase in overall chromosomal RNA synthesis. This increase is restricted, however, to puffed regions only. Evidently, histones at puffed sites are more susceptible to the action of this enzyme than are histones at nonpuffed sites. An explanation for this puzzling fact can be found in the well-known high sensitivity of "denaturated" proteins to trypsin. The conclusion to be drawn is that the activation of a chromosome region may occur by an alteration of its histone configuration that makes these molecules (1) susceptible to trypsin and (2) unable to perform their repressive function (Robert and Kroeger, 1965).

How can such an alteration of molecular configurations be induced locally and specifically by ions? Histones are bound to DNA by typical salt linkages, and it is known that salt linkages are sensitive to shifts in ionic strength. That this is also true for the DNA-histone binding forces was demonstrated by Akinrimisi, Bonner, and Ts'o (1965). Increasing electrolyte concentration causes a characteristic steep decrease in the binding coefficient between DNA and histones, and the resulting "salt profiles" are distinctly different, depending on the type of histone that prevails in the complex. Furthermore, it has been demonstrated numerous times that an increase in the ionic strength of the medium stimulates in vitro RNA synthesizing systems (for literature, see Kroeger, 1967b). This may be a consequence of large fractions of DNA becoming exempt from the action of histones and thus exposed to the action of RNA polymerase. In addition, a Mg^{++} activated system produces a qualitatively different RNA if it is further stimulated by

$(NH_4)_2 SO_4$ (Widnell, 1965), indicating that at least some of the specificity of the action of different ions is retained in such in vitro systems. However, the evidence on this specific point is sparse.

Although none of the above experiments have been performed with insect material, metazoan chromatin seems to be rather uniform, irrespective of its source, and a cautious extrapolation of these results appears warranted. Possibly by competition between cations and histone molecules for the negatively charged groups of DNA, certain electrolytes can selectively weaken DNA-histone bonds, and it seems that this sensitivity of the DNA-histone binding forces is the molecular basis of the specific reaction of chromosome segments to changes in the internal electrolyte milieu.

Tissue Differences. Do various tissues have different transport and permeability properties that create a different internal milieu in each tissue? The intracellular millieu is certainly not uniform throughout an organism, but it appears doubtful that this difference is the basis of tissue-specific activity patterns. A theory of cellular differentiation based on the internal electrolyte milieu as the main determinant meets with grave difficulties. It is easy to upset the internal ionic milieu of a cell (at least for short periods) by a variety of simple and unspecific agents. Yet these cells cling to their tissue specificity with remarkable tenacity. Although this stability may simply reflect a remarkable buffering capacity of cells against long-term disturbances of their internal milieu, a more likely alternative exists. It could be that tissues have the same internal milieus, but their chromosomal loci respond differently to this milieu. This would be the case if in the tissues the same stretches of chromosomal DNA were covered by different histones. Although this view is not new it is only recently being supported by facts (Skalka, Fowler, and Hurwitz, 1966). Therefore, hormones may alter the internal ionic milieu of different tissues in the same way but the tissues respond in a differential manner, depending on the reactivity of the chromosomal loci.

Integration of Hormone Effects

Characteristic of the action of hormones in general is the integrated nature of their effects on the cells and tissues of an organism. This question should be viewed as part of the general problem: how are genomic activities coordinated in such a way that functional metabolism ensues in the cytoplasm of a cell?

This is a formidable problem indeed. In a metazoan somatic cell, the cistrons that transliterate their information must be selected in such a way that the hundreds of enzymes synthesized to their order in the cytoplasm form a catalytic combine able to synthesize and degrade molecules along extended, often branching and interlocking pathways. Whatever the selective principle, it must contain or elaborate the blueprint for all the metabolic pathways the particular cell exhibits and in addition has to be partially specific for every cell type in the organism! Moreover, what may be called the "overall strategy of development" of an organism must ultimately reside in a coordination of these selective measures in the various parts of the body. As they change they must do so in step and in close coordination with one another. Any mistake, such as the absence of one key enzyme or the appearance of one inappropriate enzyme can be fatal to a cell and thus to the organism.

Correlation Within the Genome. Recent advances in micrurgy of cells with giant chromosomes allow for the removal of cell parts and the dissection and recombination of parts in various ways without impairing the ability of the chromosomes to puff (Kroeger, 1966a). In a series of such experiments, answers to the following questions were sought. Which part of the cell is dispensable and which part is necessary for the formation of those coherent patterns that occur during development and which may, in the sense of the above discussion, be termed "strategic patterns"? At what site or by an interaction of which parts of the cell is this "strategy" elaborated? Is it impressed upon the genome by the cytoplasm or is the coordination a purely nuclear process, arising, e.g., by an interaction of the chromosomal sites? Do cytoplasm and genome cooperate in activating any single site on the chromosomes?

The results of these experiments can be summarized as follows. (1) Transplantation of cytoplasm from Malpighian tubules or nerve tissue into the cytoplasm of salivary gland cells of *Chironomus thummi* does not alter the puffing pattern in the host cell, even if the amount of cytoplasm transferred is so large that it constitutes two thirds of the recipient cell. Such cells with "hybridized cytoplasm" shift back to the more juvenile pattern in the process of "rollback" or "rejuvenation" described previously. No influence of the foreign cytoplasm was apparent, and it was concluded that tissue-specific puff patterns are not elicited by the cytoplasm (Kroeger, unpublished results).

(2) Isolated salivary gland nuclei of the sciarid *Bradysia mycorum* also underwent a "rollback" of their puffing pattern, demonstrating that a cell nucleus devoid of all observable cytoplasm can form a more juvenile pattern. This rules out the cytoplasm as the director and coordinator of at least the rollback puffing pattern in explanted cells (Rey, 1963; see also Lezzi, 1966) and implies that the elaboration of "strategy" is a purely nuclear process. (3) A possible interaction of chromosomal sites as a means for correlating their activities was tested by removal of chromosomes or chromosome parts from explanted salivary gland cells. In the remaining chromosomes or chromosome fragments (often comprising less than one fourth of the full set) those sites again formed the typical puffs that would have appeared as a part of the overall pattern induced by "rollback"; the absence of other parts of the pattern did not influence their reaction. It was concluded that the formation of "strategic" patterns does not involve a mutual interaction of chromosomal sites; at least over relatively long distances in the chromosome set. Neighboring loci could not be separated, and their possible interaction cannot be tested by this technique. In fact, such interactions of neighboring chromosomal sites probably do exist but are irrelevant to the present discussion since the coordinative principle controlling activities all over the genome must be in a position to bridge any distance in the nucleus (Kroeger, 1963 and 1964).

These experiments were performed before the controlling function of the electrolyte milieu had been detected and created a rather puzzling situation. The genomic activity patterns did not seem to be elicited by the cytoplasm. Control seemed to reside in the nucleus, and yet patterns were not formed by a mutual interaction between subunits of the pattern. Only one possibility remained. There exists in the nuclear sap a factor to which these chromosomal sites react independently. This factor serves as an activator and coordinator and changes spontaneously in explanted cells. The subsequent finding that this "factor" consists of the electrolyte milieu and that the shift induced by explantation is a rise in the Na^+ titer resolved the puzzling situation and explained the above results. However, they do retain interest since they provide a line of evidence independent of data on the ionic regulation of genomic activities. Therefore, in reading the following discussion of the principles of intragenomic integration it should be kept in mind that the concept proposed rests on two independent lines of evidence.

It is clear that the system of gene regulation as described in this chapter differs from that described for bacteria by Jacob and Monod (1963). Although the possible separation of "operator" and "structural" elements shows a close resemblance, the coordination of genomic and cytoplasmic events and intragenomic coordination are based on entirely different principles. By means of a structural relationship to a precursor molecule, a metabolite can in the bacterial system incite the production of an enzyme specifically synthesized to react with it. One could say that the genome delivers specific units of information singly and "upon demand" of the cytoplasm.

In a system where small, unspecific, and ubiquitous molecules serve to transfer messages to the genome, an entirely different situation must prevail. Structural relationships of the type demonstrated for bacteria are ruled out as a means of transferring specific messages from the cytoplasm to the genome, and no direct feedback relationships can exist between single metabolic events (except those affecting transport and permeabilities) and specific genetic units. Instead, in response to suitable changes in the electrolyte milieu the genome is programmed to deliver enzyme recipes according to a predetermined plan, irrespective of the presence or absence of suitable substrates. This "predetermined plan" is inherent in the electrolyte sensitivities of the DNA-histone associations along the chromosome. In other words, the regulatory units in the genome must be preset to respond to the electrolyte milieu in such a way that "strategic combinations" of enzymes appear in the cytoplasm. The enzymes that appear at the same time in the cytoplasm are coupled in their appearance since the regulatory units that code for them show identical reactions to certain electrolytes. If they show only a similar instead of an identical sensitivity, the respective enzymes will appear in a close yet specific sequence. To describe the situation with a technical analogy: the genome resembles a punch tape that as a whole can be played faster or slower, can be reversed or reset to repeat a sequence, and in which the pattern of punches contains at any moment a "strategy" ensuring a specific, predetermined coordination of the subprocesses that the tape is controlling.

Integration Within Cells and Within Tissues. If all loci within the genome were sensitive to one ion species only, any titer of this ion would activate a number of loci in the genome, and this combination would be rigidly fixed. However, since in reality several ion species (Na^+, K^+, Mg^{++} plus a number of unidentified, probably organic molecules) partake in the regulation of genomic activities, their respective titers might be manipulated more or less independently by the cell and could thus be thought to furnish the cell with a certain degree of freedom in the choice of information retrieval from the genome. On the other hand, this limited freedom imposes upon the cell the task of varying the relative concentrations of ions in the cell in such a way that the final consequences of their gene-activating action are coherent and integrated at the level of cytoplasmic biochemistry.

The Na^+/K^+ transport processes function in such a way that the extrusion of Na^+ is coupled with an accumulation of K^+ in a certain fixed ratio. As a consequence, the Na^+ titer is correlated with a particular K^+ titer. The combinations can vary drastically from one tissue to the next and may vary within limits in one tissue under special conditions, but the generally observed coupling of monovalent ion concentrations leads to a linkage of the Na^+- to the K^+- inducible puffs in fixed combinations.

As a rule, transport systems for molecules other than Na^+ and K^+ seem to be energetically linked to Na^+/K^+ transport but may otherwise function independently. In fact, it may be a typical effect of some hormones to couple or uncouple such secondary transport systems to the "sodium pump" or to one another.

The variation of intracellular concentrations by movement of ions *within* the cell may be dependent upon, and therefore coupled to, other transport functions and cellular events. For instance, the transport of amino acids across the nuclear membrane is also Na^+ dependent (Allfrey, et al., 1961). It is clear that any relationships between the various forces regulating the ultimate composition of the intranuclear solute must by necessity also serve to link the activities of various chromosomal loci in the genome. However, very little information on relationships of this sort is available.

Loewenstein and Kanno (1963) have shown by electrical resistance and permeability measurements that in some tissues the neighboring cells have high permeability barriers against the surrounding medium but only 1/10,000 as much between one cell and another. The diffusion resistance is so low, in fact, that it hardly differs from that of the cytoplasm. This implies that small molecules can easily diffuse from one cell into the next and that the internal solute of large groups of cells or of a tissue forms a common pool. The authors call this phenomenon "ionic coupling."

"Ionic coupling" between adjacent cells is labile and easily disrupted by various agents, particularly if the junctional membrane is deprived of Ca^{++} by versene treatment (Nakas et al., 1966). Ionic coupling and its qualitative and quantitative control is of unusual interest to the student of gene activity since it affords the possibility of ion distribution patterns and consequently gene activation patterns. Loewenstein and Kanno (1964) suggest: "The free communication between cells may also be at the root of a number of propagated phenomena known to occur in epithelia upon injury, inflammation, infection, etc."

If, in a growing blastema, at one or more strategic points the common ionic pool is drained (for instance, by a locally increased permeability), gradients and other patterns of ionic distribution should develop in the tissue, which will eventually be translated into patterns of gene activities. When one examines what properties such ion distribution patterns might have, it becomes apparent that within limits they should be buffered against short-term, local disturbances in a way that might be described as self-regulatory in nature. If free communication between the cells was impaired experimentally, new patterns, subcenters, duplications, and multiplications of pattern elements should follow. In short, such ion distribution patterns can be expected to display features characteristic of phenomena usually categorized under the term "morphogenetic field." One can envisage that this term might soon be replaced by an expression like "field of gene activity regulation." If ions are the vehicles of this activity control, the perennial problems of regulative development, pattern formation, and related phenomena may be explained in physical and chemical terms.

CONCLUSIONS

To the questions posed in the introduction to this chapter, the following answers have been elaborated:

1. The genome continuously releases a flow of messenger (RNA) molecules that determine many and possibly all functional capacities of a cell.
2. Metamorphosis proceeds by an alteration in the composition of this flow.
3. This alteration in part is instigated by ecdysone; ecdysone and possibly also juvenile hormone alter the intranuclear electrolyte balance.
4. The genome is exquisitely sensitive to alterations in the electrolyte composition of the nuclear sap, probably because a single ionic species locally and specifically interferes with the repressive activity of histones.

5. Development appears as a progressive liberation of the intranuclear milieu from its surroundings; as a consequence, groups of genes become sequentially activated and inactivated.

Some of the prime questions as yet unanswered are as follows. What is the basis of the different reactivity of chromosome segments in the tissues? How do the hormones alter the intracellular electrolyte milieu? What other mechanisms for the regulation of gene activities might exist? How widespread is the control mechanism described in this chapter in both the animal and plant kingdoms? How do other insect hormones, (bursicon, brain hormone, and so forth,) act? (see Chapter 3 this volume).

ACKNOWLEDGMENT

Part of the research described in this chapter was aided by grants from the Schweizerischer Nationalfonds zur Förderung der wissenschaftlichen Forschung and by the Damon Runyon Memorial Fund for Cancer Research (DRG-68).

REFERENCES

Akinrimisi, E. O., J. Bonner, and P. O. P. Ts'o. 1965. Binding of basic proteins to DNA. J. Mol. Biol., 11:128–136.
Allfrey, V. G., R. Meudt, J. W. Hopkins, and A. E. Mirsky. 1961. Na-dependent "transport" reactions in the cell nucleus and their role in protein and nucleic acid synthesis. Proc. Nat. Acad. Sci. USA, 47:907–932.
Balbiani, E. G. 1881. Sur la structure du noyau des cellules salivaires chez les larves de *Chironomus*. Zool. Anz., 4:637–641.
Baudisch, W. 1963. Chemisch-physiologische Untersuchungen an den Speicheldrüsen von *Acricotopus lucidus. In* 1000 Jahre landwirtschaftliche Institute der Universität Halle.
Becker, H. J. 1959. Die Puffs der Speicheldrüsenchromosomen von *Drosophila melanogaster*. I. Mitteilung. Beobachtungen

zum Verhalten des Puffmusters im Normalstamm und bei zwei Mutanten, giant and lethal-giant-larvae. Chromosoma, 10:654–678.

_____. 1962. Die Puffs der Speicheldrüsenchromosomen von *Drosophila melanogaster*. II. Mitteilung. Die Auslösung der Puffbildung, ihre Spezifität und ihre Beziehung zur Funktion der Ringdrüse. Chromosoma, 13:341–384.

Beermann, W. 1961. Ein Balbiani-Ring als Locus einer Speicheldrüsen-Mutation. Chromosoma, 12:1–25.

_____. 1962. Riesenchromosomen. Protoplasmatologia, 6:1–161.

_____. 1963. Structure and function of interphase chromosomes. Proc. Intern. Congr. Genet., XI, The Hague, 2:374–384.

_____, and U. Clever, 1964. Chromosome puffs. Sci. Amer., 210: 50–58.

Berendes, H. D. 1965. Salivary gland function and chromosomal puffing patterns in *Drosophila hydei*. Chromosoma, 17:35–77.

_____. 1966. Gene activities in the malpighian tubules of *Drosophila hydei* at different developmental stages. J. Exp. Zool., 162:209–217.

Breuer, M. E., and Pavan, C. 1955. Behavior of polytene chromosomes of *Rhynchosciara angelae* at different stages of larval development. Chromosoma, 7:371–386.

Busch, H. 1965. Histones and Other Nuclear Proteins, New York, Academic Press.

Clever, U. 1961. Genaktivitäten in den Riesenchromosomen von *Chironomus tentans* und ihre Beziehungen zur Entwicklung. I. Genaktivierung durch Ecdyson. Chromosoma, 12:607–675.

_____. 1962. Genaktivitäten in den Riesenchromosomen von *Chironomus tentans* und ihre Beziehung zur Entwicklung. II. Das Verhalten der Puffs während des letzten Larvenstadiums und der Puppenhäutung. Chromosoma, 13:385–436.

_____. 1963a. Genaktivitäten in den Riesenchromosomen von *Chironomus tentans* und ihre Beziehung zur Entwicklung. IV. Das Verhalten der Puffs in der Larvenhäutung. Chromosoma, 14:651–675.

_____. 1963b. Von der Ecdysonkonzentration abhängige Genaktivitätsmuster in den Speicheldrüsenchromosomen von *Chironomus tentans*. Develop. Biol., 6:73–98.

_____. 1964. Actinomycin and puromycin: Effect on sequential gene activation by ecdyson. Science, 146:794–795.

_____. 1965. Puffing changes in incubated and in ecdysone treated *Chironomus tentans* salivary glands. Chromosoma, 17:309–322.

Edström, J. E., and W. Beermann. 1962. The base composition

of nucleic acids in chromosomes, puffs, nucleoli, and cytoplasm of *Chironomus* salivary gland cells. J. Cell Biol., 14:371–379.

Heims, A. 1956. Über die Kutikulamuster der Wachsmotte *Galleria mellonella*. Roux. Arch. Entwicklungsmech., 148.538–568.

Ito, S., and W. R. Loewenstein. 1965. Permeability of a nuclear membrane: Changes during normal development and changes induced by growth hormone. Science, 150:909–910.

Jacob, F., and J. Monod. 1961. Genetic regulatory mechanisms in the synthesis of proteins. J. Mol. Biol., 3:318–336.

Kroeger, H. 1963a. Chemical nature of the system controlling gene activities in insect cells. Nature, 200:1234–1235.

_____. 1963b. Experiments on the extranuclear control of gene activity in dipteran polytene chromosomes. J. Cell. Comp. Physiol., 62(1):45–59.

_____. 1964. Zellphysiologische Mechanismen bei der Regulation von Genaktivitäten in den Riesenchromosomen von *Chironomus thummi*. Chromosoma, 15:36–70.

_____. 1966a. Micrurgy on cells with polytene chromosomes. *In* Prescott, D. M., Methods in Cell Physiology, vol. II, New York, Academic Press.

_____. 1966b. Potentialdifferenz und puff-Muster. Elektrophysiologische und cytologische Untersuchungen an den Speicheldrüssen von *Chironomus thummi*. Exp. Cell. Res., 41:64–80.

_____. 1967a. Insect hormones and gene activity, in press.

_____. 1967b. Hormones, ion balances and gene activity in dipteran chromosomes. Mem. Soc. Endocr., 15:55–66.

_____, and M. Lezzi. 1966. Regulation of gene action in insect development. Ann. Rev. Entom., 11:1–22.

Laufer, H. 1963. Hormones and the development of insects. Proc. Intern. Congr. Zool., XVI, Wash., 4:215–220.

_____, and Y. Nakase. 1965. Salivary gland secretion and its relation to chromosomal puffing in the dipteran, *Chironomus thummi*. Proc. Nat. Acad. Sci. USA, 53:511–516.

_____, Y. Nakase, and J. Vanderberg. 1964. Developmental studies of the dipteran salivary gland. I. The effects of actinomycin D on larval development, enzyme activity and chromosomal differentiation in *Chironomus thummi*. Develop. Biol., 9:367–384.

Lezzi, M. 1966. Induktion eines Ecdyson-aktivierbaren puff in isolierten Zellkernen von *Chironomus* durch KCl. Exp. Cell. Res., 43:571–577.

_____. 1967. RNS- und Protein-Synthese in puffs isolierter Speicheldrüsenchromosomen von *Chironomus*. Chromosoma, 21: 72–88.

_____, and H. Kroeger. 1966. Aufnahme von Na^{22} in die Zellkerne der Speicheldrüsen von *Chironomus thummi* Z. Naturforsch., 21b:274–277.

Loewenstein, W. R., and Y. Kanno. 1963. Some electrical properties of a nuclear membrane examined with a microelectrode. J. Gen. Physiol., 46:1123–1140.

_____. 1964. Studies on an epithelial (gland) cell junction. I. Modifications of surface membrane permeability. J. Cell Biol., 22:565–586.

Nakas, M., S. Higashino, and W. R. Loewenstein. 1966. Uncoupling of an epithelial cell membrane junction by calcium-ion removal. Science, 151:89–91.

Panitz, R. 1964. Hormonkontrollierte Genaktivitäten in den Riesenchromosomen von *Acricotopus lucidus*. Biol. Zentralbl., 83:197–230.

Pelling, C. 1964. Ribonucleinsäure-Synthese der Riesenchromosomen. Autoradiographische Untersuchungen an *Chironomus tentans*. Chromosoma, 15:71–122.

Rasmussen, H., and H. F. DeLuca. 1963. Calcium homeostasis. Ergebn. Physiol., 53:108–173.

Rey, V. 1963. Das Puffmuster isolierter Kerne von *Bradysia mycorum* Frey. Diploma thesis. Eidgen. Techn. Hochschule, Zürich, 1–29.

Ritossa, F. 1962. Attivita sintetiche al livello dei puffs in *Drosophila busckii*. Atti A. G. I., 7:147–156.

Robert, M., and H. Kroeger. 1965. Lokalisation zusätzlicher RNS-Synthese in Trypsin-behandelten Riesenchromosomen von *Chironomus thummi*. Experientia, 21:326.

Rudkin, G. T. 1962. Nucleic acid metabolism in giant chromosomes of *Drosophila melanogaster*. Ann. Histochim., Suppl., 2:77–84.

_____, and S. L. Corlette. 1957. Disproportionate synthesis of DNA in a polytene chromosome region. Proc. Nat. Acad. Sci. USA, 43:964–968.

Schin, K. S., and U. Clever. 1965. Lysosomal and free acid phosphatase in salivary glands of *Chironomus tentans*. Science, 150:1053–1055.

Schurin, M. F. 1959. Localized cytochemical and submicroscopic differentiations in *Drosophila virilis* salivary gland chromosomes. Genetics, 44:534.

Sekeris, C. E., P. P. Dukes, and W. Schmid. 1965. Wirkung von Ecdyson auf Epidermiszellkerne von *Calliphora*-Larven in vitro. Hoppe Seylers Z. Physiol. Chem., 341:152–154.

———, and. N. Lang. 1964. Induction of DOPA-decarboxylase activity by insect messenger RNA in an in vitro amino acid incorporating system from rat liver. Life Sci., 3:625–631.

Shappirio, D. G., and W. R. Harvey. 1965. The injury metabolism of the cecropia silkworm. II. Injury-induced alterations in oxydative enzyme systems and respiratory metabolism of the pupal wing epidermis. J. Ins. Physiol., 11:305–327.

Siebert, G., and G. B. Humphrey. 1965. Enzymology of the nucleus. Advances Enzym., 27:239–288.

Skalka, A., A. V. Fowler, and J. Hurwitz. 1966. The effect of histones on the enzymatic synthesis of ribonucleic acid. J. Biol. Chem., 241:588–569.

Skou, J. C. 1965. Enzymatic basis for active transport of Na^+ and K^+ across cell membrane. Physiol. Rev., 45:596–617.

Slizynski, B. M. 1964. Functional changes in polytene chromosomes of Drosophila melanogaster. Cytologia, 29:330–336.

Swift, H. 1963. Cytochemical studies on nuclear fine structure. Exp. Cell Res., Suppl., 9:54–67.

Whitten, J. M. 1965. Differential deoxyribonucleic acid replication in the giant foot-pad cells of Sarcophaga bullata. Nature, 208:1019–1021.

Widnell, C. C. 1965. Characterization of the product of the RNA polymerase of isolated rat-liver nuclei. Biochem. J., 95:42p–43p.

part

two

VERTEBRATES

six

METAMORPHOSIS
IN LOWER CHORDATES

E. J. W. Barrington

Department of Zoology
The University
Nottingham, England

PROTOCHORDATA

Larval life, with its associated metamorphosis, is found in the Subphylum Urochordata as an integral and essential stage in the life history of sessile animals; it contributes to their dispersal and provides for the selection of appropriate habitats, as it does in other invertebrate groups (Barrington, 1965 and

1967). The association of urochordate metamorphosis with sessile life is clearly shown by its distribution in this subphylum, for it is particularly (although not quite universally) characteristic of the ascidians, whereas its importance is diminished in the pelagic forms that were almost certainly derived from them. A larval phase, although a nonmotile one, is still present in doliolids, but it is no longer found at all in *Pyrosoma* and the salps. Its persistence in the Larvacea is no exception to the generalization, for it is a consequence of the undoubted neoteny of these animals.

Cephalochordata

A larva stage is also found in the Subphylum Cephalochordata (Barrington, 1965), with a strikingly asymmetrical organization that has been thought to be related to its specialized mode of ciliary feeding (Bone, 1958). The need for a pelagic larva in this group can be readily understood, for the adults, despite their well-developed locomotor mechanism, are bottom-dwelling forms that have never fully exploited the potentialities of independent movement. Instead, they retain, or have redeveloped, a semisessile mode of life that is adaptively related to their complex ciliary feeding mechanism.

The cephalochordates also provide another example of neoteny. In certain circumstances the life of the larva may be prolonged into the giant amphioxides stage, which may possess as many as 34 pairs of branchial clefts (in contrast to the normal larval range of 14 to 25) and may also develop gonads. The phenomenon is of great interest, in view of the attractive suggestion that neoteny may have contributed to the derivation of vertebrates from a protochordate ancestry (Garstang, 1929). The causal factors involved in this particular instance are unknown, but Wickstead (1964) has suggested that metamorphosis in cephalochordates may be evoked by contact with the sea bottom and that the amphioxides stage may be a consequence of the contact being delayed as a result of the larva being carried into deep water. The suggestion is plausible, for we shall see abundant evidence of the importance of the sea bottom as a factor in evoking metamorphosis both in ascidians and in teleosts. Too little is known, however, about cephalochordate metamorphosis to justify further discussion in the present account, which will therefore be devoted, as far as protochordates are concerned, to an examination of metamorphosis in ascidians.

Ascidians

Any consideration of form and function in ascidians leads sooner or later to an attempt at comparison with vertebrate organization. This is an inevitable consequence of the close phylogenetic relationship between the protochordates, comprising the two subphyla metioned above, and the Subphylum Vertebrata. While dealing with ascidian metamorphosis, it is important to bear in mind that this process takes place in animals of a relatively simple organization and that it is initiated at a very early stage in their individual development. It would thus seem possible for the regulation of their metamorphic changes to demand little more physiological specialization than would be required for the normal regulation of the morphogenetic processes of early development in a direct life cycle. In contrast to this, the larvae of vertebrates may reach advanced stages of development, with a general level of organization much more complex than that of an ascidian larva, and after a very much longer period of independent life. It follows that comparisons of metamorphic processes in these two groups must be made with caution. They may well be productive, but only if care is taken not to read the complexity of the one group into the relative simplicity of the other.

Organization of the Ascidian Larva

The ascidian larva is a dual organism in which there is a sharp demarcation between the temporary organs of the larva and the rudiments of the permanent organs of the adult (Berrill, 1935 and 1947; Grave, 1944). It may be thought of as containing two quite distinct action systems, one of which has a full but brief period of functioning during the larval phase only, whereas the other is maintained in a suppressed condition until the beginning of metamorphosis. Both of these action systems begin their embryonic development together (Fig. 1), so they share a common phase of development up to and including gastrulation. From that point onward, however, two independent developmental mechanisms are operating side by side, the development of the larval structures proceeding virtually independently of that of the permanent ascidian organization.

The larval action system is concerned entirely with locomotion and with habitat selection, for the length of the larval period, although variable, is always short, and the organism does not feed. Its cells are well provided with yolk granules, and

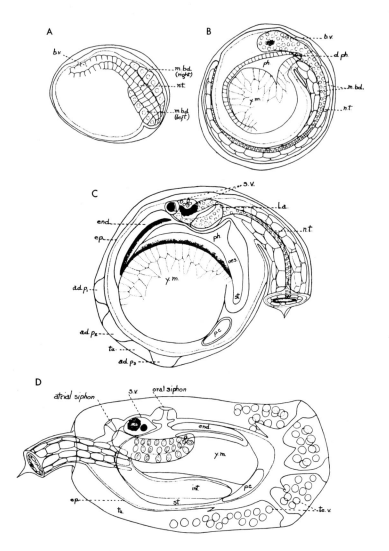

FIG. 1. Development of *Amaroucium constellatum*. A: Embryo before closure of neural folds. × 160. B: Early larva, beginning of differentiation of digestive and nervous systems. × 160. C: Lateral view of larva, with incipient adhesive papillae. × 120. D: Larva at hatching. × 120. Abbreviations: ad.p. 1,2,3, adhesive papillae; b.v., cerebral vesicle (in B); d.ph., dorsal diverticulum of pharynx; end., endostyle; ep., epidermis; int., intestine; l.a., left atrium; int., intestine; m.bd., muscle band; n.t., neural tube; oes., oesophagus; p.c., pericardial cavity; ph., pharynx; st., rudiment of stomach and intestine (in C), stomach (in D); c.v., cerebral vesicle (in C); te.v., tu., tunic; y.m., yolk mass. From Scott (1946).

226

these are more than adequate to provide for its needs, particularly since it does not grow or undergo further differentiation once it has hatched. The rudiments of the endodermal alimentary tract are well-defined (Figs. 1, 4, and 8), but these, like the ectodermal and mesodermal derivatives that will contribute to adult organisation, remain in a stage of arrested development. The means by which development to the adult organization is arrested are unknown, but the inhibition is substantially complete. In the particular case of *Styela partita* it is said to be operative long before the larva hatches (Grave, 1944); in consequence, no change in the form or even the size of this larva takes place during its free-swimming phase, even though this phase, with a maximum extent of over four days, is one of the longest recorded in the group (Table 1). Grave and Nicoll (1939) suggested that metabolic specialization might be an important factor in

TABLE 1

LENGTH OF LIFE OF THE LARVAE OF VARIOUS SPECIES OF ASCIDIANS. IN *PHALLUSIA NIGRA* THE LENGTH OF LARVAL LIFE SHORTENS GREATLY AS THE BREEDING SEASON ADVANCES. FROM GRAVE (1944).

Styela partita	9–105 hours
Phallusia (Ascidia) nigra	5–48 hours
Polyandrocarpa tincta	2–36 hours
Botryllus schlosseri	20 min to 12 or more hours
Amaroucium pellucidum	30 min to 4 1/2 hours
Amaroucium constellatum	10–100 min
Molgula citrina	5 min or less to 2 1/2 hours

determining the inhibition, with the functional larval organs characterized by a higher rate of metabolism and perhaps also by different enzyme systems.

The tail of the larva (Berrill, 1947; Grave, 1944), which is covered by an epithelium composed of a single layer of cells, is largely occupied by the notochord; above this organ is the dorsal nerve cord, below it is a solid endodermal strand, and on either side of it is a band of muscle cells (Fig. 2). The notochord consists of a linear series of about 40 cells, arranged in single file. Each cell is packed with yolk granules, which are later broken down and utilized for nutrition. The outer walls of

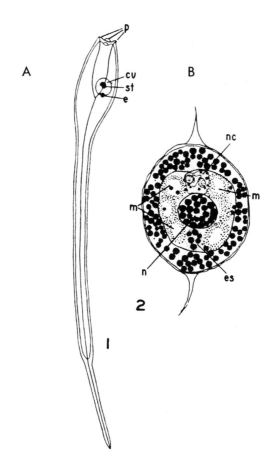

FIG. 2. The larva of *Styela (Cynthia) partita*. A: Camera outline of larva. Abbreviations: cv, cerebral vesicle; e, eye; p, papillae; st, statolith. B: Camera drawing of a transverse section of the tail; the large black dots are yolk granules. Abbreviations: es, endodermal strand; m, muscle bands; n, notochord; nc, nerve cord. From C. Grave (J. Morph., 75:176).

these cells fuse to form a continuous cylindrical covering. To this the structure owes the tensile strength that is an essential feature of the locomotor mechanism, but no doubt turgor also plays a part, for a large vacuole develops in each cell, and the cells themselves become pressed close together.

Each muscle band is composed of three parallel rows of large muscle cells. These cells number about 36 in smaller larvae, but in larger ones there may be 100 or more of them.

Each cell has a continuous cortical layer that surrounds an endoplasm containing a small nucleus and many yolk granules. Within the cortical layer are myofibrillae, which run as continuous fibrils down the length of the muscle bands, so that each band functions as a single contractile unit (Berrill, 1947). These fibrillae have been described as following a spiral course, but in the larva of *Boltenia villosa*, according to the electron microscope study of Cloney (1961a), this applies to only 28 of the muscle cells possessed by this larva, the fibrils being straight in the remainder.

Berrill (1935) has shown that the development of the larval action system differs from that of the future adult in that its cell division comes to a relatively early end. In general, all division ceases in the notochord and muscle after about one third of the embryonic period and in the neural tube after about one half or two thirds of that period. The history of these structures during the remainder of embryonic life consists of cell differentiation, together with swelling of the cells of the notochord. Because of this pattern of development, the cell numbers in these larval structures tend to be constant. Differences between larvae are therefore often a matter of cell size, dependent upon the initial egg volume and the amount of stored yolk, although the variation in the numbers of muscle cells shows that this is not always so. In contrast to this general situation, those tissues that are to contribute to adult organization, and more particularly the mesenchymal and endodermal derivatives, continue to divide throughout the whole embryonic period. Apart from the temporary inhibition of development during larval life, the development of these structures is therefore continuous with the normal growth processes of the young adult. In effect, cell division continues in them until a minimum cell size is reached, so that here, in contrast to the history of the larval action system, it is the number of the cells, and not their size, that varies with the initial volume of the egg. The full number and minimum size of the cells of the adult action system is not reached until after the completion of metamorphosis.

The Onset of Metamorphosis in the Ascidian Larva

The length of life of the ascidian larva is short, but at the same time it varies a great deal from one species to another. Grave's (1944) data (Table 1) show a minimum of 5 min or less in *Molgula citrina* to a maximum of 105 hours in *Styela partita*. These differences illustrate his contention that the larvae show a greater range of interspecific differences in organization than do the adults. His data further show that the length of larval life ranges widely even within a single species. This information, obtained from larvae that had hatched in laboratory conditions, may reflect differences in the immediate past history or physiological condition of their parents. Nevertheless, the facts suggest that the onset of metamorphosis cannot be determined solely by some form of internal clock, but that the sensitivity of the larvae to their environment may also play a part. This is not surprising; such sensitivity is an essential requisite for organisms responsible for habitat selection, and it is, of course, a well-known property of various types of invertebrate larvae.

Berrill (1947) suggests that within this range of duration there may be distinguished two main types of ascidian larvae. One type comprises those that have a short period of free-swimming life, amounting to 2 to 3 hours or less; they belong to species that are typically viviparous, with large eggs and with a long period of embryonic development. In these larvae the development of the trunk, with its future adult action system, is relatively far advanced. An extreme example of this is the larva of *Diplosoma,* in which the heart is already beating, and the organization of the young ascidian is complete in its essentials; indeed, the first bud is also present in a well-developed state. The second type comprises larvae with a long period of free-swimming life, commonly amounting to more than 12 hours; they arise from small eggs, produced mainly by oviparity, although in a few species they are of viviparous origin. In this type of larva the organization of the future ascidian is relatively far less advanced than it is in the first type.

The eye and the statocyst make important contributions to the larval action system (see Barrington, 1965). Initially the larvae are negatively geotactic. The first sign of approaching metamorphosis is often the appearance of a positive geotaxis, which in association with a negative phototaxis takes the larvae downward to sheltered areas and overhanging rock surfaces that are suitable for the modes of life of the adults. The behavior of the larvae is thus highly adaptive, and certain exceptions to the usual course of events serve to emphasize this. For example, in certain members of the family Molgulidae the free-swimming larval stage has been eliminated (Berrill, 1931 and 1955). The species concerned live on sand flats, which sustain high populations and are very uniform in character. In these circumstances there is no need for precise selection of habitat, which makes it easy to understand why the free-swimming larval stage should have been discarded.

The Progress of Metamorphosis

When the larva encounters a suitable substratum it passes rapidly into what has been called the disruptive phase of metamorphosis. An account of this has been provided by Scott (1952) in her description of the larva of *Amaroucium constellatum* (Fig. 4). The tadpoles already possess three papillae that are used for attachment in the early stage of metamorphosis. These produce a substantial and explosive discharge of secretion. The material released is similar to the layer of tunicin that has already been produced by the larval epithelium to form a thin covering to the body. The papillae differ merely in the intensity and timing of their secretory activity. They provide an illustration of the epidermal activity that, according to one current interpretation (see below), is of primary importance in the dynamics of metamorphosis. Further adhesion is provided by the secretion of additional tunicin by the ampullae, which now grow out from the mantle epithelium if they have not already done so. Their activity is another illustration of the importance of the epidermal activity at this stage.

This process of attachment is a normal accompaniment of metamorphosis, yet it is clearly not an essential element, for in some circumstances metamorphosis can proceed without any attachment having taken place at all. Cloney (1961b) has reported this to occur in *Boltenia villosa*. Normal metamorphosis in this species is usually preceded by fixation, but not invariably so. Moreover, when metamorphosis is artifically accelerated, in ways to be considered below, no attachment takes place at all, yet in all other observable respects the course of the transformation is quite normal.

The most striking external feature of normal metamorphosis in ascidians is the rapid reduction of the tail. This, together with the disappearance of the larval ganglion and receptors constitutes an abandonment of the larval action system. The tail of the larva of *Boltenia villosa* (Cloney, 1961b) stops twitching within 1 to 2 min of attachment, and then both the trunk and tail start to shorten (Fig. 3). The first sign of reduction is a rupture of the proximal end of the notochordal sheath; as a result of this the matrix and cells of the notochord start to flow out into the trunk. Meanwhile, the proximal muscle cells begin to become buckled and folded. These changes, together with the breakdown of the notochord, extend distally with great speed, with the result that after some 10 to 12 min the caudal tissues have become transformed into a cone-shaped mass lying immediately posterior to the tissues of the trunk. The cells of the epidermis also with-

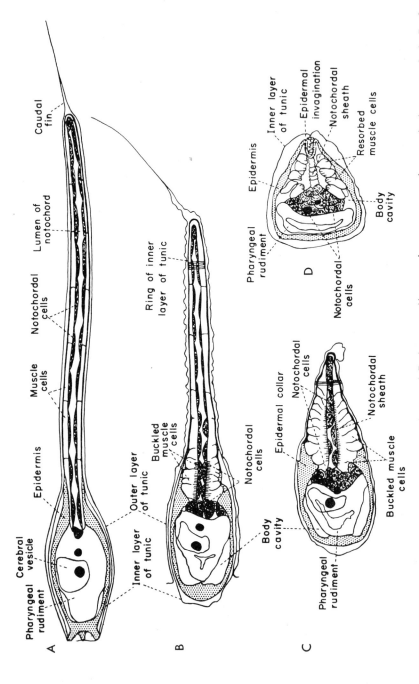

FIG. 3. Dorsal views illustrating the larva of *Boltenia villosa* and its metamorphosis. A: Larva. × 180. B: 2 to 3 min after the beginning of metamorphosis. × 180. C: 10 to 12 min after beginning of metamorphosis. × 180. D: 29 to 30 min after beginning of metamorphosis. From Cloney (1961b).

draw into the trunk region, temporarily forming a collarlike structure as they accumulate around the base of the tail.

The breakdown of the larval action system is accompanied by development and reorganization of the trunk. Scott (1952) has described this aspect in her account of *Amaroucium constellatum* (Fig. 4). The beginning of the reorganization of the internal organs is marked by a strong contraction of the trunk region of the larva. The digestive loop of the future alimentary tract, the endostyle, the mass of reserve yolk, and the heart rudiment now rotate through an arc of 90°, these changes having no effect on nutrition because the organism has not yet started to feed. Mitoses are visible in these tissues, for the movements that are imposed upon them by external contraction are amplified by their own growth and extension. In particular, the pharynx elongates, and four rows of gill clefts now come into view.

So rapidly do these changes proceed that within 5 hours the main regions of the future ascidian body are defined. In *Amaroucium* these regions are three in number: a thorax, with gill clefts and a prominent endostyle; an abdomen, with an epicardium and a U-shaped alimentary tract; and a rudimentary postabdomen. Meanwhile, the tunic has been undergoing further differentiation; the primary tunic of the larva was a simple secretion of the mantle, but now mesenchyme cells move out into it from the body wall and start to produce long fibrils.

Early on the second day of the metamorphosis of *Amaroucium* food becomes visible within the body, while histological differentiation has taken place within the alimentary tract and secretory activity has been initiated. Metamorphosis may be considered to have ended by 48 hours after the fixation of the larva to the substratum. Up to now the caudal tissues may have remained unaltered in their contracted position at the posterior end of the trunk, but by this stage they will begin to undergo dedifferentiation and absorption. However, the behavior of the tail tissues in this animal is by no means uniform. Not only may the envelope of the tail remain attached to the trunk throughout its metamorphosis, and even into the third day, but sometimes the contents of the tail are not resorbed into the trunk at all. It is of particular interest to find that the metamorphic changes of the trunk are apparently quite unaffected by these variations. This indicates that the process of formation of the ascidian body is not regulated in any way by the changes undergone by the tail. Here, then, as in the free-swimming larval phase, the two components behave as independent systems.

This independence was well demonstrated by Scott (1954) in an experiment that showed the striking capacity of these animals

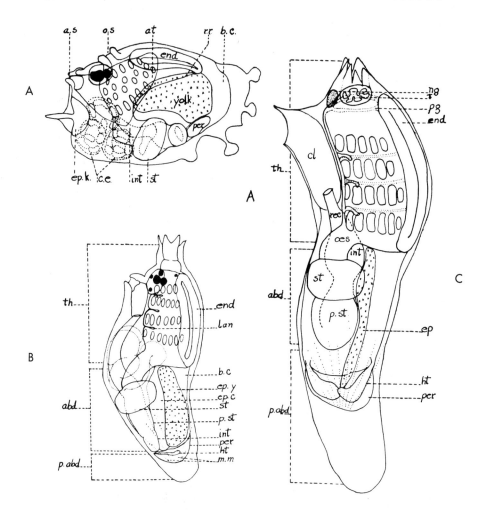

FIG. 4. Camera lucida drawings of the metamorphosis of *Amarou-cium constellatum*. A: At the beginning of metamorphosis. B: 12 hours after fixation. C: During the third day of development. Abbreviations: abd., abdomen; a.s., atrial siphon; at., atrium; b.c., body cavity; c.e., caudal elements; cl., cloacal chamber; end., endostyle; ep., epicardial tube; ep.c., epicardial cavity; ep.k., epithelial knob; ep.y., epicardial yolk; ht., heart; int., intestine; lan., languet; m.m., muscles of mantle; n.g., neural ganglion; oes., oesophagus; o.s., oral siphon; p.abd., post-abdomen; per., pericardium; p.g., peripharyngeal groove; p.st., post-stomach; rec., rectum; r.r., retropharyngeal raphe; st., stomach; th., thorax. From Scott (1952).

for dealing with adverse circumstances. She immersed larvae of *Amaroucium* in 0.001 M nitrogen mustard for 30 min. This treatment inhibited metamorphosis for two days; the tail and sensory structures disintegrated, while mitosis was suppressed in the future adult system and all dividing cells were killed, the yolk mass meanwhile being extruded. Nevertheless, organisms treated in this drastic way were able to recover. At first the adult organs started to differentiate without any cell proliferation; later, the living cells expelled the necrotic ones; after five days cell division was resumed, and the organisms began to feed and to grow.

These phenomena are not peculiar to *Amaroucium,* as is shown by Levine's (1962) observations on *Eudistoma ritteri.* In laboratory conditions the resorption of the tail in this species may proceed so slowly that all the other metamorphic changes may be completed while it is still present. On the other hand, animals in which the tail has been resorbed, but in which the reorientation of the body is only partly completed, can have further metamorphic change inhibited if they are immersed in a hypersaline medium. Such individuals, encrusted by salt crystals, have remained dormant from mid-October to mid-June. Placed in normal sea water at the end of this time, they eventually become transparent and complete their metamorphosis. Levine remarks that they looked 9 to 10 days old, whereas in terms of elapsed time their true age was nearer 9 to 10 months.

More than one attempt has been made to explain the mechanism of tail reduction. At one time the process was attributed to phagocytosis, but Conklin (1931) found no evidence for this in *Styela,* and later work has shown that it is not involved at all. Another suggestion was that the tail is forcibly contracted into the trunk by the action of the tail musculature, but this, too, has proved impossible to maintain. The changes in the form and orientation of the muscle cells (Berrill, 1947) would in themselves make it unlikely that any normal muscular contraction could be operative during this phase, and the possibility seems to be completely ruled out by electron microscope observations that reveal disarrangement of the myofibrillae (Cloney, 1961a). It must be concluded that the withdrawal of the tail is accompanied by functional breakdown of the muscular tissue, so that this tissue cannot itself be responsible for that withdrawal.

Berrill believed that the active agent might be shrinkage of the caudal epidermis. This interpretation, which was later supported by Scott (1952), has been greatly strengthened by recent observations of Cloney (1961a, and 1963, 1966). Using larvae of *Boltenia villosa* as experimental material, he studied the results of removing parts of the tail at different stages of metamorphosis. He found that a posterior fragment will not normally shorten in isolation if it has been excised after the beginning of metamorphosis, if it lies at a level posterior to the region that has already begun to shorten. This shows that the shortening process can be interrupted after it has been initiated. On the other hand, if the level of excision lies within the proximal region that has already begun to shorten, the excised fragment will shorten in isolation. This suggests that the mechanism of shortening reside within the tail tissues themselves; the tissues in which shortening has been initiated can thus continue the process in complete isolation from the trunk.

Further observations (Fig. 5) gave evidence that the epidermis may be the tissue that plays the active part in bringing about resorption of the tail in *Amaroucium constellatum* (Cloney, 1963). In this animal the process, which is normally completed within 6 min, is initiated by a rapid separation of the caudal epidermis from the underlying tissues, so that a fluid-filled subepidermal space appears underneath it. The nerve cord, notochord, and muscular tissues buckle and fold as they move toward the trunk. Meanwhile, the epidermis is also moving inward and is continuously thickening, so that it gives the impression of being under some sort of tension. Eventually it becomes concentrated to form a thick cap over the other tissues. The epidermis of an isolated distal end of a tail shows a similar proximally directed contraction and movement, while neither here nor in the stump do the muscle cells appear to be making any active contribution.

Cloney (1963) thus concludes that normal tail withdrawal is effected by active contraction of the epidermis, and he has found further support for this (1966) in an electron-micrographic study of the events of metamorphosis (Figs. 6 and 7). The principal cells (alpha cells) of the caudal epidermis contain filaments with a diameter of 50 to 70 A. Prior to contraction these are dispersed in the cytoplasm as a loose meshwork, but during contraction they become compacted and orientated in the axis of contraction. However, Cloney (1963) suggests that some form of proteolytic activity may also be involved, although there is as yet no direct evidence for the existence of any enzyme. The indirect evidence for its action is the loss of turgidity of the notochord, and the rounding up and vacuolation of its cells, for these changes could be accounted for theoretically as being a consequence of enzymatic weakening of intercellular binding. A concentration of mesenchymal cells, which Cloney (1961a) calls microblasts, can be seen at the base of the larval tail during the

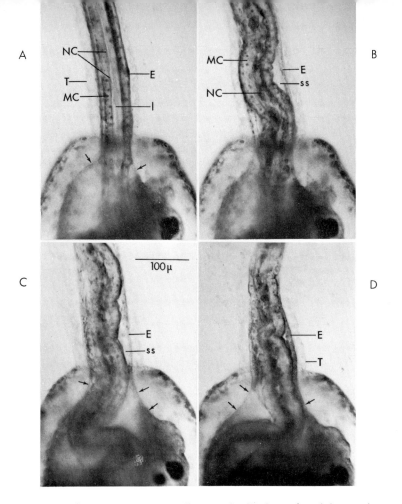

FIG. 5. *Amaroucium constellatum* A: Right side of living larva. The epidermis (E), muscle cells (MC), notochord cells (NC), notochordal lumen (I) and tunic (T) are visible. Arrows indicate the position of the epidermis within the trunk. B: Right side of the same specimen, about 1 min after the onset of tail resorption. Note the appearance of a space (ss) beneath the epidermis and the marked change in the arrangement of the notochord cells. The epidermis has separated from the surface of the muscle cells and has begun to thicken. The notochord-muscle-nerve cord complex has begun to fold as a unit without a breakdown of the binding force or cementing substances between the cells. C: Right side of another specimen about 2 min after the onset of tail resorption. The notochord-muscle-nerve cord complex has become more folded and has been partially forced into the posterior end of the trunk. The epidermis has become thicker. D: Right side of the same specimen about 3 min after the onset of tail resorption. More than half of the tail is coiled within the posterior end of the trunk. The epidermis is greatly thickened. From Cloney (1963).

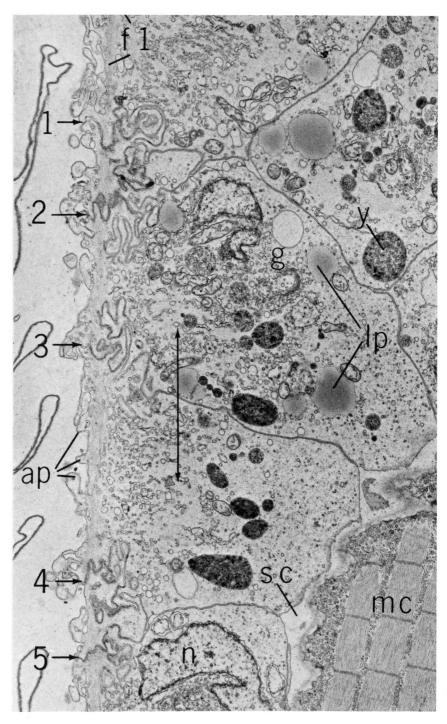

FIG. 6. (Legend on page 239)

free-swimming phase in *Boltenia villosa*. These cells could well be the source of such an enzyme, but again there is no direct evidence for this.

The Regulation of Metamorphosis in the Ascidian Larva

The elucidation of the factors that are active in the execution of ascidian metamorphosis is only one of the problems presented by this phenomenon; it is necessary also to establish what circumstances or stimuli are responsible for initiating the process. Some investigators, doubtless influenced by what we know of amphibian metamorphosis, have suggested that endocrine factors may be involved, but it is precisely here that it becomes so important to remember that the organization of urochordates is very much simpler than that of vertebrates. Extracts of both the pituitary and the thyroid glands of vertebrates have been reported to accelerate the onset of ascidian metamorphosis when added to the water in which the larvae are living, but a very wide range of substances also have this effect (Lynch, 1958 and 1961). Moreover, the results of using the hormonal preparations are not always consistent. For example, Bradway (1936) reported that a solution of crystalline thyroxine had no effect on the metamorphosis of *Clavelina huntsmani*, although she had previously obtained evidence (unpublished) that extracts of the whole thyroid had an accelerating action. Taken by themselves, such findings are certainly no evidence that either pituitary or thyroid secre-

---

FIG. 6. *Amaroucium constellatum.* Electron micrograph of a longitudinal section of a metamorphosing larva about 3 min after the onset of tail resorption. The surfaces of the epidermal (alpha) cells are beginning to form irregular protrusions (ap). Filaments are becoming increasingly compacted in the apical cytoplasm (fl). In this plane of section most of the filaments are parallel to the axis of contraction (arrow). The cell bodies of the alpha cells are beginning to elongate at right angles to the axis of contraction and to push into the subepidermal cavity (sc). Some filaments extend downward from the apex and spread out among organelles. Most of the organelles are located in the upper half of the cell. The basement membranes of the epidermis and muscle (mc) are fused into a single layer and both are attached to the sarcolemma. The basal surfaces of the alpha cells have no basement membrane. The apical contact zones of six cells are located at arrows 1 through 5. × 10,300. From Cloney (1966).

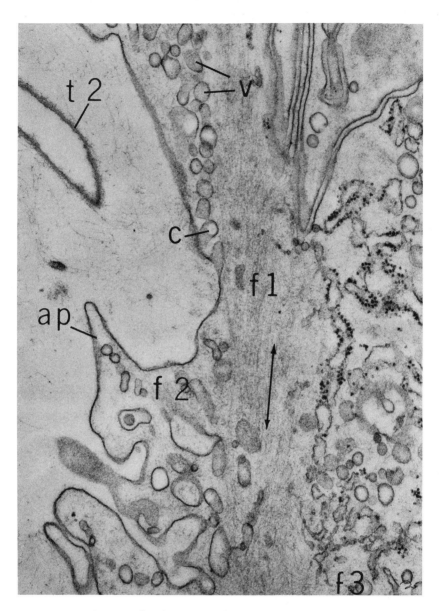

FIG. 7. Longitudinal section of the same stage as in Fig. 6, at a higher magnification. A high degree of filament orientation is apparent (f1). An arrow indicates the axis of contraction and filament orientation in the apical cytoplasm. Some elongate filaments extend downward into the cytoplasm among cytoplasmic organelles (f3). Other filaments (f2) are located in the basal region of developing apical protrusions (ap). The tunic (t2) folds as the tail is resorbed. × 49,000. From Cloney (1966).

tions are operative as specific regulatory agents within the larva; they must be critically examined in the light of the known structure of the larva.

The possibility of there being some thyroidlike action in metamorphosis is bound up with the relationship that is well-known to exist between the thyroid gland of vertebrates and the endostyle of urochordates, cephalochordates, and lamprey larvae. This relationship is clearly defined by the development of the thyroid gland of the adult lamprey out of part of the larval endostyle at metamorphosis. Assuming, then, the homology of the endostyle throughout these lower chordates (Barrington, 1965), it is reasonable to suppose that the thyroid gland evolved from the endostyle of protochordatelike ancestors. This sup-position has been fortified by the demonstration that iodine binding occurs in the protochordate endostyle, that thyroxine and triiodothyronine are present in amphioxus, and that thyroxine can be identified in extracts of the endostyle of *Ciona* (for references, see Barrington, 1965; Barrington and Thorpe, 1965). It seems probable that these substances must be of some physiological significance in the adult stages of these animals, but it has still to be shown what that significance is. As far as ascidian larvae are concerned, any suggestion that the thyroid hormones may regulate their metamorphosis encounters the difficulty that the endostyle is part of the adult action system and does not complete its differentiation until metamorphosis. Exactly how far it is differentiated in the larva is impossible to judge from published descriptions, for authors make little mention of it. In *Boltenia villosa*, e.g., the pharynx and digestive tract consist of no more than a simple cuboidal epithelium that remains relatively undifferentiated until after metamorphosis (Cloney, 1961a). In *Eudistoma ritteri*, on the other hand, the endostyle is troughlike in transverse section, with a thick base and broad arms and lined by tall columnar cells (Levine, 1962). It probably varies in its degree of differentiation, for we have seen this to be so of the adult action system as a whole; for this reason it certainly merits closer examination, particularly to see if any iodine binding can take place within it. So far, however, descriptions of larval organization provide no positive evidence that the endostyle can have any regulatory function in meta-morphosis.

One type of experiment that might be thought to have some bearing on this problem is the use of the antithyroid agents or goitrogens that inhibit the biosynthesis of the thyroid hormones. It is well known that amphibian tadpoles immersed in solutions of these substances are unable to metamorphose because of a consequential lack of thyroid secretion. Bell (1955) immersed the developing eggs of *Ciona* in a 0.001 percent solution of phenythiourea in sea water and found that the treatment produced a number of effects upon development. There was interference with melanization of the receptor structures of the cerebral vesicle, a result of inhibition of the tyrosinase required for melanin synthesis. Phenylthiourea also interfered with the normal elongation of the notochord, so that the larvae had short curved tails and could not swim. They remained in this form for five days, and some eventually attempted metamorphosis, but this was only successfully achieved in lower concentrations of the drug. Bell also used 2-thiouracil in concentrations ranging from saturation to one-tenth saturation. This allowed the production of normal tadpoles, but metamorphosis was delayed up to 12 days and was irregular in form, the chief disturbance being retardation of the absorption of the tail.

As was to be expected, normal melanization could be secured if the larvae from treated eggs were placed in normal sea water as soon as they hatched. If they were placed in certain other solutions there resulted some acceleration of tail absorption. One such solution was 0.2 percent phenylalanine; in this the tail was absorbed in 24 hours. Dihydroxyphenyl alanine, thyroxine, and tyrosine were also effective, but to an extent that diminished in that order; glycine and alanine had no effect at all.

There seems no reason for regarding these diverse effects of goitrogen treatment as indicating any participation of the thyroid hormones in normal metamorphosis, nor did Bell himself so interpret them; they could well be due to the generalized antioxidant action of goitrogens. In any case, contradictory results have been reported even in this comparatively straight-forward field of experimentation, which suggests that the larvae must be highly sensitive to the conditions in which such experiments are conducted. Thus, Lynch (1958) found that the larvae of *Amaroucium constellatum* could proceed through to the first stages of metamorphosis when they were immersed in 0.2 M thiourea, while Whittaker (1960) showed, in complete contrast to the findings of Bell, that phenylthiourea, administered in conditions apparently similar to those of the latter's experiments, had no effect upon the larval development of *Ciona*, apart from the inhibition of melanogenesis. The embryos of *Styela partita* and *Molgula manhattensis* developed equally well in the presence of the goitrogen. Metamorphosis began in the treated larvae of *Ciona* at the same time as in the controls, while those of *Styela* that were reared in phenylthiourea actually metamorphosed in advance of the control larvae. Some evidence of acceleration

was also obtained by Minganti (1957) in a study of the larvae
of *Phallusia mammillata;* these showed an acceleration of the
disruptive phase of metamorphosis, but they were unable to
complete their metamorphosis.

Even if it could be shown that an endogenous thyroidlike
secretion does have some specific action upon ascidian metamorphosis, it would still be necessary to show how its action was
released by stimulation from the external environment, for the
successful exercise of habitat selection by the larva makes it
clear that such stimulation must be involved. The thyroid gland
of vertebrates acts under the regulatory control of the pituitary
gland, this control being mediated through a feedback relationship between the two glands. As far as the urochordates are
concerned, it has been suggested that the pituitary gland may
be represented in the adults by the neural gland complex. There
is, however, little evidence that this structure has any specifically pituitarylike function, although it is arguable that it may
represent the type of sensory and glandular organ from which
the vertebrate pituitary gland could conceivably have evolved.
This problem has been considered in more detail elsewhere
(Barrington, 1965). It seems to be of little relevance in the
present context, since the neural gland complex, like the
endostyle, is part of the adult action system, and does not become fully differentiated until metamorphosis. Prior to that
moment it is represented only by rudiments of the neural gland
and its duct (the so-called "hypophysis"). The cerebral vesicle
of the larva disappears with the reduction of the larval action
system, and it is not until then that the neural gland complex
completes its differentiation; taking its origin, incidentally,
entirely from the neural tissue of the larva. Thus, it seems hardly
conceivable that any factor comparable specifically with vertebrate pituitary function could be active in the ascidian tadpole,
although it is certainly desirable that the structure of the larval
cerebral vesicle and of the neural gland rudiment should be
examined critically from this point of view. This is the more
important because, even if we are inclined to dismiss the
possibility of any pituitarylike activity, the cerebral vesicle
may well be concerned in some other way as a mediator between
the external environment and the metamorphic processes.

In the larva of *Styela partita* (Fig. 8), e.g., Grave (1944)
has shown that the duct (Fig. 8) that eventually runs from the
neural complex to the ciliated tubercle in the adult is already
identifiable, and has a tubular cavity. The future nerve ganglion
of the adult complex, however, is present only as a pear-shaped
rudiment to the left of the larval cerebral vesicle, while an

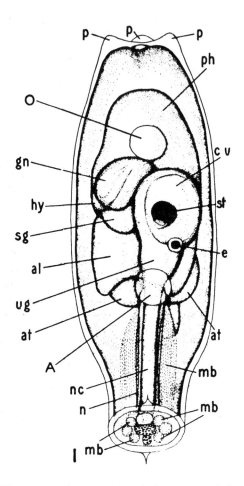

FIG. 8. The internal structure of the larva of *Styela partita*, reconstructed from whole mounts and serial sections. Abbreviations: A., trial siphon; O., oral siphon; al., alimentary canal; at., atrium; cv., cerebral vesicle; e., eye rudiment; gn., ganglion; hy., hypophysis; mb., muscle bands; n., notochord; nc., nerve cord; p., papilla; ph., pharynx; sg., subneural gland; st., statolith; vg., visceral ganglion. From Grave (J. Morph., 75:191).

oval-shaped mass of cells below this rudiment represents the future subneural gland of the adult. Grave's description of these rudiments does not suggest any signs of functional differentiation within them, but it would certainly be helpful if we had some further information on this aspect of ascidian development. What we already know, however, suggests that to visualize the regulation of ascidian metamorphosis in terms of the endocrine organization of vertebrates may be to ask for a more sophisticated mechanism than the ascidian larva is equipped to provide. A simpler mode of regulation would seem more appropriate, and the possibility of this is indicated by the results of some recent studies of the problem.

As we have suggested earlier, pituitary extracts, thyroid extracts, and goitrogens are not the only materials that have been tested on ascidian larvae. Almost every kind of biological reagent has been applied to them, in experiments that will not be recapitulated in detail here, as they have been thoroughly reviewed by Lynch (1961). The onset of metamorphosis has been accelerated by treatment of the larvae with hypotonic or hypertonic sea water, iodine, neutral red, methylene blue, Janus green, cysteine and certain other amino acids, strychnine, lactic acid, extracts of larvae and of adult tissues, urea, and certain metallic ions, including iron, zinc, and copper. Crowding of the larvae also accelerates metamorphosis (Grave, 1944), perhaps because of the accumulation of metabolic products. In contrast to these results, retardation of metamorphosis has been produced by various treatments, the reagents concerned including calcium-free sea water, urethane, other anesthetics, and excess of magnesium and of potassium.

Particular attention has been drawn to the possibility of copper being a specific activating agent in metamorphosis. This view was developed by Grave (1944) and Grave and Nicoll (1939), who, finding that an increase in the copper content of sea water tended to initiate precocious metamorphosis, suggested that this acceleration was a result of the copper poisoning the larval action system. Glaser and Anslow (1949) supported this argument with some additional evidence. For example, they showed among other things that copper was relatively abundant in the larvae of *Styela* and also in water that had been conditioned by the presence of these larvae and was known to be able to accelerate their metamorphosis. On this foundation they erected a theoretical interpretation, according to which the influence of copper was a consequence of it being adsorbed on to oxidizing enzymes; it was suggested that this would result either in activation or in poisoning, according to the number and position of the occupied sites.

Bertholf (1945), however, concluded that the effect of copper was not specific, and Whittaker (1964) has more recently found little support for this view of its supposed importance. We have referred above to his use of phenylthiourea (Whittaker, 1960).

The inhibiting action of this substance on tyrosinase is believed to be a result of it chelating the copper required as a cofactor for the enzyme. The absence of melanin in the larvae thus can be taken as evidence for the complete removal of copper from its metabolism. In later experiments (Whittaker, 1964), he therefore abolished melanogenesis in the larvae of *Styela* by phenylthiourea treatment and took this as evidence that no copper was available for them. There was no indication, however, of any inhibition of metamorphosis in these circumstances; in fact, the treated larvae metamorphosed several hours earlier than the controls. Thus, he concluded that copper could not be a significant factor in the process.

It would appear that further progress in the causal analysis of ascidian metamorphosis must depend upon relating external factors with the events that proceed within the metamorphosing larvae. At one time it was suggested that metabolic events might result in the accumulation of products up to a concentration at which they evoked the onset of metamorphosis. Berrill (1947) thought it possible that one factor in the initiation of metamorphosis might be an increasing acidity of the tissues, resulting from the accumulation of the toxic products of muscular activity. The possible importance of acidity was also argued, although from a different point of view, by Conklin (1931). He found that the onset of metamorphosis in *Styela* was accompanied by an increase in acidity, shown by a change in staining reaction with Delafield's hematoxylin from blue to reddish-brown. This, however, was not a consequence of muscle metabolism, for it occurred in abnormally developing eggs, which had not even segmented, although the nuclei had divided a number of times. The change in acidity occurred at a period of time corresponding to that at which normal metamorphosis occurred in control specimens, but it did not occur at all if nuclear division was suppressed in the experimental material. Therefore, while Conklin considered that metamorphosis might be initiated by chemical changes within the body, he suggested that these changes were in some way produced by the normal sequence of nuclear division. As Lynch (1961) points out, however, the evidence on this point is contradictory. It is true that metamorphosis can sometimes be accelerated if the swimming activity of the larvae is increased by exposing them to alternations of light and dark. Nevertheless, any suggestion that such activity is an essential prerequisite for the initiation of metamorphosis is negatived by the demonstration that metamorphosis can occur under experimental conditions in *Amaroucium* without any swimming having taken place at all.

Another possible factor to which importance has been attributed is the aging of the tissues. This concept is difficult to apply with any precision to a short-lived larva in which the length of free-swimming life is yet very variable. But as Berrill (1947) argues, the metamorphosing system is a combination of the young and actively proliferating tissues of the permanent ascidian with the fully-matured and nonproliferating tissues of the larva. In unfavorable conditions the mature and perhaps relatively senile cells might be more vulnerable, so that they would react by involution, while the young tissues of the future adult would develop at their expense. Such a concept has the attraction of transferring to the larva a process known to occur in adult ascidians, where, for example, the growing buds of *Botryllus* develop at the expense of the older buds that are resorbed.

As to what such unfavorable conditions might be, the accumulation of metabolites along the lines suggested above could be one possibility. Another is the exhaustion of the food reserves of the larval cells. Actually, this is probably less extensive than has sometimes been assumed, for Berrill (1947) noted that in *Distomus variolosus* (Fig. 9) the notochord cells were still crowded with yolk granules after tail resorption had been completed. This was true also of *Stolonica socialis*, but the yolk reserves of the muscle cells in this species were almost exhausted when metamorphosis began, while the epidermal cells had no reserves at all.

Arguing along these lines, Berrill (1947) has suggested that the immediate cause of tail resorption is a reduction of the tail epidermis, resulting from the exhaustion of its nutrient reserves. The accumulation of toxic metabolic products might be the activating factor, and from this point of view it is possible to regard the diverse effects of tissue extracts, metallic salts, and other substances as reflecting the differential susceptibility of aging cells to toxic influences. That some influence is affecting the larva as a whole, and not merely its tail, is apparent from the metamorphic changes that take place in the rudiments of the adult organs while the tail is being reduced. In some instances, indeed, there is an immediate and total reaction of the whole organism to the onset of metamorphosis. Thus, the first changes at the tip of the tail of *Dendrodoa (Styelopsis) grossularia* are accompanied also by an invasion of the larval tunic by migrating mesenchyme cells, while at the same time, the deep-red color of the tunic changes to a yellow-orange (see Berrill, 1950).

Such events are suggestive of some total chemical regulatory influence, of the type that in higher forms would be mediated by

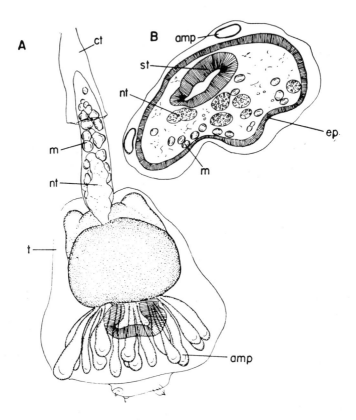

FIG. 9. Tail resorption in *Distomus variolosus*. A: Larva of *Distomus* with tail half absorbed and anterior circle of ampullae with tail cuticle in process of being sloughed and muscle and notochord tissue moving basally as disintegrating masses. B: Section through individual with tail completely absorbed, showing isolated muscle and notochord cells scattered through body cavity, and notochord cells still congested with yolk. Abbreviations: amp, ampulla; ct, tail cuticle; ep, epidermis; m, muscle cell; nt, notochord; st, stomach; t, tunic. From Berrill (J. Morph., 81:225).

hormones, but which here, as we have indicated, may be due to a less sophisticated mechanism. However, we have seen reasons for suspecting that active contraction of the epidermis is a causal factor in tail reduction (Cloney, 1963 and 1966). This implies more than a withdrawal of aging or exhausted tissue—it indicates rather that the withdrawal of the tail must be an active process. In this connection Cloney notes that potassium cyanide and sodium azide will inhibit the onset of metamorphosis, and that they will also slow down the rate of tail resorption if they are applied after the beginning of metamorphosis. This suggests the involvement of some aerobic oxidative process, since these substances are well-known inhibitors of cytochrome oxidase.

It will be obvious that we are not yet able to frame a consistent and comprehensive interpretation of the events of ascidian metamorphosis. What we have at present is a field that demands further research. What we also have, however, is a demonstration of the extent to which a developmental system can lend itself to adaptive modification, with its inherent sensitivity to disturbance brought under control and turned to the advantage of its sessile adult form.

CYCLOSTOMATA

Lampreys spawn in fresh water in the spring. Their larvae remain there for up to 5 ½ years (Hardisty, 1961), living during this time in muddy substrata, where they nourish themselves on detritus by a process of filter feeding. The metamorphosis of the larva is a relatively slow transformation that extends over a number of weeks during the summer. It brings about changes in the feeding mechanism and in the general organization of the body (particularly of the head), but biochemical changes are also involved. A new and quantitatively important plasma protein component appears in *Petromyzon marinus dorsatus* (Rall et al., 1961), while the adult of *P. planeri* has a hemoglobin different from that of the larva (Adinolfi and Chieffi, 1958; Manwell, 1960).

The subsequent history of the adults varies according to the species. Some remain in freshwater, to spawn in the following spring, an example being *Lampetra planeri*. Others, such as *L. fluviatilis* and *P. marinus*, pass down the rivers to feed and grow in estuaries and in the open sea but eventually migrate back to their freshwater spawning grounds. This return migration involves certain biochemical and physiological changes, apart from the obvious change in behavior. For example, the marine osmo-regulatory mechanism breaks down (Morris, 1960), and there is a transformation of the retinal pigment. The retina of *P. marinus* during the downstream migration contains vitamin A and the red rhodopsin; these are characteristic of marine fish. On the return migration the retina contains vitamin A_2 and the purple porphyropsin; these are characteristic of freshwater fish. Thus, these migrating lampreys may be considered to undergo two metamorphoses. The first is the larval trans-formation, preparing the migrating animal for its marine life, while the second is the transformation of a sexually maturing adult, preparing it for a return to the larval habitat (Wald, 1958).

Experimental analysis of these metamorphoses has been largely concentrated on the larval one. This, unlike the meta-morphosis of urochordates, is part of the life history of a pelagic group. In this respect it resembles that of teleosts, but there the resemblance ends, for the larval lamprey (the ammocoete larva) is in some respects a link between protochordates and vertebrates. Its feeding mechanism and general mode of life recall the habits of amphioxus, although they are provided for at a much higher level of organization, and with muscular action largely replacing the pharyngeal cilia of protochordates. These phylogenetic implications make it the more remarkable that there is no larval phase in the myxinoids (hagfish). This lack is presumably related in some way to the deep-sea life of the latter group, just as the presence of the larva in lampreys must be related to the conditions of life in certain types of freshwater streams. Indeed, it is possible that the penetration of these animals into freshwater was aided by the larval exploitation of the nutrient resources of muddy deposits.

Since lampreys and their larvae are truly vertebrates in their fundamental organization, it is natural to look to nervous and humoral factors as controlling agents in their metamorphosis. In contrast to conditions in ascidian larvae, some justification for postulating endocrine action can certainly be found in the existence in the larva of developing endocrine structures. The adenohypophysis and neurohypophysis are present, as is tissue that has been identified with reasonable assurance as chromaffin and adrenocortical tissue (Sterba, 1959); moreover, the endostyle, which gives rise to the thyroid gland at metamorphosis, is already binding iodine and forming thyroxine and triiodothyronine (for references, see Leloup and Fontaine, 1960; Barrington and Sage, 1963a).

Nevertheless, comparisons with the gnathostomes must still be made with caution. Not only is the lamprey larva itself of very primitive status, but the modern cyclostomes as a group are widely removed from the jawed vertebrates. Their primitively jawless condition is in itself an index of their isolated position within the vertebrate subphylum. Further, certain features of their organization, including their highly specialized branchial pouches and arches and their secondary development of a median nostril, show them to have had a long period of independent history (Jarvik, 1964). It is impossible to regard modern cyclostomes as in any sense ancestral to modern fish; in fact, they may well have been separated from the gnathostomes for as much as 600 million years. The implications of this phylogenetic situation are discussed in more detail elsewhere (Barrington, 1964); they are mentioned here because of their obvious bearing on the interpretation of metamorphic regulation in lampreys.

In any case, little is yet known about this regulation. Attempts to demonstrate an action of thyroid hormones, analogous with the action exerted by these in amphibians, have given only negative results (for references, see Pickford and Atz, 1957). It must be said, however, that these results can mean very little. The larval life of lampreys is a long one, and the metamorphosis is also prolonged. If any analogy can be drawn with the metamorphosis of amphibian tadpoles, it would lead us to expect the gradual deployment of precisely controlled interrelationships between increasing titers of thyroid hormones and developing sensitivity of the tissues that are to react to them (Etkin, 1964). Immersion of lamprey larvae of varying ages in arbitrarily selected concentrations of thyroxine, and for brief periods at that, is only too likely to give conditions wholly remote from those obtaining during natural metamorphosis. At this stage there is no useful purpose to be served in discussing this aspect any further.

However, it is noteworthy that Sterba and Schneider (1961) have evoked some metamorphic reactions in ammocoete larvae by immersing them for up to nine months in a 0.05 percent solution of potassium perchlorate. In these conditions two-year old larvae showed metamorphic changes in the form of the fins, in the development of guanophores in the skin, and in some advance in differentiation of the eyes, which normally remain in a condition of arrested development until metamorphosis. Potassium perchlorate is known to inhibit thyroidal biosynthesis, but it is not clear whether these responses were evoked by the lack of thyroid hormones or whether they were nonspecific results of the prolonged treatment.

Sterba (1955 and 1959) has also suggested the possibility of the involvement of adrenocortical secretion in the regulation of metamorphosis, for he found that this tissue showed marked hypertrophy in the larvae just prior to the onset of the transformation. This again is suggestive rather than conclusive, for it is always possible that the hypertrophy is itself one of the products of metamorphosis rather than a causal agent. His observations also suggested a possible involvement of the pituitary gland, for he found that injection of corticotropin could evoke the hypertrophy.

Involvement of the pituitary has also been suggested because of the results of experiments in which injection of exogenous thyrotropic hormone evoked destructive changes in the glandular tracts of the endostyle (Knowles, 1941; Olivereau, 1956). Since these tracts disappear at metamorphosis, while part of the remaining endostylar epithelium gives rise to the thyroid gland, it may seem plausible to regard such destruction as a sign of metamorphic response. Closer analysis of certain responses of the endostyle, however, has suggested that the destruction of the tracts is related in some way to hypersecretory activity in the endostyle (Barrington and Sage, 1963a and 1963b) and that goitrogen treatment can evoke this response not only in animals but also in those in which the pituitary has been completely destroyed by cautery (Barrington and Sage, 1966). This implies that the endostyle has a capacity for autonomous response and that it is not necessarily regulated by a thyrotropic feedback relationship with the pituitary, such as is found in gnathostomes. These results, of course, do not exclude the possibility that there may also be some degree of pituitary control of the organ nor that the pituitary may indeed exert some influence on metamorphosis. What they do clearly show, however, is that the physiological organization of the lamprey larva is no less complex than might have been expected of a truly vertebrate animal and that the causal analysis of its metamorphosis needs to be pursued with a more penetrating attack than it has yet received, and without the expectation that the mechanism will necessarily follow the gnathostome model.

TELEOSTEI

Metamorphosis in fish has been defined as a period during which marked changes occur in body proportion and body structures without any marked increase in length. This definition, however, is too narrow for our present purpose, for it excludes consideration of changes in function and in mode of life, which are important elements of the metamorphosis of teleosts (Barrington, 1961). It also excludes second metamorphosis. This is found, for example, in the sexually maturing eel, which undergoes changes that prepare it for moving back to its spawning grounds (D'Ancona, 1960; Wald, 1958). Thus, it will prove useful if we add to the above definition the following extension: Physiological changes, including changes in mode of behavior, may also take place during this period.

The Events of Metamorphosis in Teleosts

The classical expression of metamorphosis in teleosts is found in the transformation of the leptocephalus larva of the eel into the elver. Unfortunately, we know far less about this than could be wished, but at least it is clearly established that the transformation is physiological as well as morphological; this is to be expected because it results in a planktonic and marine existence being replaced by a free-swimming and predatory mode of life in freshwater. Changes in external proportions are conspicuous, for this metamorphosis is in part a crisis in growth (Bertin, 1956). There is marked loss in weight, which results from a loss of water and of food reserves; the water content falls from 93 percent of the total body weight to 80 percent, while there is a loss of 30 percent in dry weight. There is also a reduction in length of the body, but this is a result of shrinkage, permitted by the absence of ossification in the vertebral column.

Similar reduction occurs in other fish, an extreme example being found in *Albula vulpes*, where the transparent larva may shrink during metamorphosis to less than half of its original length (Rasquin, 1955). In this fish, and apparently also in the eel, much of the shrinkage results from the disappearance of a core of gelatinous material, which lies around the notochord in the larva and is used during metamorphosis as a source of food.

Other changes in the eel include the loss of the long and fragile larval teeth, a shortening of the intestine, accompanied by a forward displacement of the anus, and the development of pigment cells in the deep meningeal layer as well as in the skin. Respiration also increases, partly, perhaps, in correlation with the passage into a hypotonic medium, but also as a result of the physical activity expended in ascending rivers against the prevailing currents. The metamorphosis of the eel thus involves profound changes in form and function, yet it is no more than an extreme example of a phenomenon that is found in many other teleost species. Thus, *Pterothrissus gissu*, a clupeoid, develops through a compressed and transparent leptocephalid stage, with equal jaws and an anterior mouth. At metamorphosis the upper jaw grows relatively longer so that the mouth is directed ventrally; meanwhile, there is a general change to the adult form, with a development of pigmentation and with changes in the points of origin of the fins (Matsubara, 1942).

Clear documentation of the complexity of the morphological changes involved in teleostean metamorphosis have been provided by several authors. Kubota (1961), in an analysis of the metamorphosis of the conger eel *Conger myriaster*, applied relative-growth analysis to 15 body parts, taking the total length of the body as the standard, but found that the resulting curves showed peculiar shapes because the morphogenetic transformations were so complex. These transformations included shrinkage of the viscera, multiplication of muscle fibers, change of the form of the brain, the appearance of a stomach and gallbladder, the gradual disappearance of the pronephros, and the correlated appearance of the definitive mesonephric kidney.

Caldwell (1962a) has reported on the metamorphosis of *Pseudopriacanthus altus*, a marine benthic fish that lives mainly on a hard bottom. He distinguished several stages in the life history: larvae, which are pelagic; prejuveniles, which are initially pelagic, but which later migrate to the bottom; juveniles, which are fully metamorphosed, with a typically adult form; and adults, which are sexually mature. The eye provides a good example of the precision of control that has to be exerted over the growth of a particular organ during the metamorphosis. In general, the eyes of bottom-dwelling individuals of *Pseudopriacanthus* are relatively larger than are those of pelagic individuals of comparable size that have not yet started metamorphosis. This is because during metamorphosis there is a rapid and sudden increase in the relative size of eye as well as in its actual size. Once the relative size of the eye has reached its maximum, however, it maintains a rate of increase which is constant but is lower than its initial rate of increase. As a result, fish that have reached their maximum size may have eyes that are relatively smaller than the eyes of the pelagic young stages.

Another example of this is seen in a species of goatfish, *P. maculatus* (Caldwell, 1962b). Here there is an early offshore pelagic phase, which is different in appearance from the adult, the latter being adapted for bottom-dwelling life in inshore waters. Metamorphosis involves a change in pigmentation and the assumption of a more robust body form, while the scales, which are easily shed in the pelagic phase, become much more firmly fixed. Some parameters of growth are unaffected by the change in form of the body. The rate of increase of head length, e.g., is constant throughout development, as also is the relative rate of increase of postorbital head length relative to the length from snout to anal fin. Within the 50 to 60 mm range, however, which is the normal size range of metamorphosing fish, there is a sudden increase in body depth. This is a temporary phenomenon, the initial rate of increase in depth being resumed later.

These examples have all involved fish that undergo a marked change of habitat during their metamorphosis, but transformation no less complex may be undergone without any such change. This is well brought out in Ahlstrom and Counts' (1958) analysis of the life history of *Vinciguerria lucetia* (Fig. 10), a pelagic fish, 2 to $2\frac{1}{2}$ in. long, which is abundant in the eastern North Pacific. There is first a larval stage, threadlike in form and nearly colorless, which is regarded as lasting from hatching up to the first appearance of photophores. This is followed by a prometamorphic stage, with white photophores, and a midmetamorphic stage, in which there occur rapid changes in body proportions and a change in the shape of the eye from oval to round. Finally, there is a postmetamorphic stage, lasting until the pigmentation changes are completed, and leading on to the juvenile and sexually mature stages.

The changes that take place in the body proportions of this fish are considerable. There is a 20 percent increase in relative length of the head, an 80 percent increase in body depth, and an 80 percent increase in the diameter of the eye, in addition to the change in its shape. Changes are found also in other dimensions, such as the length of the intestine and the spatial relationships of the fins. Very little change in total length takes place during the metamorphosis (which is in accordance with the formal definition cited earlier), so that Ahlstrom and Counts were able to generalize the changes as a whole into a comprehensive statement: Three proportions increase relative to standard length (these being head length, eye diameter, and body depth), while three proportions decrease relative to standard length (these being the distances from the snout to the ventral fins, from the snout to the bases of the dorsal fins, and from the snout to the anus). These relationships, however, apply only to the phase of metamorphosis. The rate of growth of body parts remains the same during the juvenile and adult stages, but those three that show an increase in relative growth rate during metamorphosis retain this new rate subsequently, whereas those three that show a decrease during metamorphosis revert later to the rates of the larval period. The analysis thus is a striking illustration of the complexity of growth relationship involved in metamorphic change. We shall have to consider below how these relationships might be regulated.

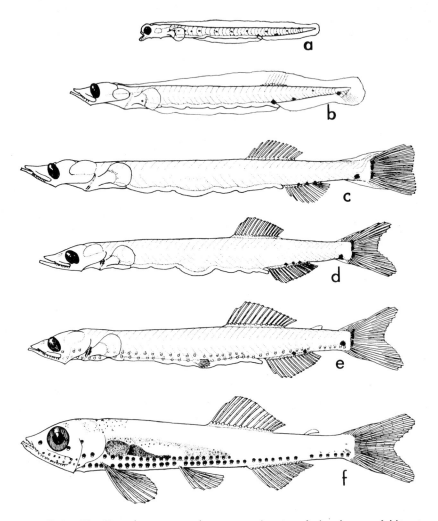

FIG. 10. Development and metamorphosis of the larva of *Vinci-guerria lucetia*. a: Larva, 2.2 mm long. b: 6.0 mm long. c: 9.0 mm long. d: 13.1 mm long. e: Prometamorphosing specimen, 15.0 mm long. f: post-metamorphosing specimen, 16.0 mm long. From Ahlstrom and Counts (1958).

Before we attempt to do this, however, it will be well to consider the type of metamorphosis in which physiological change dominates over morphological change. The classic illustration of this is the Atlantic salmon *Salmo salar*. The general circumstances of its life history are well known (Jones, 1959). After it has hatched it passes through the alevin (yolk-sac) stage to become a parr, which is adapted for life in the head-

TABLE 2

VARIATIONS IN CHEMISTRY OF TISSUES OF *SALMO SALAR*.
DATA FROM FONTAINE AND HIS ASSOCIATES AND (LIPID)
FROM LOVERN, COMPILED BY HOAR (1953).

	Parr	Smolt
Iodine, serum, y/100 ml		
Total	10.1	33.5
Thyroxine	3.1	4.3
Protein	5.6	7.0
Copper, whole blood, y/100 g	42.0	53.0
Chloride, serum, g/1 NaC2	7.2	7.17
Calcium, blood, mg/1	144.0	155.0
Glycogen, liver, mg/g fish	18.22	1.50
Chloride, muscle, g/kg fresh	0.317	0.260
Lipid, percent	3.9	1.2
Iodine value	148.5	166.0

waters of rivers. In due course the parr metamorphoses into the smolt, which swims down the river into the sea, and there develops into the sexually mature adult.

The external changes of metamorphosis in salmonids are not conspicuous, the most obvious being the loss of the characteristic pattern of pigmentation of the parr and the development of a silvery appearance as a result of the deposit of guanine in the skin. The biochemical and physiological changes, however, are extensive (Table 2) and varied, although to a large extent they are correlated with the increased swimming activity and the adaptation of the animal for marine life. One expression of this is the condition factor, which relates weight to length $(K = 100 \ W/L^3$, where L is the standard length, measured from the tip of the snout to the end of the caudal peduncle, and W is the weight). This factor is greater than 1 in the parr but falls to about 0.8 in the smolt, even though the metamorphosis takes place in the spring, at a time when the condition factor of non-metamorphosing parr is increasing. This change is not a result of reduced feeding but is a consequence of growth in length coinciding with an increase in metabolic rate (Fontaine, 1954). Associated with this is a fall in liver glycogen. Other features shown in Table 2 are the lower level of muscle chloride in the smolt and its higher levels of blood iodine and blood copper.

These changes have been held to reflect the establishment of a new equilibrium in electrolyte metabolism, adapted for a marine environment. There is evidence, e.g., that marine fish have higher levels of blood iodine and blood copper than freshwater ones. Also noteworthy in this connection is the composition of the fats of the body; in the smolt these resemble in composition the fats of marine fish, whereas in the parr they are of the freshwater type. Finally, and unrepresented in the table, there are the changes in locomotor activity and in responses, which result in the fish swimming downstream to the sea instead of maintaining station in their native waters. Before they reach the sea, however, they are already being preadapted for marine life.

When the yellow eel transforms into the migratory silver eel it undergoes changes that are sufficiently far-reaching to justify regarding this phase as a second metamorphosis (D'Ancona, 1960). The changes, which are very similar in some respects to those of smolt transformation, include an increase in the thickness of the skin and in its guanine content, changes in the form of the pectoral fins and of the head, change in osmoregulatory capacity, and enlargement of the eyes. Further, a visual pigment adapted for deep-sea vision is substituted for the previously existing one (Carlisle and Denton, 1959). The conception of second metamorphosis is not so obviously applicable to the life history of salmonids, for the characteristics of these animals during their anadromous spawning migration are not as distinctive as those of migratory eels. Moreover, it has been argued that a distinguishing feature of true metamorphosis is that it is a preparation for life in a different habitat (Wald, 1958) and not simply a response to the encountering of new stresses. From this point of view the status of the characteristics of migrating salmonids is not wholly clear. Thus, hypersecretory activity of the adrenocortical tissue is recognizable in salmonids during their spawning migration, but it is possible that this may be no more than the response of individual fish to the stress of migratory movements. The distinction between such responses and true metamorphosis is not, however, easy to draw, and it would seem reasonable to regard the well-defined metamorphoses of some species of fish as extreme examples of processes that probably operate to a less extent in many other species as well.

The Regulation of Metamorphosis in Teleosts

It seems self-evident that the complex transformations of teleost metamorphosis to a large extent must be determined and regulated from within the organism, but there is evidence that here, as in ascidian metamorphosis, the environment also plays a part, at least insofar as it can influence the onset of the process. This aspect is brought out in Breder's (1949) account of the surgeon fish *Acanthurus hepatus*, a benthic form with a pelagic larval stage.

This larva was at one time described as a distinct species, *Hepatus pawnee* (equals *Acanthurus pawnee*), just as happened when the larval stage of the eel was first discovered. In this instance the confusion arose because individuals with the typical adult form may sometimes be smaller than the largest larvae. Breder found that if the transparent larvae were caught in the open sea and transferred to tanks in the laboratory they would immediately seek shelter and begin metamorphosis; the transformation, including the assumption of adult coloration, was complete within 48 hours. He concluded that the planktonic larvae could continue to grow to a length of at least 29 mm while they remained in open water but that they could metamorphose from a length of 10 mm upward as soon as they were carried inshore or in some other way came into relationship with the sea bottom. On this interpretation, therefore, the onset of metamorphosis is not determined by the attainment of a specific size or age but is evoked by some environmental stimulus. Further, competence to respond to this stimulus must be present in individuals over a wide spectrum of age. What determines the competence is unknown, but it is reasonable to suppose that the age or maturity of the tissues would be more significant than length, for the latter might reflect the influence of secondary factors such as temperature or availability of food. That this is so is suggested by the fact that metamorphosis in *Vinciguerria lucetia* takes place at a smaller size south of latitude 25° N than it does in more northern parts of the range of this species (Ahlstrom and Counts, 1958).

Other examples of the dependence of onset of metamorphosis upon the environment have been noted by Caldwell (1962a and 1962b). The prejuveniles of *Pseudopriacanthus altus* have sometimes been regarded by fishermen as adult members of a distinct dwarf species, the reason for this being the same as in the case of the surgeon fish. Metamorphosis may be delayed, with the result that fully transformed juveniles may be smaller than some of the nonmetamorphosed prejuveniles. Here again it would seem that pelagic individuals may continue to grow if they do not encounter a suitable habitat. We have seen that successful habitat selection by ascidian larvae is favored by the emergence of a positive geotaxis. Whether any similar change occurs in these fish larvae is unknown, and it is not clear to what extent the onset of metamorphosis depends on their own adaptively directed activity and to what extent on the drift of currents.

It would be of interest to have more precise information on these matters and, in general, on the relative importance of external environment and internal organization in the determination of the onset of teleost metamorphosis. The classical view of the life history of eels certainly attaches great importance to the influence of genetic coding on the onset of metamorphosis. It is supposed that the geographical separation of the American species (*Anguilla rostrata*) and the European one (*A. anguilla*) depends upon the former coming into metamorphic condition at an earlier age than the latter. This implies that there are specific differences in rate of maturation of the larvae, these differences being adaptively related to the distances that the two species have to drift before they reach their respective continental shelfs.

The timing of the onset of metamorphosis is not, of course, the only factor that has to be taken into account in considering the role of internal regulation in teleostean metamorphosis. Whatever importance we attach to aging and to the establishment of competence in the tissues, we also have to reckon with the very complex pattern of growth and other changes. Those who have considered this aspect (and unfortunately they are very few) have understandably taken as their model the events of amphibian metamorphosis; therefore, they have looked for indications of endocrine control. These indications certainly exist, but the evidence is limited in quantity and has not always been interpreted with the precision demanded by current concepts of the organization and functioning of endocrine systems.

Murr and Sklower (1928), in a report on the metamorphosis of the eel, referred to six arbitrary stages, ranging from the leptocephalus larva to the pigmented eel (Table 3). They found that the volume of the thyroid gland increased some 14 times during early metamorphosis and that the gland was still larger in the glass eel. At stage II the secretory cells had become flatter than in stage I, the follicles being filled with colloid, as they were also in stages III and IV. In the glass eel (stage V) the follicles were empty and their walls folded, while at stage VI they were filled once again with colloid as they had been in the larva. It is very difficult to draw any satisfactory conclusion from these observations as to the role of the thyroid hormones in this metamorphosis. It should be noted that only one specimen of the glass eel stage was examined. Moreover, this information is wholly trivial by current standards in comparison with the results that have been provided by many elegant studies of thyroid

TABLE 3

THE THYROID GLAND IN RELATION TO THE METAMOR-
PHOSIS OF THE EEL *ANGUILLA ANGUILLA*. FROM MURR
AND SKLOWER (1928).

			Volume of Thyroid	Number of Thyroid Follicles
Leptocephalus	(stage I)		0.00047 cmm	13
	(stage II)	Flat shape; larval teeth lost; a little inner pigment	0.00497 cmm	17
	(stage III)	Flat shape, but head and tail clearly marked; a little outer pigment also present	0.00695 cmm	26, including 12 very small ones
	(stage IV)	Shape nearly cylindrical	Not recorded	Not recorded
Glass eel	(stage V)		0.0097	29
Pigmented eel	(stage VI)		0.01206	32, almost all of equal size

function during amphibian metamorphosis. We simply need more information. But if we take the facts as they stand, we can say that there is some indication that thyroid secretion may be important during early metamorphosis, but that maximum discharge of secretion may take place immediately prior to the glass eel stage.

In any future examination of the metamorphosis of the eel attention therefore should be given to the possibility that thyroid hormones are of particular importance in the transition from the marine to the freshwater environment. One recent finding that is relevant to this is the demonstration that cells thought to be thyrotropin-secreting ones are identifiable in the pars distalis of the elver (Knowles and Vollrath, 1965). These cells thus would be able to secrete in the elver the thyrotropin that could regulate through a negative feedback relationship, the activity of the thyroid gland. Their presence in animals that are just beginning the ascent of the rivers therefore would be in good agreement with the view that the thyroid hormones are of particular importance at this stage. On the other hand, this would not account for the evidence of thyroid hyperactivity in the flounder, when the larva metamorphoses into an asymmetrical flatfish (see Pickford and Atz, 1957), and in the herring, when it metamorphoses into its juvenile form (Buchmann, 1940). Here again, the available information has little significance as it stands, but urgently calls for exploration and amplification. For example, it would be interesting to explore further Rasquin's (1955) finding that the thyroid of *Albula vulpes* shows histological signs of extreme activity at the very beginning of metamorphosis, when the first sign of the swim bladder is becoming visible.

What is needed, of course, is not only histological studies of these situations but also experimental analysis of them. An approach to this has been provided by Vilter (1946), who treated glass eels with thyroxine solutions and found that concentrations ranging from 1/50,000 to 1/1,000,000 accelerated the development of pigment. Further, they promoted growth of the stomach, provided that in this instance the hormone was applied in progressively increasing concentrations. These findings could be held to suggest some participation of thyroid hormones in metamorphic change, having regard to the reported appearance of the gland at that time. It is difficult, however, as in all experiments in which fish are immersed in hormone solutions, to decide whether the response is truly physiological—whether, in fact, any thyroid secretion is normally present in the glass eel and, if it is, whether it exerts effects similar to those found by Vilter. He recognized this difficulty and pointed out that the results might merely be demonstrating a general pharmacodynamic action of thyroxine.

By far the most convincing evidence of endocrine regulation of metamorphosis comes from studies of the largely physiological transformation of the salmon parr into the smolt. The factors that initiate the metamorphosis are unknown. In one and the same English river the parr may molt at one, two, or three years of age (Jones, 1959). The onset has nothing to do with sexual condition for, while the parr are normally immature, certain male individuals may become sexually mature and then metamorphose afterward. According to Jones, there is some evidence that rate of growth may play a part, for it is believed that those parr that metamorphose earliest are those that have grown fastest. Growth rates are themselves likely to be determined by genetic factors, and these may be linked with other physiological parameters, including endocrine activity, so that the causal relationships may well be complex.

Regardless of how smolt-transformation is initiated, however, there is much to support the view that the thyroid gland plays an important part at this time (Fontaine, 1954). Not only does it show histological signs of increased activity, there is also evidence of some change in iodine metabolism, for there is a reduction of organic (protein bound) and inorganic iodine in the thyroid of the smolt as compared with that of the parr, while the blood iodine of the smolt is significantly higher (Table 2). Studies with radio-iodine show that the intensity of fixation of iodine by the thyroid gland rises in the early stages of the metamorphosis and that it falls again at the end. Fontaine interprets these data as showing that during smolt transformation there is a high level of production and metabolism of thyroid hormones, and that this is responsible for the high level of blood iodine. As a result, the gland loses much of its thyroglobulin, which would account for the reduction of thyroidal iodine, and is unable to increase its power of capturing iodine sufficiently to compensate for its loss of the element. Fontaine also emphasizes the significance of the increased activity of the smolt as compared with the parr. He compares this with the excitability associated with the hyperthyroid condition in man and suggests that metamorphosis and migration are a manifestation of increased neuroendocrine activity. The finding that 17-hydroxy-corticosteroids are five times more abundant in the blood of the smolt than in that of the parr suggests that the adrenocortical tissue may be involved as well as the thyroid gland.

The situation has been further analyzed by Hoar (1953), who has compared the physiological conditions of several species of salmonids belonging to the genus *Oncorhynchus*. These fish, which pass their early stages in the rivers of the Pacific seaboard of North America, offer the advantage to the investigator of presenting certain variants upon the pattern of life history seen in *Salmo salar*.

Hoar finds that the juvenile forms can be divided into two groups (Fig. 11). One of these comprises those that school as soon as the yolk sac is absorbed. Factors associated with this habit are activity at night and a preference for fast water, but there is some specific variation in these respects. The chum salmon (*O. keta*) and the pink salmon (*O. gorbuscha*) move in strong currents by day, whereas the sockeye salmon (*O. nerka*) does this only at night. This last species is relatively inactive, a characteristic associated with its lake-dwelling habit.

The second group comprises those that in the juvenile stage show marked territorial behavior, occupying and defending territory by day and being relatively inactive at night. These characteristics, which are shown by the coho salmon (*O. kisutch*) and *Salmo salar*, are associated with life in shallow streams. It is the fish of this second group, together with the lake-dwelling sockeye, that undergo metamorphosis into a smolt stage. The other two species of the first group (the chum and the pink salmon) contrast with this in that they do not pass through a smolt stage. Indeed, the pink salmon enters the sea as young fry that do not even develop parr marks, while these marks disappear early in the chum salmon (Fig. 11).

In the schooling juvenile salmonids [as well as in alewives (*Pomolobus pseudoharengus*) and smelt (*Osmerus mordax*) that behave in a similar way], the thyroid is quiescent, as judged by its histological condition. These are the fish that do not undergo smolt transformation. In the second group, comprising those that do metamorphose, the metamorphosis is initiated by changes in the pituitary gland, involving a decrease in the adenohypophysial basophils and an increase in eosinophils. Since it is well known that the pituitary operates through feedback systems, as the intermediary between the environment and certain other of the endocrine organs, including the thyroid gland, it is possible that these changes indicate a response to some environmental factor. No such factor, however, has been clearly defined.

Increased thyroid activity is clearly shown by histological evidence in the migrating smolt, but it is impossible to say whether its secretion is evoking the metamorphic changes or whether it is merely one element of them. The immersion of chum fry (group 1) in thyroxine solution has been shown to produce a significant increase in swimming rate, which suggests the possibility that the changes in the behavior of migrating coho (group 2), such as a tendency to school and a decrease in territorial behavior, may be the results of the influence of the thyroid hormones upon sensory thresholds (Hoar, 1953). It will be appreciated, however, that it is precisely because of the potentially wide-ranging effects of the thyroid hormones that precise observations are needed if we are to disentangle their influence upon morphogenetic processes from their influence upon activity.

Much attention has been focused upon the thyroid gland as a regulating agent in the metamorphosis of fish and, by implication, a wide range of action has been attributed to it. No doubt this is a consequence of the known importance of the thyroid

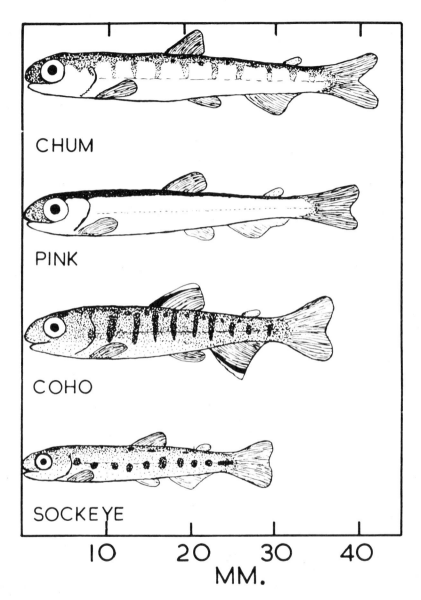

FIG. 11. Diagram showing the external distinguishing features of four species of Pacific salmon fry. For further explanation, see text. From Hoar (1958).

hormones in amphibian metamorphosis. There is, of course, no reason to assume that teleostean methods of control, evolved quite independently of amphibian methods, will be similar in pattern to these. Nevertheless, a case can be made for expecting an involvement of this gland in the metamorphosis of fish.

This case rests in part upon the fact that the thyroid hormones, from the point of view of chordate history, are ancient molecules (for references, see Barrington, 1964 and 1965; Barrington and Thorpe, 1965). There is good evidence that thyroxine is present in the endostyle of *Ciona* and that both it and triiodothyronine are present in amphioxus, as well as in the endostyle of the lamprey larva. Thus, it seems likely that the thyroidal molecules were incorporated into chordate organization at a very early stage of the group's evolution and in animals that must still have been relatively unspecialized. It is not known what function these molecules fulfill in modern protochordates; presumably, however, their establishment in early members of the group was associated with some selective advantage which, in such primitive animals, would seem likely to have been of a generalized character.

It is significant in this connection that Tata, Ernster, and Lindberg (1962), as a result of studies of the tissues of thyroxine-treated rats, concluded that thyroxine exerts a stimulating action upon a wide range of enzyme systems associated with growth and maturation. Therefore, such may have been the type of action exerted by the thyroid hormones when they were first incorporated into chordate metabolism. At the same time, they would also have constituted a reserve of potential adaptation upon which particular groups could have drawn to potentiate and regulate specific morphogenetic and physiological processes of the sort that we have seen to occur during the metamorphosis of fish.

A specific illustration of this argument is seen in the early development of trout. If newly hatched alevins are immersed in a solution of thyroxine it is found that the treatment accelerates the rate of development of the lachrymal bone of the skull (Barrington and Rawdon, unpublished). It does not necessarily follow from this that thyroxine normally influences the development of this bone. As with Vilter's experiments cited earlier, we do not known how much, if any, of this hormone is circulating in the bloodstream of these fish immediately after hatching, although thyroid follicles are certainly present and are able to bind iodine. What this evidence does suggest, however, is a model of the way in which specialized morphogenetic changes in specific life histories might have been brought under the regulating influence of the thyroid secretion, presumably through the capacity of the secretion to influence enzyme systems involved in the relevant growth processes. Needless to say, this does not dispose of the possibility of other hormones being also involved.

We have mentioned the pituitary gland and the adrenocortical tissue as being possibly implicated in teleostean metamorphosis, and it is obvious that the pituitary gland in particular, with its dual relationship with the environment and the internal medium, may well be a key factor. As with all aspects of the metamorphosis of lower chordates, however, more information is needed before further speculation can be justified.

REFERENCES

Adinolfi, M., and G. Chieffi. 1958. Larval and adult haemoglobins of the cyclostome *Petromyzon planeri*. Nature 182:730.

Ahlstrom, E. H., and R. C. Counts. 1958. Development and distribution of *Vinciguerria lucetia* and related species in the eastern Pacific. Fish. Bull. U.S. Fish. Wildlife Serv. 58:363–416.

Barrington, E. J. W. 1961. Metamorphic processes in fishes and lampreys. Amer. Zool. 1:97–106.

_____. 1964. Some endocrinological aspects of the problem of the origin of vertebrates. Ann. Soc. Roy. Zool. Belgium, 94:161–178.

_____. 1965. The Biology of Hemichordates and Protochordates. Edinburgh, Oliver and Boyd.

_____. 1967. Invertebrate Structure and Function. London, Nelson and Sons.

_____, and Rawdon. Unpublished.

_____, and M. Sage. 1963a. On the responses of the glandular tracts and associated regions of the endostyle of the larval lamprey to goitrogens and thyroxine. Gen. Comp. Endocr., 3:153–165.

_____, and M. Sage. 1963b. On the responses of the iodine-binding regions of the endostyle of the larval lamprey to goitrogens and thyroxine. Gen. Comp. Endocr., 3:669–679.

_____. 1966. On the response of the endostyle of the hypophysectomized larval lamprey to thiourea. Nature (London) Gen. Comp. Endocr., 7:463–474.

_____, and A. Thorpe. 1965. The identification of monoiodotyrosine, diiodotyrosine and thyroxine in extracts of the endostyle of the ascidian *Ciona intestinalis* L. Proc. Roy. Soc. (London) Ser. B, 163:136–149.

Bell, L. G. E. 1955. Production of abnormal metamorphosis in a tunicate. Nature, 175:1001.

Berrill, N. J. 1931. Studies in tunicate development. II. Abbreviation of development in the Molgulidae. Phil. Trans. Roy. Soc. (London) Ser. B, 219:281–346.

_____. 1935. Studies in tunicate development. III. Differential reduction and acceleration. Phil. Trans. Roy. Soc. (London) Ser. B. 225:225–326.

_____. 1947. Metamorphosis in ascidians. J. Morph., 81:249–267.

_____. 1950. The Tunicata. London, Ray Society.

_____. 1955. The Origin of Vertebrates. Oxford, Clarendon Press.

Bertholf, L. M. 1945. Accelerating metamorphosis in the tunicate *Styela partita*. Biol. Bull., 89:184–185.

Bertin, L. 1956. Eels. A Biological Study. London, Cleaver-Hume.

Bone, Q. 1958. The asymmetry of the larval amphioxus. Proc. Zool. Soc. London, 130:289–293.

Bradway, W. 1936. The experimental alteration of the rate of metamorphosis in the tunicate, *Clavelina huntsmani* (Van Name). J. Exp. Zool., 72:213–224.

Breder, C. M. 1949. On the taxonomy and the postlarval stages of the surgeon-fish, *Acanthurus hepatus*. Copeia, No. 4, 296, note.

Buchmann, H. 1940. Hypophyse und Thyroidea im Individualzyklus des Herrings. Zool. Jb., Anat. Ontog., 66:191–262.

Caldwell, D. K. 1962a. Development and distribution of the short bigeye *Pseudopriacanthus altus* (Gill) in the western North Atlantic. Fish. Bull. 203. Fish. Bull. U.S. Fish. Wildlife Serv., 62:103–150.

_____. 1962b. Development and distribution of larval and juvenile fishes of the family Mullidae of the western North Atlantic. Fish. Bull. U.S. Fish Wildlife Serv., 62:403–457.

Carlisle, D. B., and E. J. Denton. 1959. On the metamorphosis of the visual pigments of Anguilla anguilla L. J. Marine Biol. Assoc. U.K., 38:97.

Cloney, R. A. 1961a. Changes in the fine structure of striated muscle cells during metamorphosis in ascidian larvae. Anat. Rec., 139:217–218.

_____. 1961b. Observations on the mechanism of tail resorption in ascidians. Amer. Zool., 1:67–87.

_____. 1963. The significance of the caudal epidermis in ascidian metamorphosis. Biol. Bull., 124:241–253.

_____. 1966. Cytoplasmic filaments and cell movements: epidermal cells during ascidian metamorphosis. J. Ultrastruct. Res., 14:300–328.

Conklin, E. G. 1931. The development of centrifuged eggs of ascidians. J. Exp. Zool., 60:1–119.

D'Ancona, U. 1960. The life-cycle of the Atlantic eel. Sympos. Zool. Soc. London, 1:61–75.

Etkin, W. 1964. Metamorphosis. *In* Moore, J. A., ed., Physiology of the Amphibia, pp. 427–468. New York, Academic Press.

Fontaine, M. 1954. Du déterminisme physiologique des migrations. Biol. Rev., 29:390–418.

Garstang, W. 1929. The morphology of the Tunicata, and its bearings on the phylogeny of the Chordata. Quart. J. Micr. Sci., 72:51–187.

Glaser, O., and G. A. Anslow. 1949. Copper and ascidian metamorphosis. J. Exp. Zool., 111:117–140.

Grave, C. 1944. The larva of *Styela (Cynthia) partita*. Structure, activities and duration of life. J. Morph., 75:173–188.

_____, and P. A. Nicoll. 1939. Studies of larval life and metamorphosis in *Ascidia nigra* and species of *Polyandrocarpa*. Carnegie Inst. Wash. Pub. 517:1–46.

Hardisty, M. W. 1961. The growth of larval lampreys. J. Anim. Ecol., 30:357–371.

Hoar, W. S. 1953. Control and timing of fish migration. Biol. Rev., 28:437–452.

Jarvik, E. 1964. Specializations in early vertebrates. Ann. Soc. Roy. Zool. Belgium, 94:11–95.

Jones, J. W. 1959. The Salmon. London, Collins.

Knowles, F. G. W. 1941. The duration of larval life in ammocoetes and an attempt to accelerate metamorphosis by injections of anterior pituitary extracts. Proc. Zool. Soc. London, A, 111:101–109.

_____, and L. Vollrath. 1965. Cell types in the pituitary of the eel, *Anguilla anguilla* L., at different stages in the life-cycle. Z. Zellforsch., 69:474–479.

Kubota, S. S. 1961. Studies on the ecology, growth and metamorphosis in conger eel, *Conger myriaster* (Brevoort). J. Fac. Fish. Univ. Mie, 5:190–370.

Leloup, J., and M. Fontaine. 1960. Iodine metabolism in lower vertebrates. Ann. N. Y. Acad. Sci., 86:316–353.

Levine, E. P. 1962. Studies on the structure, reproduction, development and accumulation of metals in the colonial ascidian *Eudistoma ritteri* Van Name, 1945. J. Morph., 111:105–137.

Lynch, W. F. 1958. The effects of certain organic compounds and antimitotic agents on metamorphosis of *Bugula* and *Amaroecium* larvae. J. Exp. Zool., 137:117–152.

_____. 1961. Extrinsic factors influencing metamorphosis in bryozoan and ascidian larvae. Amer. Zool., 1:59–66.

Manwell, C. 1960. Comparative physiology: blood pigments. Ann. Rev. Physiol., 22:191–244.

Matsubara, K. 1942. On the metamorphosis of a clupeoid fish, *Pterothrissus gissu* Hilgendorf. J. Imp. Fish. Inst., 35:1–16.

Minganti, A. 1957. Acta Embryol. Morph. Exp., 1:37.

Morris, R. 1960. General problems of osmoregulation with special reference to cyclostomes. Sympos. Zool. Soc. London, 1:1–16.

Murr, E., and A. Sklower. 1928. Untersuchungen über der inkretorischen Organe der Fische. I. Das Verhalten der schilddruse in der Metamorphose des Aales. Z. Vergl. Physiol., 7:279–288.

Olivereau, M. 1956. Endostyle de l'ammocoete (*Lampetra planeri* Bloch) et hormone thyréotrope. C. R. Assoc. Anat., 43:636–657.

Pickford, G. E., and J. W. At. 1957. The Physiology of the Pituitary Gland of Fishes. New York, Zoological Society.

Rall, D. P., P. Schwab, and C. G. Zabord. 1961. Alterations of plasma proteins at metamorphosis in the lamprey (*Petromyzon marinus dorsatus*). Science, 133:279–280.

Rasquin, P. 1955. Observations on the metamorphosis of the bone fish, *Albula vulpes* (Linnaeus). J. Morph., 97:77–118.

Scott, F. M. 1952. The developmental history of *Amaroecium constellatum*. III. Metamorphosis. Biol. Bull., 103:226–241.

———. 1954. Metamorphic differentiation in *Amaroecium constellatum* treated with nitrogen mustard. J. Exp. Zool., 127:331–365.

Sterba, G. 1955. Das adrenal- und interrenal-System in Lebensablauf von *Petromyzon planeri* Bloch. Zool. Anz., 155:151–168.

———. 1959. Die Physiologie und Histogenese der Schilddrüse und des Thymus beim Bachneunauge (*Lampetra planeri* Bloch). Wiss. Z. Friedrich-Schiller Univ. Jena, Math. Naturwiss. Reihe 2:239–298.

———, and J. Schneider. 1961. Zur Wirkung von Kaliumperchlorat (KClO$_4$) auf Ammocoetes. Naturwiss., 48:485–486.

Tata, J. R., L. Ernster and O. Lindberg. 1962. Control of basal metabolic rate by thyroid hormones and cellular function. Nature, 193:1058–1060.

Vilter, V. 1946. Action de la thyroxine sur la métamorphose larvaire de l'Anguille. C. R. Soc. Biol. (Paris), 140:783–785.

Wald, G. 1958. The significance of vertebrate metamorphosis. Science, 128:1481–1490.

Whittaker, J. R. 1960. An in vivo analysis of tyrosinase function and melanin formation in ascidian embryos. Anat. Rec., 138:388–389.

———. 1964. Copper as a factor in the onset of ascidian metamorphosis. Nature 202:1024–1025.

Wickstead, J. H. 1964. On the status of "amphioxides" larva. J. Linn. Soc. (Zool.), 45:201–207.

seven

SURVEY OF AMPHIBIAN
METAMORPHOSIS

James Norman Dent

Department of Biology
University of Virginia
Charlottesville

A remarkable series of changes takes place when an aquatic, fishlike tadpole is transformed into a land-dwelling frog. Throughout embryonic and larval life the development of the frog has been almost entirely a gradual, unfolding process of growth and differentiation, but during the metamorphic period growth is almost halted and differentiation and degeneration occur simultaneously with dramatic suddenness. The term "metamorphosis" has broad zoological usage. It is used to designate any group of developmental changes that are completed within a period of time which is brief in comparison with the full developmental period of the individual concerned. A variety of animals undergo metamorphoses of diverse sorts. Each of the events of amphibian metamorphosis contributes toward the preparation of the developing individual for life on land, but one cannot say that that preparation is confined exclusively to the metamorphoic period, since, after all, the limbs and the lungs have been differentiating during most of the larval period.

STAGING OF ANURAN DEVELOPMENT

Development is, of course, a continuous process, but in order to make critical comparisons between different species or between different individuals of the same species it is desirable that the developmental period be divided into discrete steps or stages and that they be described in a staging table. A number of such tables have been prepared for different amphibians. The ones for anurans with aquatic larvae are quite similar to one another. Gosner (1960) has combined two of the best of them—those of Limbaugh and Volpe (1957) and Taylor and Kollros (1946)—into a simplified and generalized series that should be readily adapted for use with any frog or toad having free-swimming larvae. The larval and metamorphic stages of Gosner's series are presented here because they illustrate the sequence of external changes that are most easily observed during typical anuran metamorphosis (Figs. 1 and 2).

Note in Fig. 1 that stages 23, 24, and 25 are marked by the formation of the operculum and the consequent covering over of the external gills by its anterior component which grows backward from the hyoid arch. By stage 25 the anterior and posterior components of the operculum fuse except for a small funnel-shaped opening to the outside, the spiracle.

At about stage 23 the oral disc and rows of keratinized labial teeth and horny beaks (Fig. 3) begin to form. In stages 23 to 25 the initial formation of pigmentary patterns takes place, chromatophores of several types appearing at about stages 23 and 24.

In distinguishing between families the diagnostic feature is the form of the oral disc. Its essential peculiarities are present by about stage 26, although changes occur subsequently in the number and form of oral papillae. The tooth rows develop gradually. Although the "mature" tooth row formula of a species is usually established in the early larval stages, the relative proportions and numbers of the rows sometimes change during ontogeny.

Independent feeding commences sometime between stages 25 and 26. Primarily on this basis stage 26 is arbitrarily designated as the first larval stage.

Identification of stages 26 to 40 is made by examination of the hind limbs. Stages 26 to 30 are distinguished by changes in the ratio of length to diameter in the hind limb primordium. At stage 31 the "foot" is paddled-shaped, and in subsequent stages the configuration of the paddle is altered as individual toes are differentiated. The distinguishing criteria of stages 23 to 40 are proportional changes in the length of individual toes and in the appearance of metatarsal and subarticular tubercles.

Etkin (1932, 1955, and 1964) regards anuran metamorphosis as consisting of two phases, prometamorphosis and metamorphic climax. Prometamorphosis begins at stage 36 and is marked by the rapid elongation of the hind limbs. During stage 40 the cloacal tail piece is resorbed, shifting the position of the anus. The completion of this shift marks the beginning of stage 41. The operculum thins and becomes translucent over the developing forelimbs, forming a "skin window" through which the forelimbs erupt.

The appearance of the forelimbs marks the beginning of stage 42, the first stage of metamorphic climax. Stages 42 to 46 are characterized by the remodeling of the head and are distinguished primarily by changes in the mouth. Larval mouthparts are lost. The tympanum is formed. At stage 46 metamorphosis is essentially complete. Newly transformed young may or may not resemble the adults sufficiently to permit positive identification.

The extensive alterations in external features noted in Figs. 1 and 2 are accompanied by equally profound changes in internal anatomy such as the adaptation of the aortic arches and the hyoid cartilages and muscles for pulmonary respiration, the loss of the lateral line system, the development of a muscular tongue, and the shortening of the gut. In this chapter, however, we shall give primary attention to external morphology.

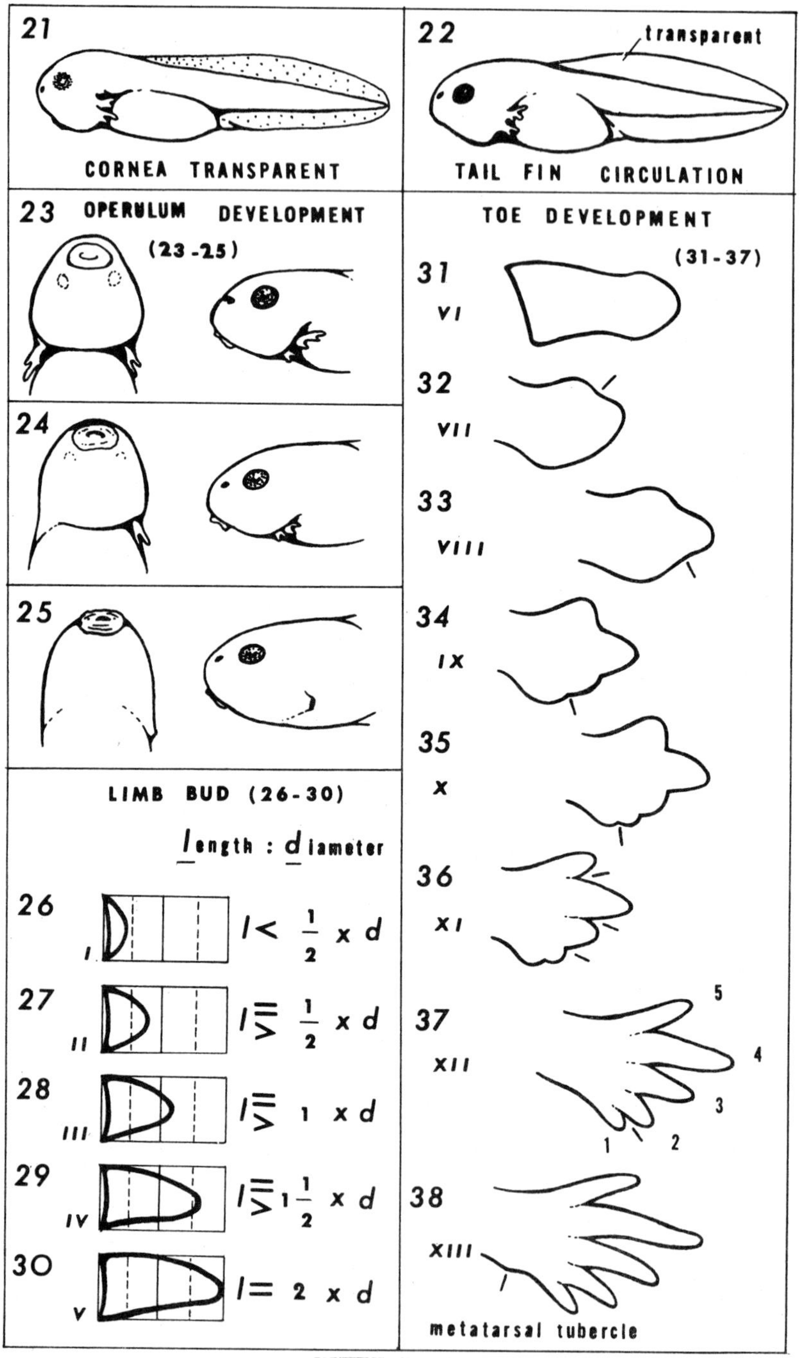

FIG. 1. Generalized stages of anuran development. Roman numerals indicate stages of Taylor and Killros. Arabic numbers indicate Gosner's stages. From Gosner, 1960.

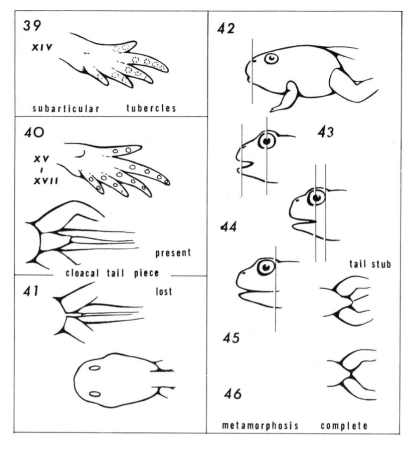

FIG. 2. Generalized stages of anuran development. From Gosner, 1960.

TYPICAL DEVELOPMENT AMONG URODELES

In the urodele the events of metamorphosis appear to be much less striking than in the anuran since the superficial resemblance of the salamander larva to the adult is much greater than that of the tadpole to the frog (compare Figs. 1 and 2 with 4).

Rather abbreviated sequences of metamorphic stages have been described for *Eurycea bislineata* by Wilder (1925), for

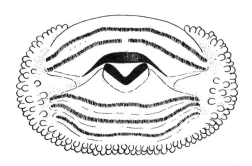

FIG. 3. Detailed diagram of oral disc from tadpole of *Leptodactylus melanotus*, a typical aquatic anuran larva. On the lateral and ventral borders are oral papillae. In the center are the horny beaks above and below the mouth. Above them are two and below them three rows of horny teeth. From Orton, 1957.

Ambystoma maculatum, *Notophthalmus* * *viridescens*, *A. jeffersonianum* by Grant (1930a and 1930b), and for *Gyrinophilus palleucus* by Dent and Kirby-Smith (1963) but external morphological changes are not sufficiently marked to substantiate a long series of stages such as that described for anurans. The only truly obvious change that is a consistent feature of metamorphosis among all urodeles is the resorption of the gills (Figs. 4, 5, and 6). Other consistent but less obvious external features are the resorption of the tail fin and the larval folds of the lower jaw, fusion of the gill slits, and the differentiation of eyelids. Also, colors and color patterns typical of certain species change from larval to adult shades and configurations. In addition to the events common to all urodeles, there are numerous changes in features peculiar to certain groups. For example, the Plethodontidae usually develop naso-labial folds during the latter stages of metamorphosis.

The internal changes of urodele metamorphosis are most extensive in the head region. Valves develop around the nares to prevent the entrance of water if the adult becomes submerged. Alterations take place in the skull and in the hyobranchial apparatus. The skeletal changes are accompanied by alterations in associated musculature. In the integument there is a loss of large glandlike cells, the Leydig cells, and the formation of a keratinized stratum corneum.

*Although *Notophthalmus* is the generic name currently accepted by systematists for the eastern spotted newt, this animal has at different times also been called *Diemictylus* and *Triturus*. It became well established as a subject for experimental studies during the time it was known as *Triturus*, and many continue to refer to it by that name in the literature of experimental zoology.

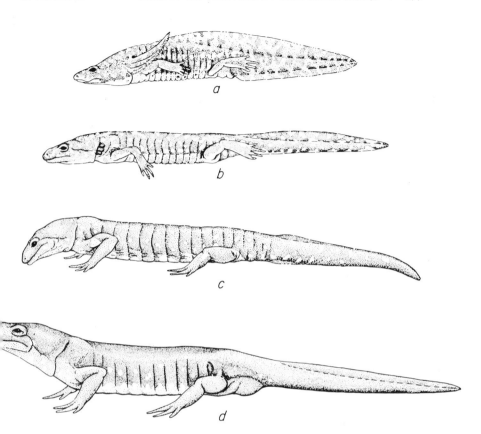

FIG. 4. *Ambystoma rosaceum* at a: larval; b: metamorphic; c: juvenile; and d: adult stages. From Anderson, 1961.

VARIATION IN AMPHIBIAN LIFE HISTORIES

Although there are many typical anurans and urodeles
whose life histories follow the patterns that have just been
described, one does not venture far into amphibian systematics
and biology without discovering that there are wide variations
upon the basic theme. In the evolution of the vertebrates the
amphibians provided the link between the fishes and the reptiles.
One tends to think of the amphibians as being in the process of
withdrawing from the water for life on land. A survey of the
various taxonomic groups discloses that there is a fairly complete gradation in a broad range between amphibians that live
completely in the water and those that live exclusively on land.
The various levels of this gradation, however, neither represent a
single orderly sequence nor links in a single evolutionary chain.

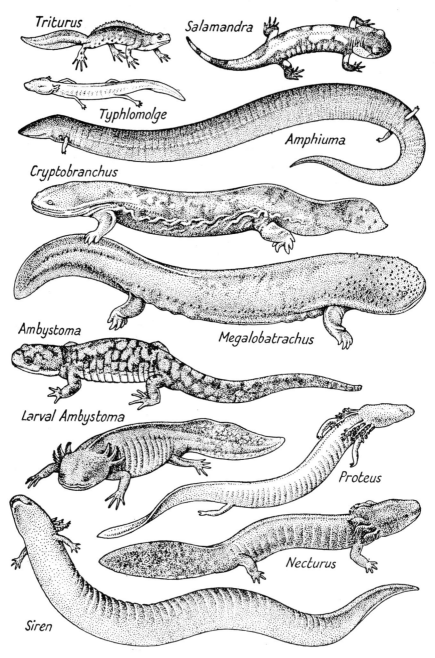

FIG. 5. Some of the various urodele amphibians (not all drawn to same scale) mentioned in the text. From Young, 1962.

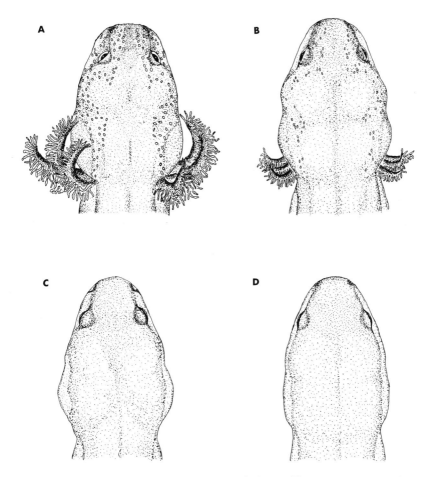

FIG. 6. The head region of *Gyrinophilus palleucus* at successive stages of spontaneous metamorphosis.

Instead, it is apparent that on several occasions not only frogs and salamanders of diverse lineage but also the legless members of Gymnophiona as well have succeeded in leaving the water entirely (Orton, 1949 and 1951). Conversely, other species have returned to water or, possibly, have never left it. Withdrawal from or return to the water are not single phylogenetic trends but rather are general tendencies that have evolved repeatedly and independently in unrelated stocks.

Among the 19 genera of the order Gymnophiona one finds some with aquatic larvae, others with direct development, and still others that are ovoviviparous. Yet they are, in effect, small and degenerate groups, and it has been decided not to give them further attention in this chapter.

COMPLETELY AQUATIC AMPHIBIANS

The completely aquatic amphibians may be divided into two categories: (1) those with aquatic larvae that complete metamorphosis in the water and then remain in it as adults, and (2) those that are neotenic.

None of the urodeles quite fit into the first category. The spotted newt, *Notophthalmus viridescens*, is completely aquatic as a larva and as an adult but following metamorphosis typically spends one to three years on land as a red eft. The eft has a tongue and a terrestrial integuement lacking lateral line organs, but passes through a second metamorphosis before returning to the water during which the tongue is lost and lateral line organs are reacquired. *Leurognathus marmorata* of the lungless Plethodontidae is rarely found outside the water but has no special aquatic adaptations as an adult.

Among the Anura the Pipidae, such as the South African clawed toad *Xenopus laevis*, never leave the water. Both larvae and adults are tongueless and have lateral line organs. Occasional aquatic genera are also found among other families such as *Batrachophrynus* and *Pseudobufo* of the Bufonidae and *Telmatobius* of the Leptodactylidae.

NEOTENY

There is some confusion in the use of the terms "neoteny" and "paedogenesis." Neoteny is a condition in which larval characters are retained for prolonged periods of time. Paedogenesis is the process by which larval individuals reproduce. A paedogenetic individual is of necessity neotenic. If a race is to be permanently neotenic it must obviously be also paedogenic.

Paedogenesis is not found among the Anura, although naturally occuring, nonmetamorphosing anuran larvae have been reported (Jurand, 1955; Saxén, 1957; Boschwitz, 1957). In some instances the larval periods of certain species or individuals have been prolonged sufficiently for them to be classed as neotenic.

Table 1 presents a listing of caudate species reported to be neotenous. All are probably paedogenic as well.

Of the genera listed as permanent larvae, Noble (1931)—upon consideration of such metamorphic features as the development of limbs, maxillary bones, loss of gills, and reduction of branchial arches—proposed that *Siren* (see Fig. 5) and *Pseudobranchus* be considered as forms that cease to differentiate at a very early stage of larval life; *Proteus* and *Necturus* as forms that reach a later stage of urodele ontogeny; *Cryptobranchus* as a form that had begun its metamorphosis; and *Megalobatrachus* and *Amphiuma* as forms that have nearly completed their metamorphosis.

The outflow of water from the mouths of urodele larvae through the internal nares (choanae) is usually prevented by the action of a simple flap of connective tissue that serves as a valve. At metamorphosis a more elaborate valve activated by smooth muscle is developed. *Necturus* and *Proteus* have choanal valves and skin of the larval type (with Leydig cells and without stratum corneum), two pairs of gill slits, and three pairs of external gills (no urodele has internal gills). Moving in the adult direction, *Cryptobranchus* and *Amphiuma* each have one pair of gill slits. *Megalobatrachus* has none. These animals have not developed eyelids. The larval character of *Siredon* and *Pseudobranchus* is indicated by the absence of hind limbs and the presence of choanal valves, external gills (three pairs in *Siren* but only one in *Pseudobranchus*), and open gill slits. The skin of *Siren* has adult structure, but that of *Pseudobranchus* is larval.

THE THYROID GLAND AND NEOTENY

With the coming of knowledge regarding the relation of the thyroid gland to metamorphosis, questions were raised regarding neotenic forms. Do they fail to metamorphose because of deficient thyroid function or have the tissues that ordinarily respond to the thyroid lost their sensitivity to it? In general, the second hormone explanation seems to be most nearly correct. *Necturus* failed more to respond to treatment with thyroxin alone, although it was in combination with adrenalin (Gutman, 1926). The treatment was lethal, and no other metamorphic changes were noted. Etkin (1955) ascribes these results to generalized effects of unfavorable conditions. Gill reduction without other changes was produced in *Siren* and *Pseudobranchus* by treatment with iodothyrine (Noble, 1924). This, also, may have geen a generalized rather than a specific response. Immersion in solutions of desiccated thyroid gland hastened the shedding of skin but had no further effect on *Cryptobranchus* (Noble and Ferris, 1929). Equivalent results were obtained in *Amphiuma* with thyroxin (Kobayashi and Gorbman, 1962). Although *Proteus* gives no metamorphic response to treatment with thyroxin, its skin undergoes changes in the adult direction upon transplantation to metamorphosing salamanders—(*Triton, Salamandra,* or *Ambystoma*)—(Reis, 1932).

TABLE 1

DEGREES OF NEOTENY AMONG THE URODELA

	Family	Genus	Species	Region
1. Permanent larvae	Sirenidae	*Siren*	*lacertina*	Southeastern U.S.
			intermedia	Southeast and Central U.S.
		Pseudobranchus	*striatus*	Southeast U.S.
	Proteidae	*Necturus*	*maculosus*	Eastern U.S.
			punctatus	Southeastern U.S.
		Proteus	*anguinus*	Central Europe
	Cryptobranchidae	*Cryptobranchus*	*alleganiensis*	Eastern U.S.
		Megalobatrachus	*japonicus*	Japan
			davidianus	China
	Amphiumidae	*Amphiuma*	*means*	Southeastern U.S.
			tridactylium	Southeastern U.S.
2. Consistently netenous in natural habitat, but metamorphosis can be induced	Plethodontidae	*Typhlomolge*	*rathbuni*	Texas
		Haideotriton	*wallacei*	Georgia and Florida
		Eurycea	*tynerensis*	Oklahoma
			neotenes	Texas
			nana	Texas
	Ambystomatidae	*Gyrinophilus*	*troglodytes*	Texas
			palleucus	Tennessee
		Siredon	*pisciformis*	Mexico

Order	Family	Genus	Species	Location
3. Occasionally neotenous in nature	Ambystomatidae	Dicampton	ensatus	West Coast of U.S.
		Ambystoma	tigrinum	United States
			talpoideum	Southeastern U.S.
			gracile	West Coast of U.S.
		Rhyacosiredon	4 species	Mexico
	Salamandridae	Notophthalmus	perstriatus	Eastern U.S.
			viridescens	Eastern U.S.
		Triturus	alpestris	Central Europe
			cristatus	Western Europe
			helveticus	Western Europe
			taeniatus	Central Europe
	Plethodontidae	Eurycea	multiplicata	Oklahoma, Arkansas, and Missouri
	Hynobiidae	Hynobius	lichenatus	Japan

283

The placement of the caverniculous salamanders *Typhlomolge* and *Haideotriton* in category 2 is perhaps questionable. In 1957 Dundee immersed a single small (33 mm snout-vent length) specimen of *Typhlomolge* in a 1:1,000,000 aqueous solution of racemic thyroxin. When no results were noted the concentration was increased first to 1:500,000 and then to 1:100,000. Immediately the labial folds, gills, and fins began to undergo gradual atrophy. Maxillae were developed and the beginnings of maxillary dentition were seen. Before the animal died at the end of 19 days, the fins and labial folds were resorbed, and the gills were reduced to mere stubs. The skin was unchanged, and no further metamorphic events were noted. It is possible that if the experiment were repeated using larger animals metamorphosis might be brought to completion. It is well known that distortion of the metamorphic pattern results when very young larvae are treated with thyroxin.

The evidence favoring the inclusion of *Haideotriton* in category 2 is much stronger. Dundee (1961) immersed five specimens of *Haideotriton* in concentrations of thyroxin ranging between 1:100,000 and 1:2,000,000. All concentrations produced metamorphic changes with about equal effectiveness. In all instances, there was a loss of fins, labial folds, lateral line organs, gills, and the coronoid bone. There were no further changes in the skull, no changes in the skin, and the eyelids were not developed. All five animals died within 25 days of the beginning of the treatment. Like the specimen of *Typhlomolge*, they were relatively small individuals, the largest being 27 mm in length. A mature specimen, the type specimen of *Haideotriton*, was reported by Carr (1939) to be 75.6 mm in length. Pylka and Warren (1958) found that an animal grown to be 43 mm long was still sexually immature. As with *Typhlomolge*, it seems likely that if larger specimens of *Haideotriton* were treated with thyroxin they might pass through a complete metamorphic sequence. It must be conceded, however, that the tissues of both *Typhlomolge* and *Haideotriton* are very resistant to the metamorphic action of the thyroid hormone and that they might be properly classed as permanent larvae.

When immersed in a solution of thyroxin at a concentration of 1:500,000, the Tennessee cave salamander *Gyrinophilus palleucus* was seen after about two weeks to begin metamorphosis with a regression of soft tissues at either side of the tip of the snout (Dent, Kirby-Smith, and Craig, 1955; Dent and Kirby-Smith, 1963; Fig. 6). The gills shrank to become mere stubs at the end of about three weeks. By this time the labial folds and tail fin were resorbed, and parasphenoid teeth, maxillary bones and teeth were formed. The formation of eyelids took several more weeks, and the differentiation of the tongue was a protracted process that took up to five or six months for completion. Rather surprisingly, in view of the length of time required for complete metamorphosis at this rather high concentration of thyroxin, a few specimens underwent spontaneous metamorphosis in ordinary springwater. The factors that stimulated this spontaneous metamorphosis have not been discovered.

Complete metamorphosis was brought about in *Eurycea tynerensis* and in *Eurycea neotines* within 18 days by immersion in a 1:500,000 solution of thyroxin (Kezer, 1952). The other species of *Eurycea* listed in the second category have not been tested, but it seems reasonably safe to assume that because of their close relation to *E. tynerensis* and *E. neotines* they also are quite responsive to the thyroid hormone. The ease with which metamorphosis is induced in the axolotl *Siredon pisciformis* is common knowledge.

The response of the species listed in category 3 to the thyroid hormone has not been tested in all instances, but it is safe to assume that they are all quite responsive. Metamorphosis occurred quite readily in *Notophthalmus viridescens*, e.g., when neotenic specimens were exposed to quite low concentrations (1:2,000,000) of thyroxin (Dent, unpublished). *Ambystoma gracile* completes metamorphosis at 18 days in a 1:500,000 solution of thyroxin (Snyder, 1956).

Thus, it is reasonably clear that the tissues of the animals in categories 2 and 3 of Table 1 are competent to respond to thyroid hormone. But what of their own endocrine glands? For many years it was generally believed that the thyroid gland was congenitally absent in *Typhlomolge rathbuni* (Emerson, 1905; Uhlenhuth, 1923), but eventually Gorbman (1957) made a careful histological study and found in each of two specimens around 100 loosely arranged thyroid follicles.

The thyroid of *Gyrinophilus palleucus* typically functions at a low level but produces sufficient hormone to induce metamorphosis when stimulated with exogenous thyroid-stimulating hormone (Dent and Kirby-Smith, 1963). The thyroid of the axolotl induces metamorphosis when stimulated by pituitary grafts from its typically metamorphosing relative *Ambystoma tigrinum*, but *A. tigrinum* larvae retain their larval form when their pituitary glands are replaced with axolotl pituitaries (Blount, 1950). In general, these observations and others made on the thyroid glands of facultative neotines indicate that their metamorphic failure results from hypofunction of the pituitary gland.

TABLE 2

EXAMPLES ILLUSTRATING THE TREND TOWARD DIRECT DEVELOPMENT WITHIN THE ANURA

Frog	Eggs Deposited in	Larval Period	Metamorphic Modifications
Rana pipiens	Ponds	Typical aquatic	None
Hyla septentrionalis	Water containing cavities of bromeliads	Typical aquatic (rapid development)	None
Hyla faber	Water-filled nests walled off from larger ponds or pools	Typical aquatic	None
Hyperolius tuberillinquis	Vegetation overhanging water	Upon hatching larvae fall into water for typical aquatic larval period	None
Leptodactylus albilabris	Froth-filled nest near pond or pool	Fluctuation of water level washes larvae into pond	None
Hemisus marmoratum	Underground nests near ponds or pools	Female digs tunnel to pond through which larvae wriggle	Lacks external gills but has horny mouth parts
Thoropa petropolitana	Spray-drenched rocks	Tadpoles remain on wet rocks	Mouth adapted for clinging to rocks, tail fins reduced
Leioplema hochstetteri	Damp situations usually (but not always) flooded before metamorphosis	Aquatic if flooded	Lacks gills; tail considered to have respiratory function.

Leptodactylus nanus	Froth within earth-covered nest distant from water	Tadpoles remain within cavity	None
Arthroleptella lightfooti	Damp moss	Larvae wriggle on moss for short time, before forelimbs emerge	No gills, gill slits, or larval mouth parts; forelimbs covered by operculum.
Cornufer hazelae	Axils for fern fronds	None	No gills, gill slits, or larval mouth parts; forelimbs covered by operculum that is continuous with abdominal respiratory folds.
Eleutherodactylus nubicola	Damp cavities under stones	None	No gills or gill slits; vestige of larval lower lip and of operculum; tail modified as respiratory structure

WITHDRAWAL FROM THE WATER

From the standpoint of evolution, several advantages have accrued to those amphibians that have taken up completely terrestrial existence. The survival value of the change is readily recognized when one becomes aware of the wide geographic distribution and the numbers of highly successful species that have acquired this mode of life (Lutz, 1948; Lynn, 1961). The aquatic larva is beset by greater numbers of predators than the developing terrestrial amphibian. On land, parental protection is feasible and often given. The hazards resulting from the drying up of temporary pools and the flooding of mountain streams are eliminated. Metamorphosis is apparently a traumatic process, as evidenced by the fact that in progenies of typical amphibians reared in protected laboratory situations the highest mortality rates are always observed during the metamorphic period. The amphibians that have achieved direct development avoid the rigors that attend the extensive remodelings of typical amphibian metamorphosis.

Adaptations that have resulted in various degrees of withdrawal from the water are found in both the Anura and the Urodela. The range of adaptation is broadest and most complete within the Anura, and we shall give first consideration to them. Gradations of withdrawal can be arranged in two series that are unsequential in the evolutionary sense. One, illustrated in Table 2, reaches its culmination with completely direct development in which strictly larval characters are almost entirely eliminated. The other, illustrated in Table 3, reaches its peak when ovoviviparity is achieved. The species listed in the left-hand columns of both Tables 2 and 3 are meant to be representatives of groups of animals that have identical or very similar life histories.

DIRECT DEVELOPMENT AMONG ANURANS

Rana pipiens is representative of all those anurans that have a typical life history in which jelly-encased eggs are laid in some body of water and in which typical aquatic larvae hatch from those eggs to eventually undergo a typical metamorphic sequence. The little West Indian tree frog *Hyla septentrionalis* is representative of those forms that lay their eggs in very small volumes of water such as those found in sections of bamboo or in the cavities created by the branching of leaves from the bases of bromeliads. Their development is morpho-

TABLE 3

EXAMPLES ILLUSTRATING THE TREND TOWARD VIVIPARITY WITHIN THE ANURA

Frog	Embryos Transported	Late Developmental Morphology
Alytes obstetricans	In strings on hind legs of male until hatching	Typical aquatic larva
Dendrobates auratus	After hatching on land, to water on back of male	Typical aquatic larva
Cryptobatrachus evansi	On back of female until hatching	Typical aquatic larva
Hemiphractus divaricatus	On back of female until development completed	Leaflike gills, simplified mouth parts, rudimentary tail (other species of each genus have less yolk, leave the female before metamorphosis, and have better developed larval characters)
Gastrotheca oviferum	In pouch on back of female until development complete	
Pipa pipa	In individual pockets within thickened dorsal skin of female	Paired spiracles; beaks and labial teeth absent
Hylambates brevirostris	In mouth cavity of female until metamorphosis completed	Typical aquatic larva
Rhinoderma darwinii	In vocal sacs of males until metamorphosis completed	Typical aquatic larvae except that horny structures are soft and skin is thin
Nectophrynoides tornieri	In uterus until metamorphosis is completed	Gill slits; suckers, horny teeth, and beaks are absent. Long, ratlike tail has low fins and a respiratory function

289

logically typical but extremely rapid. Such small deposits of water would be likely to evaporate before slowly developing larvae could metamorphose. The South American frogs *Hyla faber*, *H. pardalis*, and *H. rosenbergi* lay their eggs in small nests or puddles of water that are very close to or walled off from larger ponds or pools. *H. rosenbergi* has an additional adaptation. Its gills are modified for clinging to the surface film of the water in which it develops (Noble, 1931).

A large number of species from several genera and families attach themselves to vegetation that overhangs some body of water. In the South African *Hyperolius tuberillinquis* the eggs are contained within a stiff mass of jelly. Oftentimes, as in *Rhacophorus leucomvstax* from the Philippines, the nest is composed of froth beaten up from an albuminous secretion of the female by the limbs of one or both parents. Sometimes the nest remains relatively soft and sometimes it hardens super-ficially into a crust that resists dehydration. The female of *Chiromantis xerampolina* remains with and moistens her nest until the larvae within it are hatched, otherwise the crust becomes too hard for the larvae to break when the time comes for them to escape. Other forms such as *H. pusillus* attach their eggs individually to leaves or wrap leaves around the eggs, as do the banana frogs of the genus *Hoplophryne*. In all of these species the larva upon hatching falls into the water and takes up the existence of a typical tadpole (Cochran, 1961).

The majority of the 50-odd species of the genus *Leptodacty-lus* lay their eggs in froth-filled nests near small bodies of water that fluctuate in depth with rainfall. The nest sites are from time to time flooded and the larvae are routinely washed into the body of water before metamorphosis takes place (Dent, 1956). *Hylambates natalensis* and a few species from other families are known to build quite similar nests.

With her snout, the female of *Hemisus marmoratum* digs an underground nest chamber and remains with her eggs until they hatch. She then tunnels to the water and is followed by the larvae which, even though they become aquatic, do not develop external gills.

Thoropa petropolitana is representative of a few species of South American frogs such as *Cyclorampus pinderi* whose tadpoles are only semiaquatic in that they spend their larval period upon moist rocks and not actually within the water. Their mouths are especially adapted for clinging to the rock, and their tails are modified somewhat as respiratory organs, although gills do develop. *Leiopelma archeyi* from New Zealand is occasionally semiaquatic throughout the larval period (Fig. 7).

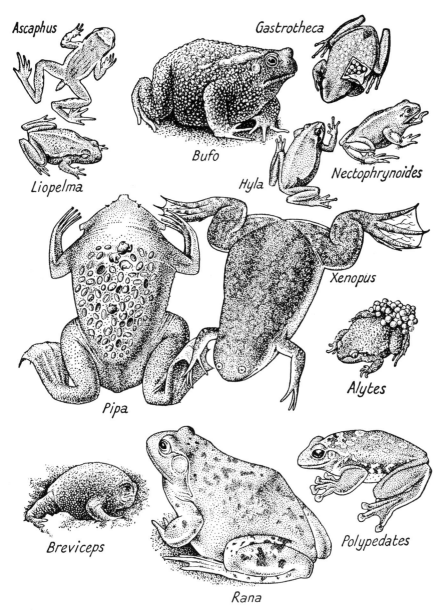

FIG. 7. Some of the anuran amphibians (not all drawn to same scale) mentioned in the text. From Young, 1962.

The eggs are laid in a damp situation, but not in the water, and the young swim only if the nest happens to be flooded before metamorphosis is complete. It has four pairs of open gill slits, but no gills form. As pointed out earlier, the anuran operculum is derived principally from a transverse dermal fold that grows backward from the hyoid region, but also from a low, ridgelike fold across the anterior part of the belly just behind the fore-limb buds (Orton, 1949). In aquatic larvae these two components are fused together prior to the formation of the forelimb bud. In *Leiopelma* fusion does not take place although the forelimb buds are covered by the anterior components (Stephenson 1951 and 1955). The tongue forms before hatching occurs. In South America *Leptodactylus nanus* represents a group of several species such as *Zachaenus parvulus* whose larvae are semi-aquatic, being laid and left throughout metamorphosis either in froth or in some moist situation some distance from water. In these animals essentially all larval features are retained and the metamorphic pattern is essentially unchanged. The South American frog *Arthroleptella lightfooti* has a semiaquatic larva but is considerably adapted in the direction of direct development with the loss of gills, gill slits, and larval mouth parts. It does retain the larval operculum. Its tail shows no special adaptations.

Frogs of the genus *Cornufer* have essentially direct develop-ment. The operculum is the only larval structure that is re-tained. The embryos are distinctive in that their abdominal walls bulge into huge saclike structures that are obviously adapted for respiration, (Fig. 8).

Eleutherodactylus nubicola is representative of the some 200 different species of over 15 other genera in which the aquatic larval period and most of the larval characters are eliminated. The young are encased within gelatinous membranes through-out the developmental period to a stage equivalent to the termi-nation of metamorphosis. Information is fragmentary concerning most of these species, but a reasonable amount of detail is avail-able concerning a few such as Arthroleptella rattrayi as well as six species of *Eleutherodactylus* (Lynn, 1942; Lynn and Lutz, 1946). In these forms gills have either disappeared completely or are present in vestigial form. Gill slits never develop, and without them neither do internal gills. Among the species of *Eleutherodactylus* that have been studied, *nubicola* is the most advanced. In this species a trace of the lower larval lip and a small vestige of the posterior opercular anlage are the only larval characters that remain (Lynn, 1942). Among the other species of *Eleutherodactylus*, *E. portoricensis*, *E. nasutus*, and *E. guentheri* have evolved to a stage nearly equivalent to that of *E. nubicola*, whereas *E. inoptatus* and *E. martinicensis* have

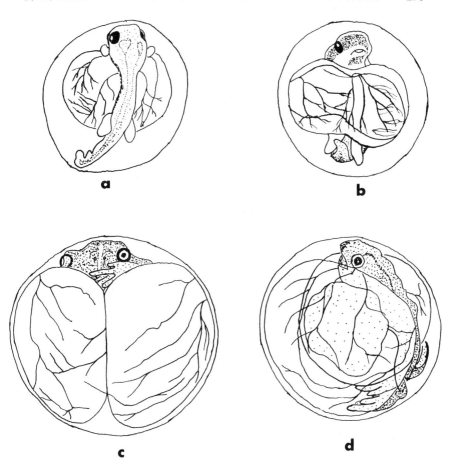

FIG. 8. Embryos of *Cornufer pelewensis* from the Palau Islands. The tremendously expanded abdominal sacs undoubtedly serve as organs of respiration. a and b are dorsal and ventral views of a young embryo, c is a ventral view of an animal nearing the hatching stage, and d is a lateral view of an advanced embryo. From Atoda, 1950.

transitory vestiges of external gills (Lynn and Lutz, 1946). In all of these animals the highly vascularized tail expands into a balloonlike structure and serves as an organ of respiration (Fig. 9a).

PARENTAL CARE AMONG ANURANS

Although they lack fetal membranes, anurans with direct development have otherwise reached a condition of oviparity equivalent to that typical of the birds and of many reptiles. The

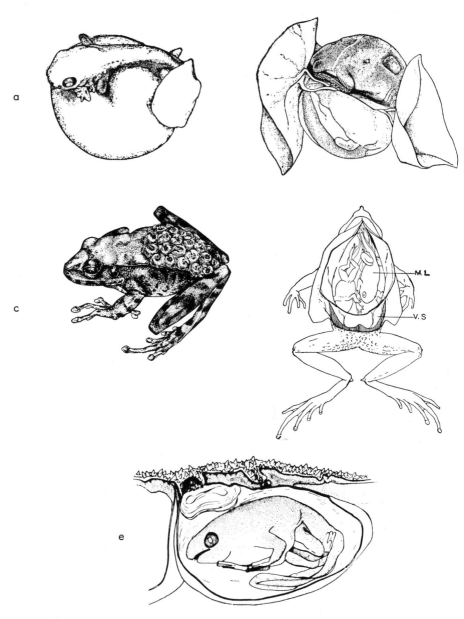

FIG. 9. a: Embryo of *Eleutherodactylus inoptatus* at early developmental stage. The short spade-shaped tail will expand into a mush-
room-shaped structure and serve as an organ of respiration. b: Advanced
developmental stage of *Gastrotheca marsupiata*. Note leaflike gills.
c: *Cryptobatrachus evansi*. A female carrying embryos upon her back.
d: Vocal sac in male specimen of *Rhinoderma darwinii* dissected to
show several partly metamorphosed larvae inside. e: Metamorphic individual of *Protopipa aspera* within a maternal dorsal pocket shown in
vertical section. From Noble, 1927 and 1931.

animals listed in Table 3 illustrate another approach to withdrawal from the water. They show a progressive increase in
parental care and handling that culminates in true ovoviviparity.
The "brooding" of eggs is not uncommon among those forms
with direct or near direct development. A parent guards the
eggs in several species of *Eleutherodactylus*, and the male of
Leiopelma guards the eggs (Stephenson, 1955). It has been
suggested by Jameson (1950) that the male of *Eleutherodactylus
latrans* wets down the eggs that it guards with urine to prevent
their drying out. Some wetting down of the encrusted froth nest
of *Chiromantis* by a guarding parent has also been reported by
Cochran (1961). The attention of the female of *Hemisus marmoratum* to her young was noted in the preceding section. The
animals cited in Table 3, however, actually transport their young
and have some quite intimate contact with them. The male of
Alytes (Fig. 7), the midwife toad, loops strings of eggs as they
are laid around his hind legs and then carries them about,
occasionally entering the water so that they are moistened,
until finally just before they hatch he enters the water and remains there until the larvae emerge from their membranes.

The males in some species of *Dendrobates* and also those
of *Phyllobates* pick up eggs after they have been laid on land
and transport them on their backs until some time after hatching
takes place. The young of both these genera as well as those of
Cryptobatrachus (Fig. 9c), in which the female provides the transportation, are deposited in the water, however, sometime prior
to the metamorphosis. *Hemiphractus* and *Gastrotheca*, the "ob-
stetrical frog" (Fig. 7), which is equipped with a pouch on its
back, vary from species to species with regard to the amount of
development that takes place while the young are being transported. In the species cited, *H. divaricatus* and *G. oviferum*,
transportation continues until metamorphosis is essentially complete but in some other species the larvae swim away before
metamorphosis begins. There is also variation in the yolk content
of the eggs from species to species, and those larvae with the
greater amounts of yolk remain longer on the back of the female
(Noble, 1927).

The Surinam toad *Pipa pipa* (Fig. 7) is well known for its
adaptation by means of which embryos are transported in
individual chambers on the back of the female. The chambers
develop when the skin thickens after the eggs have been pressed
into position on the back of the female by the belly of the male
during the mating process (Rabb and Rabb, 1960). There has
been some loss of larval characters by these larvae. Horny
mouthparts, for example, have been lost, but for the most part

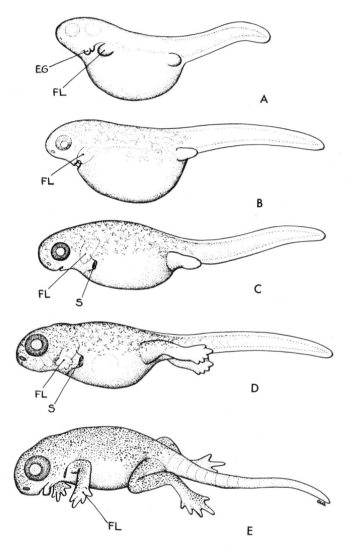

FIG. 10. Larvae removed from the oviduct of the ovoviviparous toad, *Nectophyrnoides tornieri*, at various developmental stages. In B the external gills and forelimb buds shown in A have been covered over by the developing operculum. In C operculum formation is complete and the spiracle is evident. In D metamorphosis is near as the forelimb becomes visible through the thin skin of the operculum. In E metamorphosis is underway. The forelimbs have emerged, and the tail fin has been resorbed. From Orton, 1949.

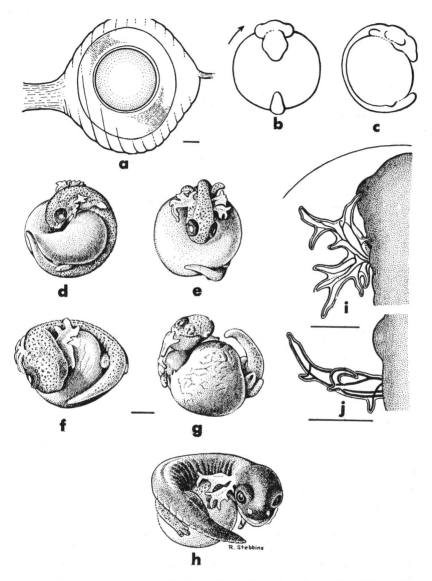

FIG. 11. Development of a plethodontid salamander (*Batracho-seps wrighti*). These diagrams are illustrative of development of most if not all, the Plethodontidae. a: Newly laid egg with its membranes. b and c: Tail bud stage showing anlagen of limbs and gills. d to g: Stage equivalent to free-swimming larva. Oral, cloacal, and nasola-bial grooves shown. h: Equivalent of premetamorphic stage. Digits well formed. i and j: Details of gills. Horizontal lines each represent 1 mm. From Stebbins, 1949.

they have the configuration of typical tadpoles and may actually feed on small organisms that come within their grasp during the last few weeks they are within their chambers (Rabb and Snedigar, 1960). A similar pattern of life history is found in two other species of *Pipa* and in the species of the closely related genus *Protopipa* (Fig. 9e), except that the larvae leave the female prior to metamorphosis.

Hylambates brevirostris is the only amphibian known to brood its eggs in its mouth, although this behavior pattern is encountered in several fishes. The female of *H. brevirostris* takes the fertilized eggs in her mouth and carries them there without eating until metamorphosis is complete (Cochran, 1961).

The reproductive adaptation of the Chilean frog *Rhinoderma darwinii* has been known since the voyage of H. M. S., Beagle but is nonetheless striking. In this species several males gather around the eggs after they have been laid and fertilized, guarding them for a brief period of time. Then one or more of the males takes a small complement of eggs into his mouth. From the mouth the eggs are moved into the vocal sac. The vocal sac gradually enlarges as the embryos increase in size (Fig. 9d). The larvae are typical in form and undergo a typical metamorphosis with the exception that the horny teeth and beaks never harden (Noble, 1927). Although the embryos have a considerable amount of yolk, some feeding may take place toward the end of the developmental period while they are still encased within the vocal sac.

In the three species of *Nectophrynoides*, ovoviviparity is attained. The larvae are equipped with gill slits and suckers, but horny beaks and teeth are absent (Fig. 10). The long, ratlike tail has very low fins. Although its surface area is not very great the tail is well vascularized and obviously has a respiratory function. This is quite apparent in *N. vivipara*. Here the uterus may contain as many as 100 larvae whose bodies tend to be located toward the central part of the uterus and whose elongate tails are arranged so as to have a maximal contact with the uterine wall (Noble, 1931). Angel and Lamotte (1944) report *N. occidentalis* to be without a spiracle. Orton (1949) states that a spiracle is present in *N. tornieri* but that it is quite small.

WITHDRAWAL FROM THE WATER BY URODELES

As is shown in Table 4, the movement from the water in the Urodela is roughly parallel to that in the Anura. Several species (including, oddly enough, the neotenic and otherwise

TABLE 4

URODELES WITH TERRESTRIAL PATTERNS OF LIFE HISTORY

	Family	Genus	Species	Region
Eggs laid on land but larvae aquatic	Ambystomidae	Ambystoma	opacum	Eastern U.S.
	Amphiumidae	Amphiuma	tridactylium	Southeastern U.S.
	Plethodontidae	Desmognathus	9 species	Eastern U.S.
		Hemidactylium	scutatum	Northeast U.S. and Southeast Canada
		Stereochilus	marginatum	Southeastern U.S.
Eggs laid on land with direct development	Plethodontidae	Batrachoseps	3 species	West Coast of U.S.
		Aneides	5 species	Appalachian Mountains and West Coast
		Plethodon	16 species	U.S. and Canada
		Ensatina	escholtzi	West Coast North America
	Proteidae	Proteus	anguinus (at lower temperatures)	Central Europe
Eggs retained in utero during development	Salamandridae	Salamandra	salamandra	Central Europe
			atra	Central Europe
	Plethodontidae	Hydromantes	5 species	Southern Europe and California
		Oedipus	30 species	Central and South America

aquatic *Amphiuma*) lay their eggs on land but near water that fluctuates in level so that the embryos are swept into it prior to hatching (Goin and Goin, 1962).

Among the urodeles, direct development is accomplished only in the family Plethodontidae. The large, yolk-laden eggs are surrounded individually with heavy gelatinous membranes. In general, there is no loss of larval characters and no deviation from the typical metamorphic pattern except that the gills are larger and longer than those of aquatic larvae (Fig. 11).

In view of its neoteny it is somewhat surprising to find that *Proteus* is often ovoviparous in the lower temperatures of its range. The European newt *Salamandra salamandra* likewise retains embryos in utero until after they hatch, sometimes apparently stimulated by low temperatures, throughout metamorphosis. *Salamandra atra* is consistently ovoviviparous, as are the plethodontids, *Hydromantes*, and *Oedipus*. As in the oviparous urodeles, with direct development there is no loss of larval characters in ovoviviparous urodeles. The intrauterine larvae of *Salamandra*, for example, develop rudimentary balancers and lateral line organs (Noble, 1931). The elongate gills of these creatures function in the exchange of respiratory gases between maternal and larval bloodstreams.

THE ROLE OF THE THYROID GLAND IN DIRECT DEVELOPMENT

In a preceding section the involvement of the thyroid gland in amphibian neoteny was commented upon. Its function in direct development is also a matter of considerable interest. As early as 1917 Hoskins and Hoskins showed that the course of typical metamorphosis was halted by removal of the thyroid gland. In 1925, Allen found some difference in *Bufo* and *Rana* in the degree to which limbs will grow in the absence of thyroid stimulation. In *Bufo* the hind limbs of thyroidectomized larvae may reach a length of 8 mm, whereas those of *Rana* remain as small buds. It is well known that administration of thyroid hormone to normal tadpoles brings about precocious metamorphosis. It seems possible, then, that direct development may consist of a telescoping of larval stages resulting from a precocious metamorphosis brought about by an early and intensive functioning of the thyroid gland, by an unusually high sensitivity of the tissues to a relatively low thyroidal activity, or by the emancipation of the tissues from the need for stimulation by the thyroid hormone (Lynn, 1961). Histological observations made by Lynn in 1936 indicated that in *Eleutherodactylus* the thyroid began to function early in the developmental period and therefore might be responsible for a precocious metamorphosis. Similar conclusions were reached by Brink in 1939 with regard to *Arthroleptella bicolor*, but Dent found that the thyroid differentiates late in the intraoval life of the terrestrial salamanders *Plethodon cinereus* (1942) and *Aneides anaeus* (1954).

Embryos of neither *Plethodon* nor *Eleutherodactylus* have survived attempts to remove the anlage of the thyroid by surgical procedures. In 1947, however, Lynn treated embryos of *Plethodon cinereus* with the goitrogen thiourea, blocking thyroid function by chemical means. Those embryos completed their development except for the resorption of the long and branched gills. Similarly, Lynn (1948) and (Lynn) and Peadon in 1955 reported results of treating with goitrogens *Eleutherodactylus ricordii* and *Eleutherodactylus martinicensis*. Three metamorphic features were affected by the treatment. The pronephoroes did not degenerate, the tail was not resorbed, and the egg tooth the animal develops just prior to hatching did not drop off as it ordinarily does. Administration of thyroxin to *Eleutherodactylus martinicensis* caused precocious degeneration of the pronephroes and resorption of the tail. Thus it seems clear that the final steps of direct development are under control of the thyroid but that in the course of evolution the greater part of the ontogenetic sequence has been freed from thyroidal control in *Plethodon* and in *Eleutherodactylus*.

ENVIRONMENTAL FACTORS IN METAMORPHOSIS

Dodd and Callan (1955) found sexually mature neotenic individuals within an otherwise typical population of *Triturus helveticus* congregated in a pond of the county of Fife in Scotland. As indicated in Table 1, neoteny has been reported to occur occasionally in several species of *Triturus*. These specimens of *T. helveticus*, however, were unique in that their thyroid glands were goiterous and tremendously enlarged. This condition could hardly be attributed to a lack of iodine in the environment since the pond is situated within a few miles of the North Sea, and the iodine content of drinking water in the nearby town of Crail is 5μ g/l. Dodd and Callan noted that kale and turnips were cultivated in fields in the vicinity of the pond. The goitrogenic effects of the brassicas is well known (see Chapter 8). Rabbits were frequently seen in the vicinity of the pond, and rabbit feces accumulated on the slopes from which water drained into the pond. Dodd and Callan concluded that this drainage water should contain the "brassica factor" at times when the rabbits were feeding on turnips and kale and that larvae overwintering in the pond might well, as a result, become goiterous and neotenic. Although it is interesting, it is unlikely that this condition described by Dodd and Callan for *T. helveticus* obtains generally among other occasionally neotenic forms.

Notophthalmus viridescens is neotenic in the lowlands of Louisiana, on Cape Cod, and on Long Island; but the majority of the neotenous individuals among the species listed in category 3 of Table 1 live in lakes located at altitudes of several thousand feet, as does *Siredon pisciformis*, the axolotl cited in category 2. Snyder (1956) has made a comparative study of the Pacific Coast salamander *Ambystoma gracile* from ponds found at sea level and from other ponds at high elevations (4,300 to 5,500 ft.) in Mount Ranier National Park. At sea level a high proportion of larvae transform into immature adults at one year of age, and most of the remainder transform at two years of age as sexual maturity is attained. A small number persist as neotenic larvae. Adult animals are found in the montane habitats, but metamorphosis appears to be rare and most of the mature animals are neotenic. Snyder states that among amphibians cold either inhibits the release of thyroid hormone or the ability of tissues to respond to its presence, and Huxley (1929) has demonstrated that below 50^0F the tissues of tadpoles are not stimulated by thyroidal material. Frieden has studied this effect extensively (see Chapter 9). Snyder states further that younger larvae respond more readily than older animals to the metamorphic effects of the thyroid hormone. This contention is supported by observations of Lipchina (1929) made on the axolotl. At high elevations the annual period of activity and growth lasts only about three months, whereas at sea level larvae may be active and feeding throughout the year. Snyder suggests that since the montane larvae reach metamorphic size at a later age they are possibly less responsive to the thyroid hormone or perhaps produce less thyroid hormone and thus do not metamorphose. The presence of some neotenic animals at sea level is accounted for by Snyder on the grounds that eggs are laid over a period of five to six weeks and that perhaps the last laid eggs give rise to animals that overwinter as larvae and reach the age at which they are resistant to the thyroid hormone. Some brief experiments of a preliminary nature appeared to give support to this hypothesis, but further studies should be made.

From an evolutionary point of view it seems reasonable that the selective pressures would be greater on the barren icy borders of a mountain lake than within its waters. Similarly, in the caves inhabited by most of the animals of category 2 in Table 1 it is usually quite apparent that food is more abundant and other conditions are more favorable to the salamander within the water than outside of it. Very likely it is these selective pressures that have brought about the rise of neoteny in caves and in mountain lakes.

Pedogenesis has never been found to occur among the Anura, but the larval period in some frogs varies greatly in length. Temperature appears to be the predominant factor involved. *Rana clamitans*, the green frog, is usually said to metamorphose after spending one winter as a larva, but Ting (1951) showed that tadpoles of *R. clamitans* metamorphosed in 92 days in the laboratory, and Martof (1952) found that great numbers of larvae metamorphosed in August from a pond that had been dry the preceding summer. He thought that overwintering larvae come from eggs laid late in the season. The bullfrog *Rana catesbeiana* also has a larval period of variable length, as shown in Table 5, which is taken from a paper by Willis,

TABLE 5

AGE OF BULLFROG TADPOLES AT TRANSFORMATION IN VARIOUS PARTS OF THE UNITED STATES[a]

Locality	Number of Winters of Life Before Transformation				Reference
	0	1	2	3	
New York			X	X	Wright (1914)
Iowa			X	X	Carlander et al. (1950)
California			X		Storer (1922)
Iowa		X			Klimstra (1949)
Florida		X			Fla. D. Ag. (1952)
Louisiana	X	?			George (1940)
Gulf States	X	X			Viosca (1934)

[a] From Willis, Moyle, and Baskett (1956).

Moyle, and Baskett (1956). These figures indicate that the larval period increases with the length and severity of winters.

The length of the larval period may also be increased in urodeles without the occurrence of paedogenesis. Many individuals of *Eurycea bislineata* metamorphose in their second year, but some (presumably those from eggs laid late in the first year) metamorphose in the third year (Wilder, 1924; Duellman and Wood, 1954). In southern Europe *Triturus vulgaris* metamorphoses in the fall of its first summer, but in northern Russia it hibernates for one winter as a larva (Terent'ev, 1965), no doubt because the summers in the latter region are not long enough or warm enough for it to complete its larval development in one of them.

For reasons discussed in Chapter 8, in looking about for environmental features that may be responsible for neoteny in any given group of amphibians one always gives consideration to the iodine content of the water. Actually, no one has yet reported finding neotenous larvae in water with an iodine content too low to support metamorphosis in other amphibian species. Blair (1961) reported that one of two specimens of neotenic *Gyrinophilus palleucus* metamorphosed after three months in a rather strong solution of sodium iodide, but the other was still unchanged after six months, and as was pointed out earlier Dent and Kirby-Smith (1963) found that specimens of this species occasionally metamorphose spontaneously in spring water under laboratory conditions. Although the induction of metamorphosis in the axolotl by the application of iodine has been reported (Ingram, 1928), the amount given was relatively large (Lipchina, 1929). It seems safe to conclude that low iodine content of water is not ordinarily a cause of neoteny.

It is to be expected that larvae deprived of food would soon stop growing and differentiating. As far back as 1878 Yung reported that amphibian larvae are highly susceptible to nutritional deficiency and that their development is conditioned by the nature of the food. In 1887, Barfurth noted that under certain conditions the development of tadpoles was accelerated by starvation. This phenomenon was investigated in detail by D'Angelo, Gordon, and Charipper (1941). They found that up to a critical period occurring in the early stages of hind-limb development metamorphic progress is slowed down and then halted by inanition so that tadpoles can be held for considerable periods of time in a "stasis" condition. Having passed the critical stage, the rate of metamorphosis indeed is increased by inanition. Possibly inanition accelerates the degenerative phases of metamorphosis. D'Angelo, Gordon, and

Charipper observed that the thyroid and pituitary glands of starved animals underwent atrophic and degenerative changes. Stasis tadpoles metamorphose readily after either immersion in thyroxin solutions or injection with pituitary material. The thyroid glands of stasis animals that are metamorphosing after treatment with thyroxin are histologically inactive, but those of pituitary-injected tadpoles give histological evidence of marked activity. On the basis of these observations it was concluded that the failure of starved animals to metamorphose is directly related to a decreased production and release of thyrotropic hormone from the anterior hypophysis.

Any naturally occurring inanition would be likely to be associated with crowding, and crowding itself appears to have a direct effect on the growth of amphibian larvae. It was Yung (1885), again, who first made observations on the relation of crowding to the delay in tadpole metamorphosis. His work was followed by that of others; notably, Adolph in 1931 and more recently Richards (1958 and 1962), Rose (1960), and Akin (1966). Adolph saw that uncrowded animals reached a much larger size than crowded ones and that they metamorphosed in a much briefer period of time. Rose observed that whenever a group of R. pipiens embryos were put in a rather confined space all began to grow after hatching, but at different rates. Those that grew more rapidly at first and became larger than their bowl mates continued to grow if the water was changed daily, whereas those that lagged behind stopped growing and failed to eat even when abundant food was supplied to them. On the other hand, the stunted animals grew if they were removed and put into other containers, giving greater "lebensraum." Richards (1958) showed that if small tadpoles were put into culture water in which large tadpoles had been growing the growth of the small tadpoles was completely or almost completely inhibited, indicating that some sort of inhibitory product is thrown off into the medium by the larger tadpoles. Further, the inhibitory effect could be removed by heating the culture water to 60°, by centrifugation, by sonification, or by filtration. Thus, the inhibitory product is a rather large particle.

In an aquarium where both large and small animals were present and the small ones were growing poorly and dying out, the largest animals were just as large as large animals that had been growing in isolation (Rose, 1960). This indicates that the large animals were unaffected by anything produced by the small tadpoles or that the small ones were neither producing stimulatory nor inhibitory substances. The growth of small tadpoles was supported, on the other hand, by culture water from

METAMORPHOSIS: A PROBLEM IN DEVELOPMENTAL BIOLOGY

large tadpoles after it had been treated with a proteinase. At least some of the inhibitory material, then, must be a protein. Richards (1962) reported that the inhibitory agent is associated with a type of algal cell in *R. pipiens.* Akin (1966) showed that the agent is elaborated by the posterior half of the gut in the growing tadpole. The algae pass through the gut and apparently transport the agent to the water. Akin also confirmed earlier reports that the agent is largely species-specific.

There are no reports of the inhibitory effects of crowding in nature, but such effects must exist since in the laboratory one rapidly growing large tadpole can appreciably retard the growth of small tadpoles in as much as 75 liters of water (Rose, 1960).

There have been reports that various electrolytes have accelerating or inhibitory effects on metamorphosis. Lynn and Wachowski (1951), however, are of the opinion that these apparent electrolytic effects are caused by changes in the hydrogen ion concentration of the medium rather than by any specific effects of the ion in question. Marzulli in 1941 confirmed earlier observations of Rosen (1938) to the effect that acidity below pH 4.8 and alkalinity above pH 11.0, respectively accelerate and retard the metamorphosing action of thyroxin. Marzulli further demonstrated that if thyroxin is injected its effects are not dependent on the pH of the culture medium. He concluded that the greater effectiveness of thyroxin dissolved in an acid culture medium results from the fact that it is taken up more actively by the tissues at acid rather than alkaline pH levels. For further discussion of the uptake of thyroxin, see Chapter 9.

Disclos (1959) reported increased metamorphic rates among tadpoles of *Alytes obstetricans* given supplemental illumination, and Guyétant (1964) found that growth and metamorphosis were accelerated in larvae of *R. temporaria* maintained in constant illumination at 2,000 and 4,000 lux, whereas tadpoles kept in permanent darkness grew more slowly. It seems likely that the effects of illumination upon development will be found to be quite complex. Possibly they are mediated through the neuro-secretory pathways of the hypothalamus. This area of investigation is relatively untouched and may be the source of very interesting results in the future.

ACKNOWLEDGMENT

The author wishes to thank Professor W. Gardner Lynn, Dr. James Peters and Dr. Doris Cochran for their kindness in reading and commenting on the text. The help of Mrs. Jan Redick in preparing illustrations is gratefully acknowledged.

REFERENCES

Adolph, E. F. 1931. Body size as a factor in the metamorphosis of tadpoles. Biol. Bull., 61:376–386.

Akin, Gwynn C. 1966. Self-inhibition of growth in *Rana pipens* tadpoles. Physiol. Zool., 39:341–356.

Allen, B. M. 1925. The effects of extirpation of the thyroid and pituitary glands upon the limb development of anurans. J. Exp. Zool., 42:13–30.

Anderson, J. D. 1961. The life history and systematics of *Ambystoma rosaceum*. Copeia, 1961:371–376.

Angel, F., and M. Lamotte. 1944. Un crapaud vivipare d'Afrique occidentale, *Nectophrynoides occidentalis* Angel. Ann. Sci. Nat. (Zool.), 6:63–89.

Barfurth, D. 1887. Die Ruckbildung des Froschlarvenschwanzes und die sogenannten Sarcoplasten. Arch. Mikrobiol. Anat., 29:35–60.

Blair, A. P. 1961. Metamorphosis of *Pseudotriton palleucus* with iodine. Copeia, 1961:499.

Blount, R. F. 1950. The effects of heteroplastic hypophyseal grafts upon the axolotl, *Ambystoma mexicannum*. J. Exp. Zool., 113:717–739.

Boschwitz, D. 1957. Thyroidless tadpoles of *Pelobates syriacus* Boettger H. Copeia, 1957:310–311.

Brink, H. E. 1939. A histological and cytological investigation of the thyroids of *Arthroleptella bicolor villiersi* and *Bufo angusticeps* during normal and accelerated metamorphosis. Proc. Linn. Soc. Lond., 151:120–125.

Carr, A. F., Jr. 1939. *Haideotriton wallacei*, a new subterranean salamander from Georgia. Occasional Papers Boston Soc. Nat. Hist., 8:333–336.

Cochran, Doris M. 1961. Living Amphibians of the World. New York, Hanover House.

D'Angelo, S. A., A. S. Gordon, and H. A. Charipper. 1941. The role of the thyroid and pituitary glands in the anomalous effect of inanition on amphibian metamorphosis. J. Exp. Zool., 87:259–277.

Dent, J. N. 1942. The embryonic development of *Plethodon cinereus* as correlated with the differentiation and functioning of the thyroid gland. J. Morph., 71:577–601.

_____. 1954. Observations on iodine metabolism in embryos of the terrestrial salamander *Aneides anaeus*. Anat. Rec., 118:294.

_____. 1956. Observations on the life history and development of *Leptodactylus albilabris*. Copeia, 1956:207–210.

_____, and J. S. Kirby-Smith. 1963. Metamorphic physiology and morphology of the cave salamander *Gyrinophilus palleucus*. Copeia, 1963:119–130.

_____, J. S. Kirby-Smith, and Doris L. Craig. 1955. Induction of metamorphosis in *Gyrinophilus palleucus*. Anat. Rec., 121:429.

Disclos, P. 1959. Influence régulatrice de la lumière sur le développement de têtrards *d'Alytes obstetricans* Laur. soumis à un traitment thyroxinien. C. R. Acad. Sci., 249:1277–1279.

Dodd, J. M., and H. G. Callan. 1955. Neoteny with goitre in *Triturus helveticus*. Quart. J. Micr. Sci., 96:121–128.

Duellman, W. E., and J. T. Wood. 1954. Size and growth of the two-lined salamander, *Eurycea bislineata rivicola*. Copeia, 1954:92–96.

Dundee, H. A. 1957. Partial metamorphosis induced in *Typhlomolge rathbuni*. Copeia, 1957:52–53.

_____. 1961. Response of the neotenic salamander *Haideotriton wallacei* to a metamorphic agent. Science, 135:1060–1061.

_____, and A. Gorbman. 1960. Utilization of radioiodine by thyroid of neotenic salamander, *Eurycea tynerensis* Moore and Hughes. Physiol. Zool., 33:58–62.

Emerson, E. T. 1950. General Anatomy of *Typhlomolge rathbuni*. Proc. Boston Soc. Nat. Hist., 32:43–74.

Etkin, W. E. 1932. Growth and resorption phenomena in anuran metamorphosis, I. Physiol. Zool., 5:275–300.

_____. 1935. The mechanisms of anuran metamorphosis. I. Thyroxine concentrations and the metamorphic pattern. J. Exp. Zool., 71:317–340.

_____. 1955. Metamorphosis. *In* B. H. Willier, P. A. Weiss, and V. Hamburger, eds., "Analysis of Development" pp. 631–663. Philadelphia, Saunders.

_____. 1964. Metamorphosis. *In* John A. Moore, ed., "Physiology of the Amphibia." New York, Academic Press, pp. 427-468.

Goin, C. J., and O. B. Goin. 1962. Introduction to Herpetology. San Francisco and London, Freeman.

Gorbman, A. 1957. The thyroid gland of *Typhlomolge rathbuni*. Copeia, 1957:41–43.

Gosner, K. L. 1960. A simplified table for staging anuran embryos and larvae with notes on identification. Herpetologica, 16:183–190.

Grant, Madeline P. 1930a. Diagnostic stages of urodele metamorphosis. With references to *Amblystoma punctatum* and
Triturus viridescens. Anat. Rec., 45:1–25.

_____. 1930b. Diagnostic stages of metamorphosis in *Amblystoma
opacum* and *A. jeffersonianum*. Anat. Rec., 47:330.

Gutman, A. B. 1926. Metamorphosis in *Necturus maculosus* by
means of thyroxin-adrenalin treatment. Anat. Rec., 34:133–
134.

Guyétant, R. 1964. Actions comparée de la lumière et de
l'obscurité sur la croissance et la metamorphose des têtards
de *Rana temporaria* L. Ann. Sci. Univ. Besancon-Zool.,
Physiol., 19:77–98.

Hoskins, E. R., and M. M. Hoskins. 1917. On thyroidectomy
in amphibia. Proc. Soc. Exp. Biol. Med., 14:74–75.

Huxley, J. S. 1929. Thyroid and temperature in cold blooded
vertebrates. Nature, 123:712.

Ingram, W. R. 1928. Metamorphosis of the Colorado axolotl by
injection of inorganic iodine. Proc. Soc. Exp. Biol. Med.,
26:191.

Jameson, D. L. 1950. The development of *Eleutherodactylus
latrans*. Copeia, 1950:44–46.

Jurand, A. 1955. Neoteny in *Xenopus laevis* Daud., Folia Biol.,
3:315–330.

Kezer, J. 1952. Thyroxin induced metamorphosis of the neotenic
salamanders *Eurycea tynerensis* and *Eurycea neotenes*.
Copeia, 1952:234–237.

Kobayashi, H., and A. Gorbman. 1962. Thyroid function in
Amphiuma. Gen. Comp. Endocr., 2:279–282.

Limbaugh, Beverly A. and E. P. Volpe. 1957. Early development
of the Gulf Coast Toad, *Bufo valliceps* Wiegmann. Amer.
Mus. Novitates, 1842:1–32.

Lipchina, L. P. 1929. The dependence of the process of metamorphosis in axolotls on factors of age, coloring and sex.
Zh. Eksp. Biol. Med., 13:73–78.

Lutz, Bertha. 1947. Trends towards non-aquatic and direct
development in frogs. Copeia, 1947:242–252.

_____. 1948. Ontogenetic evolution in frogs. Evolution, 2:29–39.

Lynn, W. G. 1936. A study of the thyroid in embryos of *Eleutherodactylus nubicola*. Anat. Rec., 64:525–539.

_____. 1942. The embryology of *Eleutherodactylus nubicola*, an
anuran which has no tadpole stage. Carn. Inst. Wash.
Contrs. Embryol., 190:27–62.

_____. 1947. The effects of thiourea and phenylthiourea upon the
development of *Plethodon cinereus*. Biol. Bull., 93:199.

_____. 1948. The effects of thiourea and phenylthiourea upon the development of *Eleutherodactylus ricordii*. Biol. Bull., 94:1–15.

_____. 1961. Types of amphibian metamorphosis. Amer. Zool., 1:151–161.

_____, and Bertha Lutz. 1946. The development of *Eleutherodactylus guentheri Stdnr*. 1864, Bol. Museu Nacional—Zool., 71:1–46.

_____, and Annie M. Peadon. 1955. The role of the thyroid gland in direct development in the anuran. *Eleutherodactyplus martinicenis*. Growth, 19:263–286.

_____, and H. E. Wachowski. 1951. The thyroid gland and its functions in cold-blooded vertebrates. Quart. Rev. Biol., 26:123–168.

Martof, B. 1952. Early transformation of the greenfrog, *Rana clamitans* Latreille. Copeia, 1952:115–116.

Marzulli, F. N. 1941. The effects of hydrogen ion concentration upon the metamorphic pattern of thyroxin- and iodine-treated tadpoles. J. Gen. Physiol., 25:623–647.

Noble, G. K. 1924. The "retrograde metamorphosis" of the Sirenidae. Anat. Rec., 29:100.

_____. 1927. The value of life history data in the study of the evolution of the amphibia. Ann. N.Y. Acad. Sci., 30:31–128.

_____. 1931. Biology of the Amphibia. New York, McGraw-Hill.

_____, and E. J. Farris. 1929. A metamorphic change produced in *Cryptobranchus* by thyroid solutions. Anat. Rec., 42:59.

Orton, Grace L. 1949. Larval development of *Nectophrynoides tornieri* (Roux), with comments on direct development in frogs. Ann. Carn. Mus., 31:257–277.

_____. 1951a. Direct development in frogs. Turtox News, 29:2–6.

_____. 1951b. The tadpole of *Leptodactylus melanonotus* (Hallowell). Copeia, 1951:62–66.

Pylka, J. M., and R. D. Warren. 1958. A population of *Haideotriton* in Florida. Copeia, 1958:334–336.

Rabb, G. B., and Mary S. Rabb. 1960. On the mating and egg-laying behavior of the Surinam toad, *Pipa pipa*. Copeia, 1960:271–276.

_____, and R. Sneidgar. 1960 Observations on breeding and development of Surinam toad *Pipa pipa.* Copeia, 1960:40–440.

Reis, Karolina. 1932. La métamorphose de greffes hétéroplastiques de la peau des amphibiens néoténiques *(Proteus anguineus)*. C. R. Soc. Biol. Paris, 109:1015.

Richards, Christina M. 1958. The inhibition of growth in crowded Rana pipiens tadpoles. Physiol. Zool., 31:138—151

_____. 1962. The control of tadpole growth by alga-like cells. Physiol. Zool., 35:285-296.

Rose, S. M. 1960. A feedback mechanism of growth control in tadpoles. Ecology, 41:188-199.

Rosen, S. H. 1938. Effect of pH upon metamorphosing action of thyroxine on tadpoles. Proc. Soc. Exp. Biol. Med., 38:171-176.

Saxén, L. 1957. Schilddrusenaplasie als Ursache von partieller Neotenie. Acta Endocr., 24:271-281.

Snyder, R. C. 1956. Comparative features of the life histories of *Ambystoma gracile* (Baird) from populations at low and high altitudes. Copeia, 1956:41-50.

Stebbins, R. C. 1949. Observations on laying, development, and hatching of the eggs of *Batrachoseps wrighti*. Copeia, 1949:161-168.

Stephenson, N. G. 1951. Observations on the development of the amphicoelus frogs, *Leiopelma* and *Ascaphus*. J. Linn. Soc. (Zool.), 42:18-28.

_____. 1955. On the development of the frog, *Leiopelma hochstetteri* Fitzinger. Proc. Zool. Soc. London, 124:785-795.

Taylor, A. C., and J. J. Kollros. 1946. Stages in the normal development of *Rana pipiens* larvae. Anat. Rec., 94:7-23.

Terent'ev, P. V. 1965. Herpetology. Springfield, Virginia, U.S. Department of Commerce.

Ting, H. P. 1951. Duration of the tadpole stage of the green frog, *Rana clamitans*. Copeia, 1951:82.

Uhlenhuth, E. 1923. The endocrine system of *Typhlomolge rathbuni*. Biol. Bull., 45:303-324.

Wilder, Inez W. 1924. The relation of growth to metamorphosis in *Eurycea bislineata* (Green). J. Exp. Zool., 40:1-112.

_____. 1925. The morphology of Amphibian Metamorphosis. Northampton, Massachusetts, Smith College Press.

Willis, Y. L., D. L. Moyle, and T. S. Baskett. 1956. Emergence, breeding, hibernation, movements, and transformation of the bullfrog, *Rana catesbeiana*, in Missouri, Copeia, 1956:30-40.

Young, J. Z. 1962. The Life of the Vertebrates. New York, Oxford University Press.

Yung, E. 1878. Contributions a l'histoire de l'influence des milieux physiques sur les etres vivants. Arch. Zool. Exp., 7:251-282.

_____. 1885. De l'influence des variations du milieu physiochemique sur le developpement des animaux. Arch., Sci. Phys. Nat., 14:502-522.

eight

HORMONAL CONTROL OF
AMPHIBIAN METAMORPHOSIS

William Etkin

Department of Anatomy
Albert Einstein College of Medicine
Bronx, New York

INTRODUCTION

If instead of reviewing the published endocrine studies on amphibian metamorphosis we ask questions concerning the endocrine control of the process from the viewpoint of developmental physiology, we become impressed more with the lacunae in our knowledge than with the strength of the separate threads. In any event the general endocrine interrelations in this field have been reviewed in some detail (see reviews by Allen, 1938, and Bounhiol, 1942; Lynn and Wachowski, 1951; Etkin, 1955, 1964; Kollros, 1961). Here we propose to examine metamorphosis from the viewpoint of the physiology of animal development rather than to inquire into the role of the separate endocrine glands. Before we can do that, however, we must summarize the main outlines of the endocrine relations among vertebrates generally in order to provide the framework within which we can ask our questions concerning control of metamorphic change by the hormones.

GENERAL ENDOCRINE RELATIONSHIPS RELATED TO THE CONTROL OF METAMORPHOSIS

No detailed citations to the literature will be given for this discussion of endocrine interrelationships, but such references can be found in recent summaries of the field such as the recent volumes on *Neuroendocrinology* (Martini and Ganong, 1966 and 1967) and *The Pituitary Gland* (Harris and Donovan, 1966) and in standard textbooks of endocrinology.

The thyroid hormones (TH) are iodine-containing derivatives of tyrosine whose chemistry is detailed in Chapter 10. The principal hormone is thyroxine. The thyroid gland has an iodine-trapping mechanism whose efficiency as determined with radioiodine (I^{131}) is one measure of thyroid activity. The histological picture presented by the thyroid is also a clear indicator of its physiological state. Abundant cytoplasm and release of colloid from the follicles indicate active glands. However, where iodine uptake is prevented by goitrogens, a histological picture of activity is associated with the failure to release potent hormone.

The thyroid gland can function autonomously at a low level, but higher levels of activity are dependent upon activation by a hormone, thyrotropin, or thyroid-stimulating hormone (TSH), produced by the anterior lobe of the pituitary. The level of activity of the pituitary-thyroid (PT) axis is under control through two known mechanisms.

One of these is by way of feedback of thyroid hormones that inhibit the activity of the TSH cells, thus stabilizing the PT axis at a particular level. There is good evidence that this negative feedback of TH upon TSH production operates primarily at the pituitary level, directly inhibiting the TSH cells.

The second mode of regulating TSH activity is by way of a thyrotropin releasing factor (TRF) produced in the hypothalamus. TRF is presumed to be a neurosecretory material reaching the anterior pituitary by way of the pituitary portal veins that drain the median eminence of the hypothalamus. At present the chemical nature of TRF has not been clarified nor have the neural cells from which it arises been identified. It is believed, however, to differ from the peptides that constitute the classical neurosecretory substances produced in hypothalamic nuclei (preoptic nucleus in amphibians) and stored in the neural lobe of the pituitary (see the recent review by Reichlin, 1966). In stimulating TSH production, TRF may be thought to act by partially desensitizing the pituitary to the negative feedback action of TH and thereby permitting the level of the TP axis, the so-called thyrostat, to rise.

A word of clarification is needed with regard to the concept of neurosecretion. This has undergone marked development in recent years (Knowles and Bern, 1966). Originally neurosecretion was identified by characteristic, although not specific, staining reactions in light microscopy, i.e., neuronal granules positive to aldehyde fuchsin or chrome alum haematoxylin. Physiological, histochemical, and electronmicroscopical evidence has compelled the recognition that such material is related primarily to the pars nervosa although also occurring in the median eminence (Oota and Kobayashi, 1963). This latter region, however, has been shown to be rich in monoamines and in peptides differing from those of the nervosa. In the present discussion the neurosecretory system will be considered to include in addition to the classical neurosecretory pathway to the posterior lobe of the pituitary:

1. Neurons that produce other specific chemicals released into the bloodstream in the median eminence.
2. The median eminence with its primary capillary bed intimately related to neurosecretory fibers.
3. The portal veins that drain blood from the primary capillary bed of the median eminence into the secondary capillary bed of the pars anterior of the pituitary (see Fig. 8).

These endocrine and neuroendocrine interrelations are applicable to amphibian metamorphosis. As early as 1912, Gudernatch reported that the feeding of thyroid-gland preparations to young tadpoles precipitated metamorphic changes. It was soon demonstrated—particularly by M. Allen, Hoskins, and Hoskins and P. E. Smith (see reviews)—that the pituitary gland of the tadpole controls thyroid activity and that the latter is the immediate agent of metamorphic change (also see Chapter 10 for evidence on direct action of thyroid hormones). The neuroendocrine relations governing metamorphosis were worked out more recently. The evidence is convincing here, too, that the hypothalamus influences pituitary TSH activity by way of a TRF passed. into the capillaries of the median eminence.

Another pituitary hormone that recently assumed a role in our understanding of metamorphosis is prolactin, which like TSH is a protein product of the anterior lobe of the pituitary. It is known to be active in stimulating body growth in several vertebrates (Meites and Nicoll, 1965) and has recently been found to have antithyroid activity in tadpoles (see frontispiece E and F; Etkin and Gona, 1967; Gona, 1967). In mammals and probably in amphibians (see below) prolactin appears to be under inhibitory rather than stimulatory control by the hypothalamus (Everett, 1966).

THE METAMORPHIC PATTERN IN A TYPICAL ANURAN

In Chapter 7 the variety of developmental patterns among amphibians was described. However, the endocrine analysis with which we are concerned here has been carried out largely on a few species of anurans. To follow this analysis it will be most useful to have a more exact and quantitative delineation of the developmental pattern relative to metamorphosis in a typical Ranid, *Rana pipiens*. This is provided in Figs. 1 and 2. The principal points to be noted here are as follows. The first post-

FIG. 1. A. Normal tadpoles of *Rana pipiens* at beginning and at end of growth phase. B. Normal tadpoles: a = day before emergence of foreleg (E − 1); b = E + 0; c = E + 1; d = E + 2; e = E + 4. C. Results of treating early tadpoles with strong concentrations of thyroxine (243 ppb). D. Normal metamorphic morphology produced in large thyroidectomized tadpole treated with a patterned sequence of increasing concentrations of thyroxine. E. Results of treating a large hypophysectomized tadpole as in D. From Etkin, 1964.

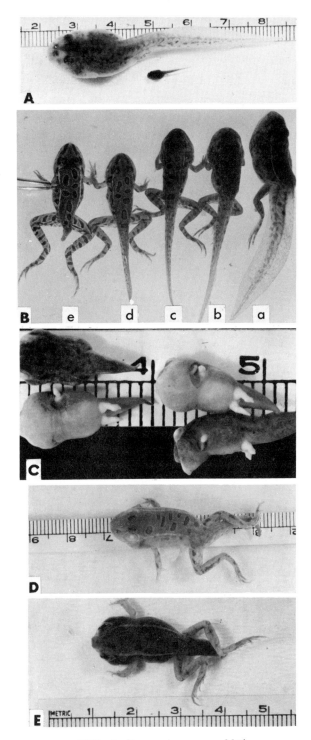

FIG. 1. (Legend on page 316)

embryonic period is characterized by much growth with very little change in form. This is here designated the growth or premetamorphic period and lasts about seven weeks at conventional room temperatures (22 to 25°C). This is followed by the period designated prometamorphosis and characterized by differential growth of the hind legs. During this period of about three weeks, the legs grow from about 2 mm to about 20 mm, whereas the body growth increases only from about 55 mm total length (body length, 18 mm; tail length, 37 mm) to 65 mm (body length, 21 mm; tail length, 44 mm). It is easy to follow the progress of the animal through prometamorphosis by noting the ratio of hind-leg length to body length (HL/BL).

The animal has definitely entered prometamorphosis when the HL/BL ratio exceeds 0.2, and it reaches the end of that period when this ratio approaches 1.0. During the latter part of prometamorphosis certain minor morphological changes may be observed in the intact animal. For example, the resorption of the anal canal piece or ACP (the basal lobe of the ventral fin that carries the anal opening out into the left side of the tail) occurs when the HL/BL ratio is about 0.6. In a day or two thereafter at a ratio of about 0.8 the first signs of the degeneration of the opercular skin over the gill chambers (the skin window for the forelegs, SWFL) can be seen on the right side. The corresponding change on the left is the reduction of the tubular wall of the spiracular opening from the gill chamber. In one or two days thereafter (Fig. 2) the forelegs emerge, usually within a few hours of each other, and the changes from the narrow tadpole mouth to the wide frog mouth begin with the shedding of horny teeth and beaks. The emergence of the forelegs and loss of tadpole mouthparts constitute the last phase of prometamorphosis and the beginning of metamorphic climax. The following week of climax is that in which the dramatic changes described in Chapter 7 take place rapidly but in a definite order (Etkin, 1932).

As noted in Chapter 7, the position of any given specimen in the metamorphic spectrum can be conveniently described in terms of the numbered stages of Taylor and Kollros (1946), Nieuwkoop and Faber (1956), and Gosner (1960). However, for the experimental analysis it is important to recognize the exact quantitative and temporal relations of metamorphic changes as depicted in Fig. 2. By use of the information in this figure it is possible to derive the concept of slowly accelerating metamorphic activity during prometamorphosis with climax recognizable as a burst of morphological change. In the design of experiments it is possible by use of these tables to select

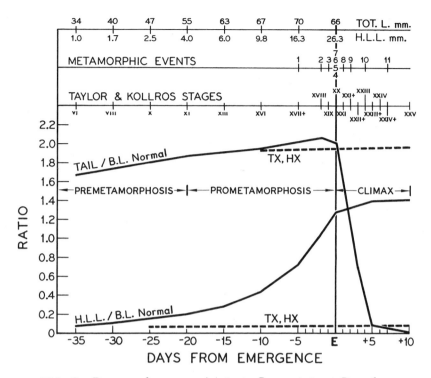

FIG. 2. Pattern of metamorphosis in *Rana pipiens*. Data from one batch of normal animals raised at 23°C ± 1 shown by solid line. Comparable data for thyroidectomized animals (TX) and hypophysectomized animals (HX) are shown by broken lines. The metamorphic events indicated in the figure by number are as follows: 1. Anal canal piece—first definite reduction. 2. Anal canal piece reduction completed. 3. Skin window for the forelegs clearly apparent. 4. Loss of 2d (both) beaks. In experimental animals this is the most satisfactory criterion for the beginning of climax. 5. Emergence of first foreleg to appear. 6. Emergence of second foreleg (E). 7. Mouth widened to level of nostril. Events 4, 5, 6, and 7 usually occur within a period of 24 hours. 8. Mouth widened to level between nostril and eye. 9. Mouth widened to level of anterior edge of eye. 10. Mouth widened past level of middle of eye. 11. Tympanum definitely recognizable. By use of the data of this table it is possible to classify individual animals in terms of days before or after the beginning of climax (E). After Etkin, 1964, with some corrections on the T and K staging.

animals at particular stages and to predict the course of events to be expected in normal animals.

It should be noted that the widely used stages of Taylor and Kollros describe the entire range of tadpole development and are not directed at the analysis of metamorphosis per se. They do not recognize the differential acceleration of hind-leg growth as the initiation of metamorphosis but regard this process as beginning in what we designate here as late pro-metamorphosis (Taylor and Kollros stage XVIII). They also do not differentiate a climax phase. Descriptively, the procedure of Taylor and Kollros is highly useful, but it obscures the experimental analysis. As will be seen later, early leg growth (stages XII to XVIII) is dependent upon activation of the thyroid gland and is thus considered here to be part of metamorphosis. Furthermore, the endocrine balance undergoes a profound change at the beginning of climax so that the precise delineation of this phase is essential for an adequate understanding of the hormonal control of metamorphosis.

The most important consideration that emerges from this analysis is that the postembryonic developmental cycle of a typical anuran involves three phases: (1) a growth phase characterized by rapid growth and little morphological change, (2) a prometamorphic phase with reduced body growth rate and with morphological changes proceeding at a progressively accelerating pace, and finally (3) a phase of metamorphic climax in which body growth has ceased and differentiative changes proceed with extreme rapidity. We may center our analytic discussions, therefore, upon the special endocrine characteristics of each phase and the regulation of the transition from one to the next.

THE ROLE OF THE ENDOCRINES IN THE GROWTH PHASE OF TADPOLE DEVELOPMENT

It is obvious that at least morphologically all the elements necessary for metamorphic activity are present in the early tadpole, the hypothalamus, the pituitary, the thyroid, and the tissues. We may then ask: Why does not the animal transform immediately? Many possibilities suggest themselves, and we may consider the more plausible of these seriatum:

1. Are the tissues initially insensitive or relatively insensitive to thyroid hormone? Such a change in sensitivity might determine the time of initiation of metamorphic activity. The evidence, however, seems to indicate clearly that this is

not the case. It is indeed true that the tissues of the embryo seem to be insensitive to thyroxine as seen in the often-repeated observation that embryos develop normally in thyroxine solution and do not show metamorphic change (e.g., leg growth or tail resorption) until reaching the definitive tadpole stage (stage I)—for earlier literature see Etkin, 1955. On the other hand it is also clear, as in Gudernatch's original experiments, that the postembryonic tadpole's tissue is capable of giving metamorphic responses to thyroid hormone. In a brief study reported only in abstract form, Etkin (1950) attempted to determine more precisely just when the tissues acquire thyroxine sensitivity. He did this by exposing embryos of R. pipiens to immersion in strong thyroxine solutions (or implantation of thyroxine crystals), beginning at successively later stages. He observed that embryos exposed before embryonic stage S-23 (see Chapter 7) did not develop metamorphic changes any earlier than did those whose exposure began at stage S-23. On the other hand, those exposed at later stages showed the first evidence of response at successively later periods. He concluded, therefore, that the tissues first became sensitive at about stage S-23 and are not influenced by exposure at earlier stages. There is a latent period of about three days in the appearance of metamorphic change, even when late tadpoles are exposed to strong thyroxine—1 part per million (ppm). The first changes do not appear in the above experiment until the animals are in stage S-25. Recent experiments by Prahlad and De Lanney (1965) with embryos of the axolotl likewise indicate early acquisition of thyroxine sensitivity. Furthermore, the pattern of change in the embryos of R. pipiens exposed at stage S-23 is the same as that in animals exposed later. This suggests that the general tissues, as observed externally, acquire sensitivity at the same time and approximately to the final degree.

Of course, the above experiment does not preclude the possibility that sensitivity in special tissues may appear at different times, nor does it satisfactorily answer the question of whether the level of sensitivity may not change gradually during tadpole life. Indeed, in Chapter 10 and later in this chapter evidence is presented that sensitivity to thyroid in neural and perhaps other structures may appear late in tadpole life.

There have been many attempts to show that sensitivity of tissues to thyroxine increases during tadpole development (e.g., Heady and Kollros, 1964). These are discussed more fully in Chapter 10. However, the present author does not regard the evidence available on this point as satisfactory for two reasons: (1) When, as in the experiments that claim to demonstrate changes in sensitivity, normal tadpoles of different ages are compared in their reactivity, the older animals start from a more advanced baseline since their tissues have been exposed for a longer time to conditioning by low levels of thyroid hormone present in the tadpole. (2) The differences in sensitivity reported are small, less than a factor of two times and therefore as compared to the changes in thyroid level (see below) can play only a minor role in determining normal metamorphic change. In some cases (Prahlad and De Lanney, 1965) differences in time of first appearance of metamorphic change in animals treated as embryos have been interpreted as indicating differences in time of acquisition of sensitivity. However, such differences may represent merely differences in latent period of response. In summary, then, except for certain nervous structures, the tadpole's tissues appear to be ready to respond to the metamorphic stimulus throughout the growth phase of development. Changes in sensitivity play a minor, if any, role in determining metamorphic pattern.

2. A second possibility to be considered is that the thyroid gland may not be capable of forming the necessary hormone during the growth phase. However, the earliest studies (e.g., Smith, 1920) have shown that the thyroid gland differentiates normally in the absence of the pituitary. In the normal animal, moreover, the gland forms detectable levels of T_4 in the early tadpole stage (16 mm total length in *R. pipiens*), as shown by Flickinger (1964). The tadpole's thyroid also responds to pituitary TSH at all stages of tadpole development (D'Angelo et al., 1941; Gordon et al., 1945) and even in the embryo (Etkin, 1939 and 1966a; Kaye, 1961). Therefore, there is no reason to suspect that the thyroid of the tadpole is incapable of responding appropriately to a metamorphic stimulus during any part of the growth phase. We must look higher than the thyroid in the hypothalamus-pituitary-thyroid axis for the explanation of the failure of the tadpole to metamorphose during this period.

If we ask next whether the pituitary is capable of effective levels of TSH production during this period, we must again answer that it is. The most direct and satisfactory evidence for this would be the demonstration of the responsiveness of the tadpole pituitary to a hypothalamic TRF factor. However, as is discussed below, evidence from this source is not yet available. But other evidence does indicate clearly that the tadpole's pituitary is capable of producing an effective TSH during tadpole life. One such bit of evidence is the demonstration that when the pituitary (adenohypophyseal) primordium and thyroid primordium are placed close together in the embryo, the thyroid is precociously activated (Etkin 1939 and 1966a). This shows that even at early stages the pituitary is capable of producing an effective TSH. The evidence derived from the effects of goitrogens in tadpoles further demonstrates that this capacity for producing TSH continues through tadpole life. The administration of such goitrogens leads to hypertrophy of the thyroid (for literature, see Etkin, 1964, and Hanaoka, 1967). This action, like the similar action in mammals, works by preventing the iodination of the molecule in the gland and, therefore, renders its hormone production ineffective. The lack of thyroid hormone in the goitrogen-treated tadpole removes the feedback inhibition normally exerted by thyroid hormone upon TSH production. The excess TSH produced by the pituitary of the goitrogen-treated tadpole stimulates the thyroid to increased growth and to the abundant secretion of its physiologically ineffective product. We have recently found this goitrogen effect to obtain even in the early tadpole (*unpublished results). Thus, we are led to regard the pituitary of the early tadpole as capable of producing the TSH necessary for the induction of metamorphosis but restrained from doing so because of the inhibition of its TSH-secreting cells by negative feedback from thyroxine produced by the thyroid. The premetamorphic period may be regarded as one in which the pituitary-thyroid axis is maintained in a steady state at an extremely low level of activity because of the great sensitivity of the TSH cells of the pituitary to negative thyroid feedback. The level of this steady state is so low that the amount of thyroid hormone produced is not sufficient to make the normal animal deviate perceptibly from the thyroid-ectomized one (Fig. 1).

As the growth curve of the animal suggests, and as has been recognized and emphasized by Gudernatch and other early workers in the field, there is a reciprocal relation between the rate of overall body growth and the rate of metamorphic change (Fig. 1). Therefore, we may inquire as to the significance of the endocrine factors in maintaining the high growth rate of the premetamorphic period. It was recognized early that thyroid treatment inhibits growth even as it promotes metamorphosis. Steinmetz (1952 and 1954) studied this phenomenon quantitatively by measuring the growth rate of tadpoles immersed in various concentrations of thyroxine and treated with the goitrogen, propothiouracil (PTU). He showed that distinct inhibition of the growth rate occurs at the lowest concentration of thyroxine measurably affecting leg growth and that the goitrogen stimulates the tadpole's growth. From this he inferred that the level of thyroid hormone in the premetamorphic animal is maintained at an extremely low level, less than that equivalent to one part thyroxine per billion parts of water. Our own unpublished work with thyroxine concentration applied to normal tadpoles fully confirms Steinmetz's results, as illustrated in Fig. 3. Thus it is clear that the low steady state of the PT axis is an essential factor in maintaining the characteristic high growth rate of the premetamorphic period.

In recent years it has come to be realized that prolactin (or a prolactinlike molecule) plays a significant role in amphibian physiology (see the review by Meites and Nicholl, 1965). Berman et al. (1964) and Nicoll et al. (1965) reported a stimulation of growth in normal tadpoles by prolactin, and Etkin (1964) and Etkin and Gona (1967) reported such stimulation in hypophysectomized animals. These studies indicate an antagonism between thyroid hormone and prolactin. The antithyroid activity of prolactin has been found at low doses to act peripherally (Nicoll et al., 1965) and to act as a goitrogen at high dosage level (Gona, 1967). In any case it appears that the retardation of growth to be seen in the hypophysectomized tadpole is to be ascribed at least in part to the absence of the prolactinlike factor. Further support of this concept is derived from the report of Etkin and Lehrer (1960). They found that the transplanted pituitary induces growth in hypophysectomized hosts in excess of that of the normal (Fig. 4). This suggests that the production of a prolactinlike hormone in the amphibian, like

FIG. 3. Normal animal (above) compared to experimental animal raised in 3 to 9 ppb thyroxine. Note difference in size but not in time of metamorphosis.

its production in the mammal, is under inhibitory control by the hypothalamus.

The concept of the neuroendocrine relationships responsible for the high growth rate and the low metamorphic tendency in the premetamorphic tadpole that emerges from this evidence may be summarized as follows. The hypothalamus is only minimally active in producing a TRF or a prolactin-inhibiting factor. By this activity it only partially retards prolactin production and does not appreciably stimulate TSH production. Consequently, the negative feedback of thyroxine upon the activity of the TSH cells prevails and keeps the PT axis at a very low level. The high level of prolactin and low level of thyroid hormone favor a high growth rate and no appreciable metamorphic change during this period.

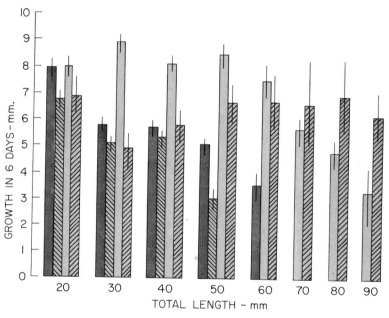

FIG. 4. Rate of growth of tadpoles of *Rana pipiens*. All animals of same batch. Individual growth curves kept for each animal and amount of growth in a six-day period as derived from these growth curves is plotted at different stages of development. Controls entered metamorphic climax at 65 to 70 mm. Hypophysectomized animals generally failed to grow above 60 mm.

THE REGULATION OF THE PATTERN OF TISSUE RESPONSE

The concept of the low-level steady state of the metamorphic mechanism during the growth phase of the tadpole's life raises most directly the question of how this system is disrupted to permit metamorphosis to take place. Before we can examine this question, however, it is necessary to arrive at some understanding of endocrine activity during metamorphosis so that we can appreciate what the nature of the transition from one condition to the other might be. The clue to this was given by the analysis of the pattern of thyroid activity in relation to the pattern of metamorphic change.

It will be recalled from a preceding section and Figs. 1 and 2 that the prometamorphic period is characterized by rapid growth of the hind legs and other less conspicuous changes that are spread over about three weeks in *R. pipiens*. This is followed by about a week of climax, during which profound changes in morphology occur. The relation of developmental and histological changes in the thyroid gland to these events was early subjected to extensive studies (for literature, see Allen, 1938; Etkin, 1955; and Fox 1966). The results in different anuran species indicate that during the period of prometamorphosis the relative growth rate of the thyroid is high and the gland reaches a maximum size at the end of this period (Fig. 10). The histological picture of moderate increase in cell height accompanied by enlargement of follicles indicates cell activity and storage of hormone. In early climax, however, the epithelium reaches a maximum height and the follicles show a reduction of colloid which, particularly in smaller species, brings on partial collapse of the follicles. This picture was early interpreted as indicating an increasing release of thyroid hormone during prometamorphosis and a very high level of activity at climax (see the review of Etkin, 1955; Schrekenberg, 1956). At the end of climax the histological picture shows a return to a flat epithelium and to follicles distended with colloid, thus indicating a deactivation of the thyroid.

Modern studies have attempted to apply recently developed techniques to the analysis of thyroid activity in relation to metamorphosis. These have included chemical studies with and without radioiodine (Saxen et al., 1957a and b; Bowers et al., 1959; Leloup and Fontaine, 1960; Kaye, 1961; Flickinger, 1963), electrical conductivity measurements (Gorbman and Ueda, 1963), and enzyme studies (Yamamoto, 1964; Dowling and Razevska, 1966). In a general qualitative way these studies have supported the morphological investigations mentioned above since most

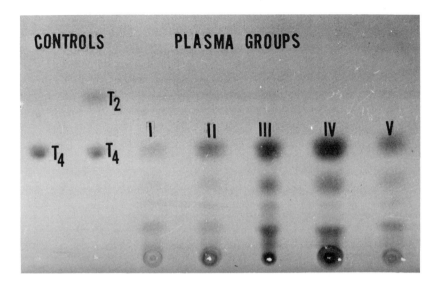

FIG. 5. Chromatographic identification of thyroxine (T_4) in plasma of tadpole in various stages of development. The stages are as follows: I = T + K, stages VI to X, premetamorphosis; II = T + K, stages XI to XV, early prometamorphosis; III = T + K, stages XVI to XIX, late prometamorphosis; IV = T + K, stage XX, early climax; V = T + K, stages XXI to XXIV, late climax. A semi-quantitative estimate of total T_4 (bound and unbound) can be made by densitometer studies of such chromatograms. It indicates a rise in T_4 during prometamorphosis to a peak at the beginning of climax with a fall thereafter. Chromatogram and data courtesy of James Race.

authors interpret their findings in terms of increasing activity with the approach of metamorphic climax. However, the quantitative refinement that one could wish for from such studies was not forthcoming. For example, Saxen et al. found no clear increase in protein-bound iodine in prometamorphosis and only a twofold increase at climax. Whereas these authors and Kaye reported a large increase in I^{131} uptake, this uptake peaked in mid- or late prometamorphosis rather than at climax. Similarly, the conductivity measurements of Gorbman and Ueda indicated the greatest change in midprometamorphosis and a return to the premetamorphic level at climax. Flickinger was able to detect thyroxine in peripheral tissues only at climax. Yamamoto followed T_4-deiodinase activity through precisely defined stages of metamorphosis and reported a great increase during prometamorphosis peaking at climax, falling abruptly thereafter. Although the physiological significance of this deiodination is not clear, the parallelism to metamorphic activity is suggestive of changes of hormone level. Unfortunately, the results of Dowling and Razevska are not in agreement with the findings of Yamamoto's study. The reason for this difference remains unexplained. Needless to say, each of these techniques has its complexities of interpretation, the analysis of which would take us far afield at this point. Therefore, without going into detail, the present author may summarize his interpretation that these studies reinforce the concept that prometamorphosis is marked by an increase in thyroid activity, much of which goes into storage of hormone in follicles. However, they fail to clarify in any quantitative way the changes of level of effective hormone. Particularly, they fail to define the effective hormone level responsible for climax changes. It is to be hoped that this admittedly personal evaluation of the results of these methods constitutes a challenge to a critical application of biochemical and biophysical methods to this problem. There is as much to be gained in the clarification of the methods as well as in the understanding of thyroid action in metamorphosis by such a study. A most promising application of modern biochemical methodology to this problem is the attempt to measure T_4 and T_3 levels in the blood directly by chromatographic separation (Race and Cameron, 1966). Preliminary results by this method support the concept of increasing concentration of thyroid hormone during prometamorphosis to a maximal at climax with a decrease thereafter. But a more precise quantification of hormone level is not yet available.

An indirect method for evaluating thyroid function quantitatively is that of studying metamorphic change in young tadpoles, preferably thyroidectomized animals, during immersion in thyroxine solutions of various concentrations. An early study (Etkin, 1935) demonstrated that low concentrations (3 to 10 parts thyroxine per billion parts of water) yielded good leg growth, but later metamorphic change was protracted at this hormone level. Higher concentrations (100 to 1,000 ppb) on the other hand yielded climax events at near normal rates but did not permit sufficient time for leg growth to attain normal dimensions before tail resorption was induced. The general inference drawn from these studies was that a normal pattern of metamorphic change could be induced only by an extended period of treatment with a low concentration of T_4 followed by immersion in high concentration. This inference has been repeatedly confirmed in many subsequent studies in this laboratory (see Fig. 6 for an example).

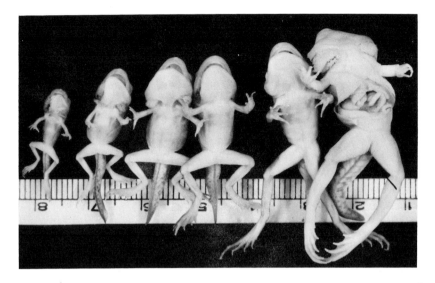

FIG. 6. Tadpoles of R. *pipiens*. Second from right is an untreated control fixed three days after emergence of forelegs when tail resorption is half completed. The maximal size attained by this animal was 68 mm. The animal at right was a thyroidectomized animal induced to metamorphose by a patterned application of increasing concentrations of thyroxine after reaching 90 mm. To the left are a series of normal animals similarly treated beginning at various early stages and fixed at midclimax. Note the normal morphology induced by the pattern of increasing concentration of hormone in contrast to the abnormalities induced by single concentrations as shown in Fig. 1. From Etkin, 1965b.

More recently we have attempted to give this concept more precise quantification by studying the relation of level of immersion to rate of a quantifiable event of prometamorphosis (leg growth) and of climax (tail resorption). The graph (Fig. 7) shows that the maximal rate of leg growth comparable to that in normal animals may be attained in concentrations of 10 to 20 ppb, whereas maximal rates of tail resorption require well over 200 ppb for this induction. The general conclusion that may be drawn from these studies is that normal prometamorphosis may result from a thyroid activity level equivalent to 3 to 20 ppb, whereas as climax is approached the level of activity of the gland must increase by a factor of 10 or more. This increase must occur within a day or two of the beginning of climax (emergence of the forelegs).

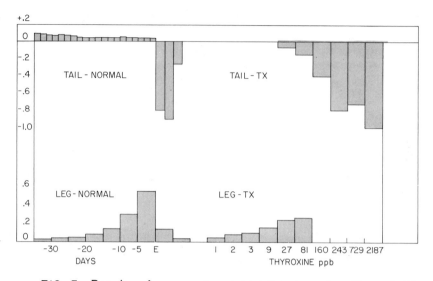

FIG. 7. Results of an experiment (right) to test the effect of different concentrations of thyroxine (Tx) on hind-leg growth and tail resorption in half-grown normal tadpoles. For comparison the rates of change of leg and tail in normal metamorphosis are shown at the left. The rates of change are expressed as proportions of body (snout to anus) length to make the data of smaller experimental animals comparable to controls. Each bar for the tail shows the ratio change over a two-day period in normal animals and for days 3 to 5 after exposure to Tx for the experimentals. Leg ratios are shown for five-day periods in normals and days 3 to 8 in experimentals. It may be noted that in the normals the legs grow most rapidly in the five-day period before climax begins (E), and tail reduction begins after E and drops by 0.8 of the body length in each of the next two two-day periods. In the experimental animals it can be seen that the rate of leg growth produced by 27 ppb thyroxine is about maximum. Animals in concentrations higher than 81 ppb do not survive long enough to provide adequate data, although observations shows that their legs do not grow faster than those in animals at 27 ppb. The tail, on the other hand, does not show its maximal rate of reduction until the concentration of 243 ppb is reached. It may be concluded that maximal leg growth such as occurs during late prometamorphosis requires a Tx concentration about one tenth that necessary for the maximal rate of tail resorption.

   It should be noted parenthetically that Frieden (Chapter 9) advocates the application of thyroxine by injection rather than immersion because he finds a low level of absorption of the hormone from the medium. We cannot agree with this viewpoint for two reasons: (1) the equilibrium level of absorption is irrelevant as long as it varies with the external level and (2) after injection the internal level does not remain constant since loss by excretion and degradation are rapid, as shown by his own studies. Of course, immersion studies do not tell us directly what the equilibrium level of hormone is within the animal's body, but Kollros (1963) has shown that the hormone's concentration is maintained at a highly constant level by the immersion method.

   This type of evidence then leads to the concept that the level of thyroid hormone action rises progressively during prometamorphosis and undergoes an explosive increase by a factor of at least 10 times at climax. The most immediate question raised by this concept is that of the significance of this changing thyroid hormone level for the induction of the normal sequence and spacing of metamorphic events. This question is dealt with in Chapter 10, where the mode of action of the thyroid hormones is analyzed. We continue here with the endocrine analysis by asking how this pattern of thyroid activity is regulated.

THE CONTROL OF LEVEL IN THE PITUITARY-THYROID AXIS

   Since thyroid activity above the minimal level as found in the hypophysectomized tadpole is dependent upon TSH production, it could be assumed that the activation of the thyroid in metamorphosis is induced by an increase of TSH release from the pituitary. Exploration of the morphology of the pituitary therefore might be expected to yield as clear a picture of activation as did the studies of the thyroid discussed above. There have been repeated studies of this problem, but although a general qualitative agreement with this concept has been reported, the clarification of the quantitative interrelations is not impressive (for older literature, see Etkin, 1955 and 1964). Recent studies by Kerr (1966) in *Xenopus* and by Kiremidjian and Ortman (1966) in *R. pipiens* have indicated an increase in the supposed TSH cells (identified as Aldehyde fuchsin positive basophils). Yet the amount of the increase, even admitting that the level of activity of a cell is not readily inferred from its staining reaction, does not seem entirely consistent with the inference from the thyroid pattern. Kerr emphasizes that there is no evidence of hormonal discharge in the pituitary at the time of metamorphic climax. The identification of the TSH cell as a basophil is itself uncertain. Several authors (Dent, 1961; Ramaswami, 1962) have presented evidence pointing to an acidophil as the source of TSH (see discussion in van Oordt, 1963, 1966). The study of this problem at the electron microscope level by Dent and Gupta (1967) again indicates some increase in the supposed TSH cells but not as great a change at climax as was to be anticipated. The recent finding of the antithyroid activity of prolactin suggests that instead of a simple increase in TSH there may be a shift in proportion of TSH to prolactin production that accounts for the activation of the thyroid gland. Indeed, the criteria for identifying the TSH cell (response to goitrogens, thyroxine, etc.) will have to be reconsidered in the light of a possible role for prolactin in controlling thyroid activity. In any case it is apparent that further quantitative work will be required before we can specify the nature of the change in the pituitary activity that is responsible for the patterning of thyroid activity during metamorphosis.

But whatever may be the precise nature of the change in the pituitary, it is clear that the signal initiating and controlling the pattern of metamorphosis must come from the pituitary. Therefore, we may ask whether the pituitary is autonomous, i.e., whether it determines its own rate of activity by some sort of built-in clock mechanism or whether it is subject to some external control. The remarkable fact that throughout the vertebrates, however diverse their brain-pituitary morphology may be, the connection between the two structures is always maintained suggests that the pituitary is under control by the CNS (Scharrer and Scharrer, 1963). Furthermore, the clarification of the morphological relationship by the demonstration of the neurosecretory system and the pituitary portal system of blood vessels strongly reinforces this viewpont. Before the nature of the neurosecretory system was understood, this problem had been attacked in relation to anuran metamorphosis by isolating the gland from the brain. In 1938, Etkin showed that if a tadpole's own pituitary were transplanted in the embryo the animal would usually grow very well but would show at best a retarded and protacted metamorphosis. Nonetheless, the capacity of at least the most successful cases for inducing prometamorphosis was taken to indicate the essential independence of the pituitary from its connection to the brain, a connection then thought of in terms of conventional innervation. In 1940, Uyematsu reported the converse experiment in a toad, removing the region of the embryonic neural plate that gives rise to the infundibular lobes of the hypothalamus and thereby isolating the epithelial pituitary. He also reported his animals to show prometamorphosis, but he found them unable to complete climax changes. This failure he ascribed to a degeneration of the isolated gland at climax. But despite this evidence, which speaks for the concept of an autonomous clock mechanism in the pituitary as the controlling factor in metamorphosis, when the nature of the neurosecretory and the pituitary portal system and hypothalamic influence on TSH production was elucidated in mammals, the need to reexamine this question was recognized. We were able to confirm our earlier work with embryonic grafts and extended it to grafts of differentiated glands placed into hypophysectomized hosts (Etkin, 1964). In these studies the animals were maintained into climax, and it was found that the hosts to successful grafts, though often completing prometamorphic development, invariably entered a metamorphic stasis at climax. Clearly, then, graft activity was capable of activating the thyroid to the low levels responsible for prometamorphic change but not to the high level necessary for climax events. It was apparent that the failure at climax was not due to a degeneration of the gland at that time since the gland was found to be maintained morphologically and also was seen to continue the production of its growth and pigmentation-regulating factors in spite of the metamorphic stasis. We were also able to confirm Uyematsu's findings of similar capacities in pituitaries isolated by removing part of the embryonic hypothalamic region.

There have been many reports in the last 10 years confirming the necessity of the presence of the hypothalamus for the completion of metamorphosis (Chang, 1957 and 1958; Srebo, 1961; Bounhiol and Remy, 1962; Hanaoka, 1963; Voitkevitch, and Chekh, 1964; Weber, 1964; Bounhiol et al. 1964; Remy and Bounhiol, 1965; Hanaoka, 1967). However, Guardabassi (1961) reported completion of metamorphosis after removal of the hypothalamus. It should be understood that failure of metamorphosis in short-term experiments or in experiments in which the animals fail to grow vigorously does not necessarily imply hypothalamic control of TSH function since injury or starvation by themselves can inhibit metamorphosis. However, in our experiments and those of Remy and Bounhiol there can be no doubt of the vigor of the animals since many achieved gigantic size without completing metamorphosis. At least in these experiments, then, it is clear that isolation of the pituitary from the hypothalamus specifically inhibits it from attaining a high level of TSH activity. It is possible that the discordant results reported by Guardabassi are the consequence of incomplete removals accompanied by regenerative repair, which is possible in the tadpole's nervous system. In the opinion of this author it appears to be clearly established that the high level of thyroid activity necessary for metamorphic climax can be maintained by a pituitary gland only if it has its normal connection with the brain. In urodeles also it is clear that the metamorphic process that corresponds to climax in anurans depends upon normal hypothalamic relations with the pituitary. A barrier inserted between these two structures (see frontispiece D) effectively prevents metamorphosis, provided it completely separates them (Etkin and Sussman, 1961). A low prometamorphic level, however, can be maintained by the isolated pituitary in anurans.

On the other hand, some evidence indicates a considerable measure of independence of the pituitary TSH production from hypothalamic control in amphibians. Dent (1966) reported that molting in the newt, in which this process is known to be dependent upon the thyroid, is maintained by pituitaries isolated from the brain. Iodine metabolism, though reduced in toads with pituitary grafts, is higher than in hypophysectomized animals (Rosenkilde, 1964; van Dongen et al., 1966). We regard such evidence as consistent with that derived from metamorphic studies where the isolated pituitary is found to sustain prometamorphic change. It is possible that the role of thyroid in the molting of these amphibians is merely permissive. Though necessary at a minimal level, it does not determine the rhythm of molting by its variation (Jorgensen and Larsen, 1960).

One is tempted to infer from the evidence given above that the pituitary TSH system is autonomous for low levels of activity and requires hypothalamic cooperation only for the highly activated state. However, if we think of the hypothalamic-pituitary interrelationship in terms of neurosecretion rather than conventional innervation it is apparent that inference is not justified. Presumably, the significance of the pituitary portal venous system lies in the greater efficiency it provides for the transfer of chemicals produced in hypothalamic neurons to the cells of the anterior pituitary. Thus, it appears likely that though this system of direct transfer of neurosecretion may be essential for maximal stimulation of the pituitary, a lower level of TSH activity may be maintained by the transfer of neurosecretion through the systemic circulation. Such a low level of stimulation could reach a graft wherever it was located. To my knowledge this possibility has not yet been tested directly by removing the possible source of the neurosecretion. The evidence on brain removal mentioned above either does not include the areas presumed to contain the relevant pericarya (Uyematsu, Bounhiol, Chang, and Hanaoka) or is too fragmentary and incompletely analyzed (Voitkevich and Guardabassi) to permit judgment. Further studies should clarify this critical point. At present it appears most logical to accept the possible transfer of hypothalamic substances in diluted form through the systemic circulation as the explanation of the low and moderate levels of TSH function reported in isolated pituitaries.

Of course, a most direct approach to this question could be derived from experiments with extracts of the hypothalamus that have thyrotropin-releasing properties (TRF). Such TRF preparations have been developed for mammals in several laboratories (see the review by Reichlin, 1966). However, Bowers and Schally, working with their TRF preparation, failed to find evidence of TSH release in the tadpole (personal communication). In our laboratory, work with a TRF prepared by Dr. Roger Guillemin that was potent in tests on rodents likewise failed to elicit activation of metamorphosis, even when large amounts were injected directly into the heart. Presumably the chemistry of the amphibian TRF must differ from that in mammals, but no adequate studies of an amphibian TRF are yet available. The possibility should also be kept in mind that a shift in the prolactin-TSH balance rather than a simple release of TSH may be necessary for metamorphic activity.

Our consideration of the hypothalamic-pituitary-thyroid-tissue axis in relation to metamorphosis thus leads us to the concept that at the beginning of prometamorphosis the hypothalamus initiates the changes, in some way stimulating the pituitary-thyroid axis. This activation process builds up during prometamorphosis to a subtotal activation of the axis by the beginning of climax. At the end of metamorphosis the hypothalamus apparently stops its stimulation of the PT axis since the latter becomes inactive, although we have no direct evidence on this point. Such a concept raises the question of the control of the hypothalamus: Does it, rather than the pituitary, contain the ''clock'' mechanism that determines the timing and pattern of metamorphosis?

THE ACTIVATION OF THE METAMORPHIC MECHANISM

Since the evidence indicates that the control of the metamorphic process depends upon the hypothalamic neurosecretory apparatus, it was desirable to investigate the development of this mechanism. Wilson et al. (1957) reported on the morphology of this system in the western tree frog (*Hyla regilla*) and showed that the classical neurosecretory material of the posterior lobe (see above) appears early in development. However, they did not follow the differentiation of the portal vessels and median eminence in detail. When this was studied in *R. pipiens* (Etkin, 1963 and 1965a) in correlation with metamorphic change, it was found that in the premetamorphic tadpole these parts of the neurosecretory apparatus are poorly differentiated. The anterior lobe of the pituitary is broadly adherent to the thin floor of the hypothalamic lobes with a diffuse network of capillaries lying between the two (Fig. 8). The capillaries of this network derive their blood from hypothalamic arteries and feed into the capillary system of the anterior pituitary. During prometamorphosis this system differentiates in the neural floor, becoming shorter and thicker as the capillaries sink into the neural substance. The anterior lobe separates from the neural tissue except at its anterior tip, where it remains attached by the few large venous channels that drain the primary capillary bed. These constitute the pituitary portal veins draining the now-differentiated median eminence as found in the adult; when the animal enters climax, this median eminence system is well advanced although not completely differentiated (Fig. 8).

It is evident that this morphological development is entirely consistent with the concept that some hypothalamic substance is fed from the neurosecretory fibers in the hypothalamic stalk into the capillary bed of the anterior lobe. In the premetamorphic animal this system, being only diffusely organized, presumably carries a minimum of hypothalamic substance. As the system matures during prometamorphosis and the median eminence differentiates, the amount of material transported increases to reach a level sufficient to achieve the high-level activation of the PT axis at metamorphic climax.

If this hypothesis is valid, then the question of hypothalamic control could be studied by examining the differentiation of the median eminence region in the thyroidectomized larva. If the hypothalamus is autonomous in its differentiation, the median eminence should mature in spite of the failure of the thyroidless larva to metamorphose. The examination of this question showed that this was not so (Etkin, 1963 and 1965b). In the thyroidectomized larva the median eminence region retains its larval character (see frontispiece B). However, if such a larva is artificially induced to metamorphose in a normal pattern by the application of graded concentrations of thyroxine, the median eminence is seen to differentiate as in the normally transforming animal (see frontispiece C). Thus, it is apparent that the median

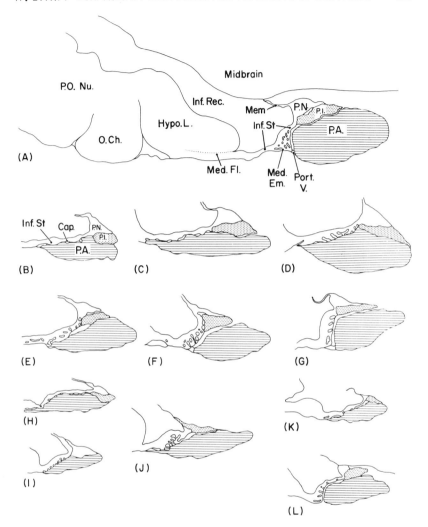

FIG. 8. Camera lucida drawings of sagittal sections of the pituitary region. A: Adult frog, B: premetamorphosis; C: early prometamorphosis; D: late prometamorphosis; E: beginning of climax; F: midclimax. G: post-climax. A to G show *Rana pipiens*. H: Early prometamorphosis; I: late prometamorphosis; J: one day before E. H to J show *Rana sylvatica*. K: mid-prometamorphosis; L: early climax. K to L show *Bufo americanum*.

eminence, part of the hypothalamic mechanism that is presumed to control the PT axis, is itself controlled by thyroid hormone. Evidently, then, there is a circular mechanism involving a positive feedback of thyroid hormone to the hypothalamus. This suggests that the differentiation of the hypothalamic mechanism is gradually brought about by the action of thyroid hormone. This feedback process starts in the early larva at an extremely slow rate because of the low level of thyroid activity in the premetamorphic period. Since it contains a positive feedback element, however, this circular system accelerates slowly at first then more rapidly and finally ends in a burst of activity as any circular system with positive feedback must (Etkin, 1963).

This intriguing possibility could be tested in a number of ways. One such test is to expose early larvae to low concentrations of thyroxine (1 to 9 ppb) for some time. Such exogenous thyroxine in this hypothesis, should, accelerate the maturation of the endogenous hypothalamic mechanism responsible for activating the animal's own PT axis. Animals thus treated should metamorphose earlier than controls and should show a normal pattern of climax events. Repeated attempts in which different concentrations of exogenous hormone were applied in various combinations however, failed, to produce an acceleration of metamorphosis (Etkin, unpublished data). Of course, the thyroxine-treated animals were smaller at metamorphosis than controls because the hormone inhibited their growth rate, as explained above (Fig. 3). This result raised the possibility that the hypothalamic system, as certain other neural elements (see Chapter 10), does not acquire its sensitivity to thyroxine until late in the premetamorphic period. An experimental analysis of this point showed that it was indeed so (Etkin, 1966b). Animals (R. pipiens) treated with graded concentrations of thyroxine from early larval stages and thus brought into mid-climax much earlier than normal failed to show any morphological advance of the median eminence region over the larval condition. On the other hand, animals that were so treated as to be only slightly precocious did show such development (Fig. 9). Thus, it is clear that until a short time before the normal animals enter prometamorphosis, the median eminence region, and presumably the rest of the hypothalamic neurosecretory apparatus, is insensitive to positive thyroid feedback. The feedback cycle thus begins about a week before the commencement of metamorphosis in normal development and builds up quickly through prometamorphosis to climax.

Thus we are led to consider that the timing of the beginning of metamorphosis is regulated by a clock mechanism in the hypothalamus that times the acquisition of hormone sensitivity in that organ. On the other hand, the pattern of thyroid hormone buildup that, as we have seen previously, determines the pattern of metamorphic change is determined by the positive feedback

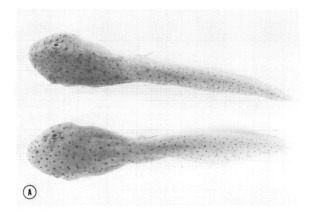

FIG. 9. Photographs of bullfrog (*R. catesbeiana*). In this experiment the animals were set up in matched pairs at the same stage of development—approximately at E – 20 (top group, A). The experimental animal received 1 mg prolactin three times a week, controls received saline injections. Controls went through normal metamorphic climax (lower animal, group B), whereas prolactin injected animal stopped metamorphosis about 10 days after injections began (upper animal, group B).

system of thyroxine to the hypothalamus. In order to form a more comprehensive picture of the mechanism regulating development in larval life of the frog we must now add the newly acquired knowledge of the role of prolactin in promoting body growth and inhibiting metamorphosis in tadpoles as discussed above. Since prolactin is under inhibitory control by the hypothalamus, the positive feedback of T_4 to the neurosecretory system presumably inhibits prolactin activity while at the same time stimulating the PT axis. In Fig. 10 an attempt is made to depict the interaction of these elements in the life history of the anuran larva.

METAMORPHOSIS AS A DEVELOPMENTAL PHENOMENON

I propose in this section to speculate more broadly than, in the stress of scientific investigation and writing, scientists commonly permit themselves to do. Since the ideas expressed are very general, no detailed documentation will be offered.

Evolution and developmental mechanisms in amphibians

Although a few fossil larvae are known, they contribute little to an understanding of the evolution of metamorphosis beyond the fact that it was present in paleozoic labyrinthodonts. General biological considerations, however, permit some resonable speculations. Metamorphosis in urodeles is a developmental adaptation permitting the change from water to land environment. The basic mode of feeding by predation and the associated locomotor mechanisms, however, remain unchanged. Presumably this was the situation in primitive amphibians. In anurans, on the other hand, the larva generally feeds as a free-swimming scavenger, herbivore, or filter feeder. In metamorphosis it changes to a predator which depends upon powerful leg action for its saltatory locomotion. The significance of the prometamorphic phase in anuran transformation appears to lie chiefly in providing time for the legs, whose development had been repressed during the larval phase, to grow before the transition to land is made at metamorphic climax. In urodeles the limbs develop in the way usual among vertebrates, during embryonic stages, and are not involved in metamorphosis. This evolutionary process must, of course, have operated through modification of the mechanics of development. From this point of view, the changes of prometamorphosis, principally limb growth, have been brought into the metamorphic picture by the evolution of a developmental mechanism separating limb differentiation from the general embryonic processes and suppressing it during the premetamorphic period. The action of thyroid hormone, then, appears as the factor which removes this initial inhibition of limb development. We see here an example of a phenomenon appearing frequently in the mechanics of development. This is that control of development is effected by a balance between inhibiting and disinhibiting factors operating on a protoplasmic mechanism with very broad developmental capacities. We see this type of developmental control in gene action at the molecular level, in fertilization phenomena, and in field effects in organ determination.

At the level of endocrine action we again see that developmental control is effected by a balance between inhibition and disinhibition rather than by simple stimulation. The PT axis is kept at a low level of activity in the growth phase of the tadpole's development by negative feedback, and at metamorphosis its activation is brought about by disinhibition of this feedback by hypothalamic action. It is possible that the hypothalamic controlling mechanism of the pituitary has been inhibited for the duration of the larval period by some evolutionary change in the genome. In that case what we have described above as the positive feedback of thyroxine to the hypothalamus would be another instance of the disinhibition of development by thyroxine.

The complexity of the push-pull type of interaction in governing metamorphosis is further emphasized by the discovery of the role of prolactin as a thyroid antagonist in amphibian development (Fig. 9). Whether this substance acts at the peripheral level or as a goitrogen or in both ways its role again emphasizes that development is controlled by a dynamic balance of plus and minus factors. A fascinating aspect of this particular interaction is the manner in which it appears to have been seized upon as the mechanism for the evolution of a "second metamorphosis" in the common newt (see Chapter 7). After a first metamorphosis that produces the land form, this animal returns to the water for breeding in a second period of transformation (see frontispiece A). This second metamorphosis has been shown to be under the influence of prolactin (Grant, 1961). We must now view this change as a shift in the balance between the pituitary factors, prolactin and TSH, rather than as an activation of one of them. First metamorphosis is induced by a shift in favor of TSH, second metamorphosis by a return to the predominance of prolactin. What brings on this second shift is yet to be explored.

Insect and Amphibian Metamorphosis

The analogy between insect metamorphosis and that of amphibians has often been commented upon (see Scharrer and Scharrer, 1963). In both, the brain acting through a neuro-

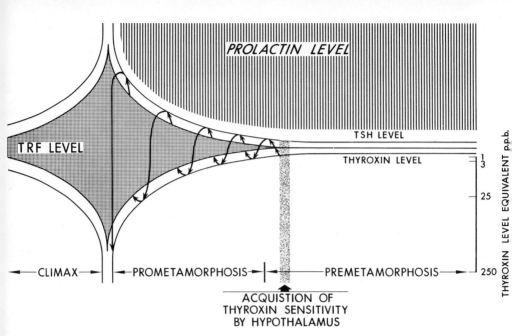

FIG. 10. Diagram illustrating the interaction of endocrine factors in determining the time and pattern of anuran metamorphosis. In the early premetamorphic period the thyroxin level is very low and remains so until just before prometamorphosis begins. At this time, the hypothalamic TRF mechanism becomes sensitive to positive thyroxin feedback, thereby initiating prometamorphosis. The increase in TRF provoked by the action of the initial thyroxin level upon the hypothalamus stimulates increased TSH release, which acts back to raise the thyroxin level. This leads to a spiraling action which raises the thyroxin level and thereby induces prometamorphosis with its characteristic sequence of changes. The positive feedback cycle leads to maximal activation of the pituitary-thyroid axis, thereby bringing on metamorphic climax. During early premetamorphosis, prolactin is produced at a high rate (vertical lines). With the activation of the hypothalamus, the production of prolactin drops under the inhibitory influence of hypothalamic activity. As the level of TSH rises during prometamorphosis, that of prolactin decreases. The growth rate of the animal therefore falls, and the metamorphosis-restraining activity of prolactin diminishes. Thus the premetamorphic period in which growth is active and metamorphosis is inhibited is characterized by the predominance of prolactin over TSH. The reverse holds during metamorphosis. The time of shift in hormone balance is determined by the initiation of positive thyroid feedback to the hypothalamus. This varies greatly between species. The pattern of change during metamorphosis is regulated by the pattern of the feedback build-up and is much the same in most anurans.

342

secretory mechanism controls the endocrine apparatus which governs tissue response through hormone release. Until recently one feature of the insect system seemed to be lacking in vertebrates. In insects the hormone of the corpus allatum acts as a modulator inhibiting the action of ecdysone (see Chapter 3). We now see, however, that there is an analogous situation in amphibians, with prolactin playing the role of modulator to thyroid activity. Perhaps the analogy will suggest ways in which factors that are found to regulate balance in one system can be applied to the other.

Metamorphosis and Puberty

A final area of speculation deserving comment is the analogy between amphibian metamorphosis and puberty in mammals. There are striking similarities in the mechanism of sexual regulation and metamorphosis. In each, the hypothalamic neurosecretory system appears dominant, controlling the pituitary (gonadotropin or TSH) which controls the basic endocrine gland (gonad or thyroid). This in turn regulates the response of the peripheral tissues. Within this system, likewise, there is a negative feedback relation which makes this, too, a balanced system.

In the prepuberal mammal as in the amphibian larva the lower levels of the control sequence are capable of response much before they are actually called upon to act (see Critchlow and Bar Sela, 1967; Donovan and Van der Werff Ten Bosch, 1966). Thus the sex accessories and secondary sex characters can respond to gonadal stimulation long before puberty in most mammals. Likewise the gonads and the pituitary show early responsiveness. The critical factor determining the time of puberty then lies in the activation of the hypothalamus just as it does in metamorphosis. Beyond this point, however, the analogy appears to break down. Properly placed lesions in the hypothalamus have been shown to accelerate puberty so that the hypothalamic gonadotropic releasing mechanism appears to be under inhibitory control of other neural centers. This has never been shown to apply to amphibian metamorphosis. On the other hand no positive feedback system of hormones to the hypothalamus has been described for the mammal as it has for the amphibian larva. Could this be because the possibilities suggested by the analogy have never been explored?

REFERENCES

Allen, B. M. 1938. The endocrine control of amphibian metamorphosis. Biol. Rev. 13:1–19.

Berman, R., H. Bern, C. Nicoll, and R. Strohman. 1964. Growth-
promoting effects of mammalian prolactin and growth
hormone in tadpoles of *Rana catesbeiana*. J. Exp. Zool.,
156:353–359.

Bounhiol, J. J. 1942. Le Determinisme des Metamorphoses
Chez les Amphibiens. Paris, Hermann.

——, and C. Rémy. 1962. Nouvelles observationes sur le
freinage de la morphogénèse chez le têtard privé de
diencephale. C. R. Soc. Biol., 156:2037–2039.

——, P. Disclos, and Ch. Rémy. 1964. Influence de la lumière
sur la métamorphose des amphibiens anoures privés de
leur diencéphale avec ou san remplantation. Ann. Endocr.
(Paris), Suppl. 25:19–29.

Bowers, C. Y., A. Segaloff, and B. Brown. 1959. Factors
affecting the thyroid gland uptake of I^{131} of the *Rana
catesbeiana* tadpoles. Endocrinology, 65:882–888.

Chang, C. R. 1957. Hypothalectomy in *Rana pipiens* neurulae.
Anat. Rec., 128:531.

——. 1958. Hypothalectomy in amphibian embryos. I. Its
effects on the development of the pituitary gland. Sci. Rec.
(Chinese) New Ser., 2:297–301.

Critchlow, V., and M. E. Bar-Sela. 1967. Control of the onset
of puberty. *In* Neuroendocrinology, Martini, L., and W.
Ganong, eds., vol., 2, 101–162. N.Y., Academic Press.

D'Angelo, D., A. Gordon, and H. Charipper. 1941. The role of
the thyroid and pituitary glands in the anomalous effect
of inanition on amphibian metamorphosis. J. Exp. Zool.,
87:259–277.

Dent, J. N. 1961. Cytological response of the newt pituitary
gland to thyroidal depression. Gen. Comp. Endocr., 1:218–
232.

——. 1966. Maintenance of thyroid function in newts with
transplanted pituitary glands. Gen. Comp. Endocr., 6:401–
408.

——, and B. L. Gupta. 1967. Ultrastructural observations of
the developmental cytology of the pituitary gland in the
spotted newt. Gen. Comp. Endocr., 8:000.

Donovan, B. T., and J. J. van der Werff Ten Bosch. 1965.
Physiology of Puberty, Baltimore, Williams and Wilkins.

Dowling, J. T., and D. Razavska. 1966. Thyroxine metabolism
by amphibian skin during metamorphosis and molting. Gen.
Comp. Endocr., 6:162–169.

Etkin, W. 1932. Growth and resorption phenomena in anuran metamorphosis I. Physiol. Zool., 5:275–300.

——. 1935. The mechanisms of anuran metamorphosis I. Thyroxine concentration and the metamorphic pattern. J. Exp. Zool., 71:317–340.

——. 1938. The development of thyrotropic function in pituitary grafts in the tadpole. J. Exp. Zool., 77:347–377.

——. 1939. A thyrotropic field effect in the tadpole I. J. Exp. Zool., 82:463–496.

——. 1950. The acquisition of thyroxine sensitivity by tadpole tissues. Anat. Rec., 108:541.

——. 1955. Metamorphosis. In Willier, B. H., P. A. Weiss, and V. Hamburger, eds, Analysis of Development, pp. 631–663. Philadelphia, Saunders.

——. 1963. The metamorphosis activating system of the frog. Science, 139:810–814.

——. 1964. Metamorphosis. In Moore, J., ed., Physiology of the Amphibia, pp, 427–468. New York, Academic Press.

——. 1965a. The phenomena of amphibian metamorphosis. IV. The development of the median eminence. J. Morph., 116:371–378.

——. 1965b. Thyroid feedback to the hypothalamic neurosecretory system in frog larvae. Neuroendocrinology, 1:45–64.

——. 1966a. Development of TSH function in frog embryos. Program of the Endocrine Society, 48th Meeting, p. 90.

——. 1966b. Hypothalamic sensitivity to thyroid feedback in the tadpole. Neuroendocrinology, 1:293–302.

——, and A. Gona. 1967. Antagonism between prolactin and thyroid hormone in amphibian development. J. Exp. Zool., 165:249–258.

——, and R. Lehrer. 1960. Excess growth in tadpoles after transplantation of the adenohypophysis. Endocrinology, 67:457–466.

——, and W. Sussman. 1961. Hypothalamo-pituitary relations in metamorphosis of Ambystoma. Gen. Comp. Endocr., 1:70–79.

Everett, J. W. 1966. The control of the secretion of prolactin. In Harris, G., and B: T. Donovan, eds., The Pituitary Gland. Berkeley, University of California Press.

Flickinger, R. A. 1963. Iodine metabolism in thyroidectomized frog larvae. Gen. Comp. Endocr., 3:606–615.

——. 1964. Sequential appearance of moniodotyrosine, diiodotyrosine, and thyroxine in the developing frog embryo. Gen. Comp. Endocr., 4:285–289.

Fox, H. 1966. Thyroid growth and its relationship to metamorphosis in *Rana temporaria*. J. Embryol. Exp. Morph., 16:487–496.

Gona, A. 1967. Prolactin as a goitrogenic agent in amphibia. Endocrinology, in press.

Gorbman, A., and K. Ueda. 1963. Electrical properties of thyroid follicles in normal and thyrotropin-injected frogs and in premetamorphic and metamorphic tadpoles. Gen. Comp. Endocr., 3:308–311.

Gordon, A. S., F. D. Goldsmith, and H. A. Charipper. 1945. The effects of thiourea on amphibian development. Growth, 9:19–41.

Gosner, K. L. 1960. A simplified table for staging anuran embryos and larvae with notes on identification. Herpetologica, 16:183–190.

Grant, W. C. 1961. Special aspects of the metamorphic process: second metamorphosis. Amer. Zool., 1:163–171.

Guardabassi, A. 1961. The hypophysis of *Xenopus laevis* after removal of the anterior hypothalamus. Gen. Comp. Endocr., 1:348–363.

Hanaoka, Y. 1963. The effect of hypothalectomy at open neurula embryos in *Rana pipiens*. Amer. Zool., 3:509.

_____. 1967. The effects of posterior hypothalectomy upon the growth and metamorphosis of the tadpole of Rana pipiens. Gen. Comp. Endocr., 8:647–665.

Harris, G. W., and B. T. Donovan. 1966. The Pituitary Gland. Berkeley, University of California Press.

Heady, J., and J. Kollros. 1964. Hormonal modification of the development of plical skin glands. Gen. Comp. Endocr., 4:124–131.

Jørgensen, C. B., and L. O. Larsen. 1960. Hormonal control of molting in amphibians. Nature, 185:244–245.

_____, and L. O. Larsen. 1964. Further observations on molting and its hormonal control in *Bufo bufo* (L.). Gen. Comp. Endocr., 4:389–400.

Kaye, N. W. 1961. Interrelationships of the thyroid and pituitary in embryonic and premetamorphic stages of the frog, *Rana pipiens*. Gen. Comp. Endocr., 1:1–20.

Kerr, T. 1966. The development of the pituitary in *Xenopus laevis* Daudin. Gen. Comp. Endocr., 6:303–311.

Kiremidjian, L., and R. Ortman. 1966. Differential cell count study of the anterior pituitary during metamorphosis of *Rana pipiens*. Amer. Zool., 6:301–302.

Knowles, F., and H. Bern. 1966. Neurosecretion. In Martini, L., and W. Ganong, eds., Neuroendocrinology. New York, Academic Press.

Kollros, J. J. 1961. Mechanism of amphibian metamorphosis: hormones. Amer. Zool., 1:107–114.

———. 1963. Immersion as a method of thyroxine administration in amphibian metamorphosis studies. Develop. Biol., 7:1–10.

Leloup, J., and M. Fontaine. 1960. Iodine metabolism in lower vertebrates. Ann. N. Y. Acad. Sci., 86:316–353.

Lynn, W. G., and H. Wachowski. 1951. The thyroid gland and its functions in cold-blooded vertebrates. Quart. Rev. Biol., 26:123–168.

Martini, L., and W. Ganong. 1966 and 1967. Neuroendocrinology, vols. 1 and 2. New York, Academic Press.

Meites, J., and W. Nicoll. 1966. Prolactin. Ann. Rev. Physiol. 28:57–83.

Nicoll, C. S., H. A. Bern, D. Dunlop, and R. C. Strohman. 1965. Prolactin, growth hormone, thyroxine, and growth of tadpoles of *Rana catesbeiana*. Amer. Zool., 5:738–739.

Nieuwkoop, P. D., and J. Faber. 1956. Normal Table of *Xenopus laevis* (Daudin). Amsterdam, North-Holland Publishing Co.

Oota, T., and H. Kobayshi. 1963. Fine structure of the median eminence and the pars nervosa of the bullfrog, *Rana catesbeiana*. Z. Zellforsch., 60:667–681.

Prahlad, K. V., and L. E. DeLanney. 1965. A study of induced metamorphosis in the axolotl. J. Exp. Zool., 160:137–145.

Race, J., and J. Cameron. 1966. A method for the detection of the thyroid hormones in the plasma of amphibian larvae by thin layer chromatography. Amer. Zool., 6:302.

Ramaswami, L. S. 1962. Endocrinology of reproduction in fish and frog. Gen. Comp. Endocr., Suppl. 1:286–299.

Reichlin, S. 1966. Control of thyrotropic hormone secretion. *In* Martini, L., and W. Ganong, eds., Neuroendocrinology, pp. 445–536. New York, Academic Press.

Remy, Ch., and J. J. Bounhiol. 1965. Gigantisme experimental chez le tetard du crapaud accoucheur (Alytes Obstetricians Laur). Gen. Comp. Endocr., 5:697.

Rosenkilde, P. 1964. Regulation of thyroid function in the toad *Bufo bufo*. Gen. Comp. Endocr., 4:74–81.

Saxen, L., E. Saxen, S. Toivonen, and K. Salimaki. 1957a. Quantitative investigation on the anterior pituitary-thyroid mechanism during frog metamorphosis. Endocrinology, 61:35–44.

———, E. Saxen, S. Toivonen, and K. Salimaki. 1957b. The anterior pituitary and the thyroid function during normal and abnormal development of the frog. Ann. Zool. Soc. Zool. Bot. Fennicae "Vanamo," 18:1–44.

Scharrer, E., and B. Scharrer. 1963. Neuroendocrinology. New York, Columbia University Press.

Schreckenberg, M. G. 1956. The embryonic development of the thyroid gland in the frog, *Hyla Brunnea*. Growth, 20:295–313.

Shellabarger, C. J., and J. R. Brown. 1959. The biosynthesis of thyroxine and 3:5:3'-Tri-iodothyroxine in larval and adult toads. J. Endocr., 18:98–101.

Smith, P. E. 1920. The pigmentary growth and endocrine disturbances induced in the anuran tadpole by the early ablation of the pars buccalis of the hypophysis. Amer. Anat. Mem. No. 11.

Srebro, Z. 1961. The influence of brain injuries on the development of *Xenopus laevis*. Folia. Biol., 9:119–129.

Steinmetz, C. 1952. Thyroid function as related to the growth of tadpoles before metamorphosis. Endocrinology, 51;154–156.

———. 1954. Some effects of thyroxine and antithyroid compounds on tadpoles and their relation to hormonal control of growth. Physiol. Zool., 27:28–40.

Taylor, A. C., and J. J. Kollros. 1946. Stages on the normal development of *Rana pipiens* larvae. Anat. Rec., 94:7–24.

Uyematsu, T. 1940. Experimentelle Untersuchungen uber die Entwicklung der Hypophyse bei Anuren (Bufo). Ökajimas Folia Anat. Japan, 19:391–457.

van Dongen, W. J., C. B. Jorgensen, L. O. Larsen, P. Rosenkilde, B. Lofts, and P. G. van Oordt. 1966. Function and cytology of the normal and autotransplanted pars distalis of the hypophysis in the toad *Bufo bufo* (L.) Gen. Comp. Endocr., 6:491–518.

van Oordt, P. G. 1963. Cell types in the pars distalis of the amphibian pituitary. *In* Benoit, J., and C. Da Lage, eds., Cytologie de l'Adenohyphyse. Paris.

———. 1966. Changes in the pituitary of the common toad, *Bufo bufo*, during metamorphosis, and the identification of the thyrotropic cell. Z. Zellforoch., 75:47–56.

Voitkevich, A. A., and T. K. Chekh. 1964. Effect of extirpation of embryonic anlagen of the neurosecretory-hypophyseal system in amphibia. Dokl. Acad. Sci. USSR, 159:802–806.

Weber, W. 1964. Entwicklung und Function des neurosekretorischen Systems von *Salamandra salamandra*. Z. Zellforsch., 66:35–65.

Wilson, L. D., J. A. Weinberg, and H. A. Bern. 1957. The hypothalamic neurosecretory system of the tree frog, *Hyla regilla*. J. Comp. Neurol., 107:253–271.

Yamamoto, K. 1964. Changes in thyroxine deiodinase of the frog, *Xenopus laevis* Daudin, during metamorphosis and growth. Gen. Comp. Endocr., 4:360–369.

nine

BIOCHEMISTRY OF
AMPHIBIAN METAMORPHOSIS

Earl Frieden

Department of Chemistry and
The Institute of Molecular Biophysics
Florida State University
Tallahassee

HISTORY AND INTRODUCTION

Amphibian metamorphosis is an important postembryonic developmental process in which nonreproductive structures of the larval form of the amphibian change drastically to an adult form during a brief discrete period. The dramatic nature of the morphological transformations during this transition have excited biologists since the beginning of this century. The basic hormonal controls of this process were established by Gudernatsch, Allen, and others in the 1912 to 1930 period. A significant extension of the hormonal control of amphibian metamorphosis has been described by Etkin (1964) in the text edited by Moore and in this volume. Two other recent reviews dealing with the effects of the thyroid hormones on growth and differentiation have also been published by Shellabarger (1964) and Dodd and Matty (1964). Classical anatomical studies culminated in careful staging by Taylor and Kollros (1946). A survey of metamorphic events in amphibia principally at the morphological and cytological levels by Dent and Kaltenbach is included in this volume. Cytological studies involving electron microscopy are now beginning to emerge. Thus, a significant literature characterizing the biological aspects of this developmental phenomenon has accumulated over the past 50 years.

Our knowledge of the chemical and molecular changes associated with the biological transitions of amphibian metamorphosis is of a much more recent vintage. The process of metamorphosis is one of the classic examples of differentiation and of comparative and developmental biochemistry. It embodies all of the features of a remarkable adaptation during the transformation of an aquatic larva to a terrestrial frog. It also illustrates one of the most dramatic effects of the thyroid hormone, or any hormone for that matter. The rapid changes in cell type and function have been frequently compared to changes occurring in tumor cells. Despite the obvious import of this system, prior to 10 years ago only a limited number of papers had appeared, chiefly from the laboratories of Baldwin, Munro, Urbani, Wald and Frieden. Since then, numerous significant papers have emerged by Brown, Cohen, Frieden, Gross, Paik, Tata, Weber, Wilt, and their coworkers. In the first comprehensive review of this subject in 1961, Frieden and Bennett and Frieden (1962) pointed out the essential adaptive features of most of the biochemical changes then known about amphibian metamorphosis. This concept remains as a useful guide for cataloging many of the significant biochemical changes summarized in Table 3, to be discussed later. Valuable reviews covering various portions of this subject have recently been authored by Brown (1964), Cohen (1966), Frieden (1961 and 1967), Tata (1965), Urbani (1962), and Weber (1966a and b).

While the nature of the hormonal control of amphibian metamorphosis has been widely accepted for many years, precise information about the levels of endogeneous hormones has only recently been published. Shellabarger and Brown (1959) were able to identify monoiodotyrosine, diiodotyrosine, T_4*, and traces of T_3 in the thyroid gland of *Xenopus laevis* tadpoles during the metamorphic climax or "critical" stage in development. In *Rana pipiens,* Kaye (1961) found that <1, 12, and 43 percent of injected I^{131} was found in the thyroid during pre- and pro- metamorphosis, and metamorphic climax, respectively. Flickinger (1964) has followed the development of the synthesis of iodinated tyrosines and, later, T_4 in the glands of the early larvae. Etkin's (1964) and Kollros' (1961) proposals as to a "stoichiometric" or "threshold" overall metamorphosis-activating mechanism are experimentally based on exogenous T_4, but can be rationalized with expected T_4 secretion rates. Experimental problems of studying trace levels of unstable compounds in small animals have made definitive experiments difficult. In a recent study of the metabolism of T_3 and T_4 in the bullfrog tadpole, Yamamoto et al. (1966) also used exogenously administered T_4 and T_4 to compare the fate of these hormones at 25° and 6°C.

RELATIVE ACTIVITY OF THYROID HORMONES AND ANALOGS IN THE TADPOLE: INHIBITION OF METAMORPHOSIS

In the 1950's a considerable literature developed concerning reports that numerous analogs of T_3 and T_4 were many times more active than T_3 or T_4 (Pitt-Rivers and Tata, 1959; Money et al., 1960). This inordinately high activity of the side chain acid analogs has now been shown to be due to the use of the unique method of testing compounds by simply immersing tadpoles in solutions of these compounds (Frieden and Westmark, 1961; Frieden et al., 1965). As shown in Table 1, when tested with a single injection, T_3 is more active than all side-chain variants.

---

*The following abbreviations are used in this paper: T_3—3,5-3'-tri-iodo-L-thyronine; T_4—L-thyroxine; RNA—ribonucleic acid; m-RNA—messenger RNA; DNA—deoxyribonucleic acid; AMP—adenylic acid; GMP—guanylic acid; ATP—adenosine triphosphate; Hb—hemoglobin; HbA—adult Hb, type A; HbF—fetal HB, type F.

Only the new analog, $3'$-isopropyl-3, 5-diiodothyronine, is more active. There is a reasonable agreement with the relative activities of these compounds in the rat, also shown in Table 1, eliminating the anomalous feature in this structure-activity relationship. It is of interest that Kaltenbach and Clark (1965) found that cholesterol pellet implants of T_3 and T_4 side-chain analogs produced comparable molting responses in the adult newt rather than anomalously high activities. Our evidence thus supports the view that the single injection method is the most informative way of comparing the relative biological activities of T_3 and T_4 analogs, since it eliminates the important variable of the rate

TABLE 1

COMPARATIVE THYROMIMETIC ACTIVITIES OF T_3 AND T_4 ANALOGS IN THE TADPOLE[a]

Compound	Relative Activity in the Rat	Relative Activity in the Tadpole by Injection	Estimated Ratio of Activities in the Tadpole Injection/Immersion
L-thyroxine	1.0	1.0	10–17
L-3,5,3′-tri- iodothyronine	5.0	10.0	25–100
D-3,5-3′-tri- iodothyronine	1.3	5.0	45
D-thyroxine	0.2	0.3	7
L-3′-isopropyl-3,5- diiodothyronine	8.0	30.0	100
L-3′-ethyl-3,5- diiodothyronine	3.0	6.0	120
L-3′-methyl-3,5- diiodothyronine	1.2	5.0	100
3,5,3′,5′-tetraio- dothyropropionic acid	0.4	3.0	1
3,5,3′-triiodothyro- acetic acid	0.3	7.0	3
3′-isopropyl-3,5- diiodothyroacetic acid	0.4	5.0	2.5

[a]Data principally from Frieden and Westmark (1961), Pitt-Rivers and Tata (1959), and Wahlborg et al. (1964); Money et al. (1960).

of penetration of these compounds. This point is emphasized by the data in the last column of Table 1, in which the various compounds are compared for their injection and immersion activities. All of the alanine compounds have ratios of injected to immersion activities greater than 10 except D-T_4. All of the acid side-chain compounds have much smaller ratios, reflecting relatively higher activity when tested by immersion. The absorption of the naturally occurring hormones T_3 and T_4, administered by immersion, is unexpectedly low. Using I^{131} labeled T_3 and T_4, Yamamoto et al. (1966) found that no more than 3 percent T_3 or 5 percent T_4 were absorbed in 24 hours at 25^0 when tadpoles were immersed in 10 nM T_3 or T_4. Less than one half of these amounts is absorbed at $6°$. The question as to which method of administration is best to initiate changes most closely resembling those that occur during normal metamorphosis is, obviously, more complicated and is very sensitive to the concentration of hormones available at different stages of development. This point has been emphasized by Etkin (1964) in proposing a "stoichiometric" interpretation of thyroid hormone action. Etkin estimated that the hormone level in the prometamorphic (period of hind-leg growth) tadpole to be equivalent to 1 to 20 parts per billion (ppb) T_4 in the immersion fluids. At the metamorphic climax (beginning with the eruption of forelimbs) this amount rises to 200 ppb T_4. With the proper corrective procedures, either method of administration should be amenable to the emulation of spontaneous development.

The poor absorption of T_3 and T_4 may not be sensitive to many environmental factors other than temperature, but it may be an important factor in experiments in which other test substances are administered simultaneously with T_3 or T_4 for their effect on induced metamorphosis. Since many experiments have been performed in this way, the interpretation of data on inhibition or enhancement of immersion-induced metamorphosis remains in doubt. Without additional evidence, it is not possible to separate the quantitative effects of permeability (or penetrability) from quantitative effects on the peripheral tissues. We have strongly recommended the injection of T_3 or T_4 in order to eliminate the rate of uptake of T_3 or T_4 as a variable (Frieden and Westmark, 1961; Frieden et al., 1964; Frieden, 1967). Only limited success has attended experiments designed to find chemical inhibitors of metamorphosis in vivo, e.g., such compounds as actinomycin D, thalidomide, penicillin, and thyroxine analogs. Several groups of compounds, including certain pyrimidines, steriod hormones, and vitamin-A-like compounds, have also been noted as enhancers of T_3 or T_4 action. But all these experiments employed the immersion technique, and their interpretation can be challenged.

Since normal metamorphosis is dependent upon the output of thyroid hormone by the thyroid gland, any goitrogenic substance—e.g., thiourea, thiouracil, perchlorate ion—that suppresses thyroid gland function will prevent metamorphosis. These effects can be overcome by supplying exogenous thyroid hormone. The recent observation of Bern and coworkers and Etkin and Gona (1967) that metamorphosis may be retarded by injection of the pituitary hormone prolactin suggests the possible importance of this and other pituitary hormones.

EFFECT OF TEMPERATURE ON ANURAN METAMORPHOSIS: RENEWAL AND ARREST OF T_3 INDUCTION

The fact that the frog is a poikilotherm permits the introduction of a major new parameter in studies of the effect of thyroid hormones on metamorphosis. The influence of temperature on the metamorphosis of amphibia was first reported by Hertwig in 1898. Thus, it was early recognized that metamorphosis was favored in midsummer and retarded in the winter. A recent confirmatory study of the effect of cold on spontaneous metamorphosis was outlined by Delsol and Flatin (1962). In 1929, Huxley noted qualitatively the temperature sensitivity of the response of tadpoles to thyroid powder. In a quantitative study (Frieden et al., 1965), we confirmed the intense temperature sensitivity of tadpoles to T_3 using the tail decrease response in vivo. No T_3 effect was observed after up to 100 days incubation at $5°$.

More recent experiments presented in Fig. 1 (Frieden et al., 1967) show the effect of $5°$ temperature increments on the tail decrease and the shift in ammonia to urea excretion, a chemical index of anuran metamorphosis. Relatively small effects on either tail decrease or urea excretion are observed between 20 and $30°$. Below $20°$, marked reduction in T_3 effects occurred until no effect was observed even after 100 days incubation at $5°$. In a study of the effect of temperature on the formation of liver carbamylphosphate synthetase, Tatibana and Cohen (1965) noted a strong temperature dependence at $15°$ for the induction of this enzyme in T_4-treated tadpoles. However, in the tail decrease and the urea response, the critical temperature for an

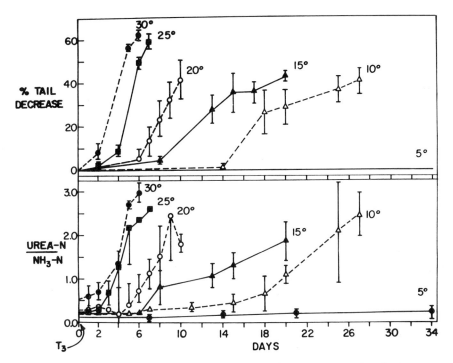

FIG. 1. Effect of six temperatures on the response of tadpoles to a single dose of triiodothyronine. Tadpoles were injected with 0.30 nmoles/g of tadpole at day zero. The percent decrease in tail length, urea-N, and ammonia-N were measured every day during periods of rapid change. Groups of 10 tadpoles were maintained with no food at 5 to 30° in separate 100 ml water, which was changed as needed. Urea was determined by a modified butane-dionemonoxime-thiosemicarbizide method sensitive to 0.1 μg in 5 ml sample; NH_3 by standard Nessler technique. Data from Ashley et al. (1968).

in vivo T_3 effect seems to be close to 5°, although there is an appreciable change in the urea-N excretion at 10 and 15°.

A striking effect was observed when animals were injected with T_3 on the first day and maintained at 5° for almost 80 days and then transferred to 25° (Fig. 2). The ensuing response at 25° was rapid and comparable to animals kept at 25° from the time of injection. Conversely, both the tail and urea response can be arrested by shifting tadpoles from 25 to 5°. These data provide a confirmation of earlier work on tail decrease effects (Frieden, 1964).

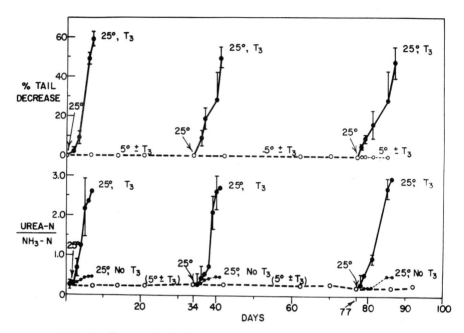

FIG. 2. Renewal of the T_3 response at $25°$ after tadpoles were held at $5°$ for extended periods. A single injection of 0.30 nmoles/g of tadpole was administered at day zero, and the percent decrease in tail length, urea-N, and ammonia-N were measured as described above. When no T_3 is injected, no change in tail length was noted when tadpoles were changed to $25°$, but there is a measurable increase in urea to ammonia ratio ($25°$). Even after 110 days, T_3-injected tadpoles held at $5°$ showed no significant change in tail length or urea to ammonia ratio. Data from Ashley et al. (1968).

Survival and Effect of T_3 at $5°$

These experiments raise two important questions about T_3 effects on the tadpole. The first question relates to what happens during the prolonged incubation at $5°$. Does the hormone survive at $5°$ to become effective at $25°$? In a recent study of the metabolism of labeled T_3 and T_4, the maximum survival time of injected T_3 increased from 1 day at $25°$ to 11 to 15 days at 5 to $6°$, raising the possibility of some T_3 remaining at $5°$ (Yamamoto et al., 1966). The amount of surviving hormone, however, does not produce the in vivo effects observed. Moreover, unpublished evidence is accumulating for early metabolic effects on RNA and protein metabolism at $5°$ in tadpoles injected with T_3.

The Great Temperature Sensitivity of Thyroid Hormone Effects

The second problem is to account for the enormous tempera-ture sensitivity of the liver-urea and tail responses. Prior to a few recent experiments, we could only speculate about this. Is it due to phase changes in lipid structures, the unusual temper-ture sensitivity of certain enzymes, changes in the structure of water, alterations in water-biopolymer, RNA-DNA, or DNA-protein interactions? Protein biosynthesis in bacteria also show a remarkably similar temperature sensitivity (Goldstein et al., 1964). It also has been observed that temperature strongly modifies the nature of the polyribonucleotide polymer produced by highly purified RNA polymerase using synthetic DNA templates (Nishimura et al., 1966). We have recently studied the effect of the 25 to 5° shift for certain metabolic reactions that will be described in more detail in a later section (Eaton et al., 1967). No effect of 5° was observed on the incorporation of C^{14}-phenyla-lanine into liver protein. Possible effects were noted on the incorporation of adenine, guanine, and hypoxanthine into the acid-soluble pool. A significant reduction was observed on the incorporation of hypoxanthine and guanine into RNA and in the AMP/GMP of RNA initiating from adenine or guanine. A com-parison of the effects of 5° and 25° on selected tadpole responses is shown in Table 2. These experiments are only the beginning of efforts to elucidate the nature of the temperature effect on the response of the tadpole to thyroid hormones. The low-temperature arrest of metamorphosis should prove to be a valuable clue to the basic molecular changes accompanying the differentiating process in the amphibian.

BIOCHEMICAL EFFECTS: ADAPTATION AND THE COMMON DENOMINATOR OF THYROID HORMONE FUNCTION

It is the main purpose of this chapter to discuss the most significant and revealing biochemical changes induced in tadpoles as a response to endogenous or exogenous thyroid hormones. The principal systems about which some experimental data is available are summarized in Table 3. We shall consider the first six items in some detail, refer only briefly to the changes in the skin and eye, and merely mention the last two items be-cause of the meagerness of the data available about them. Early knowledge of all of these systems was included in previous reviews by Frieden (1961) and Bennett and Frieden (1962). It

TABLE 2

COMPARISON OF TEMPERATURE RESPONSES IN TADPOLES[a]

Property	5/25° Effect
1. O_2 Consumption	1/7
2. Max. survival $t_{1/2}$ of T_3	14
Max. survival $t_{1/2}$ of T_4	20
3. Tail decrease by T_3, T_4	<1%
4. Urea excretion	1/7
5. Urea increase with T_3, T_4	<1%
6. Carbamyl-PO_4 synthetase with T_3	1/10
7. Kinetics of glutamate dehydrogenase by T_3	1/3
8. phe* → protein* ($\pm T_3$)	1/1 (none)
9. Adenine*, guanine* → acid soluble pool*	2
10. Hx*[b] → acid soluble pool*	1/4
11. Adenine* → RNA*	1/1 (none)
12. Guanine*, Hx* → RNA*	1/2, 1/5
13. Adenine*, guanine* → AMP*/GMP* of RNA	1/2, 1/3

[a] Data from Eaton et al. (1967), Frieden et al. (1965), and Cohen (1966).
[b] Hx* = radioactive hypoxanthine.

should be emphasized that most of the biochemical studies are confined to the anurans, with relatively little data on the urodeles or apoda.

In trying to assemble and integrate the crucial ideas about what happens in metamorphosis, we were impressed previously with the adaptive nature of the essential biochemical changes and the variety of the responses in tadpole tissues induced by thyroid hormones. As noted in Table 3, of special adaptive significance is the change from ammonotelism to ureotelism, a characteristic response of animals to the restriction of water in the environment, the switch from the tight oxygen binding by tadpole hemoglobins to the more ready oxygen unloading by frog hemoglobins, the induction of the biosynthesis of serum albumin to contribute to homeostasis, and the development of more aggressive gut proteases to prepare the frog for its more carnivorous diet.

To explain the ability of different tadpole tissues to respond uniquely to T_3 or T_4, it was necessary to invoke an idea that was difficult to test experimentally, that of "inherent tissue sensitivity." The conclusion that T_3 or T_4 must affect these

BIOCHEMICAL SYSTEMS KNOWN TO BE EXTENSIVELY MODIFIED DURING ANURAN METAMORPHOSIS

Tissue, Organ	Biochemical System	Change	Comments
1. Entire animal	Respiration	No increase; decrease in certain species	Calorigenic responses still possible
2. Erythrocytes	Hemoglobin (Hb)	Repression of tadpole Hb synthesis induction of frog Hb synthesis	Adaptive oxygen binding
3. Serum proteins	Serum protein bio-synthesis (in liver)	Induction of biosynthesis of serum albumin, ceruloplasmin, etc.	Probably necessary for hemeostasis
4. Liver	RNA biosynthesis	Increased RNA turnover	Thyroxine-mediated genetic expression via DNA
5. Liver	Urea production	Induction of urea cycle enzymes	Transition from ammonotel-ism to ureotelism
6. Tail	Synthesis of hydro-lytic enzymes of lysosomal type	Stimulation of cathepsin, phosphatase β-glucuronidase, etc., synthesis	Leads to tail resorption
7. Skin	Collagen biosyn-thesis	Collagenolysis in tail; deposition in back, head	Skin strengthening
8. Eye	Light sensitive pigments	Shift to rhodopsin	Repression of porphyropsin (retinene$_2$) synthesis
9. Intestine	Digestive enzymes	Shift from carbohydrases to proteases	Change from herbivorous to carnivorous
10. Limb buds	Proteins, nucleic acid	Development and growth of tissues (skin, nerve, etc.)	Locomotion on land

tissues in some selective way seemed inescapable. New evidence suggests that thyroid hormones may affect different tadpole tissues in essentially an identical way. Two tadpole tissues that frequently have been used as an illustration of different metabolic orientations are the liver and the tail. The liver is primed to produce many new proteins through a typical protein biosynthetic mechanism. But the tail eventually is resorbed, and protein synthesis must eventually suffer a complete breakdown. Yet, as discussed in detail in the section on tail resorption, the available evidence indicates that a directed protein synthesis must precede tail resorption. Thus, we may have a common denominator for the multiplicity of biochemical effects in anuran metamorphosis. It will be of great interest to see if other tissues that undergo extensive resorption, e.g., gills and intestine, also show an early macromolecular synthetic phase.

Genetic Basis for the Hormonal Control of Metamorphosis

Advances in our understanding of modern genetics have provided the basis for the development of new hypotheses about hormone action and metabolic control. In applying these principles to amphibian differentiation, we must first assume that the tadpole has all the genetic machinery to become a frog and that metamorphosis represents a change in genetic expression. While this is a very general postulate, there is some evidence supporting this in the amphibian. Over 30 years ago, Kaywin (1936) in a cytological study of frog liver during metamorphosis noted that most liver cells undergo transition without significant degeneration, division, or replacement. Great emphasis, as indicated in Table 1, has been placed on the many and broad changes in proteins that accompany metamorphosis. The genetic control of information transcription and translation is expected to be ultimately reflected in terms of the synthesis of specific proteins or enzymes. Recently, on the basis of electrophoretic studies that revealed differences in numerous proteins and enzymes in several tissues, Manwell (1966) proposed that at least some of the numerous differences in the synthesis of proteins are the result of differences in gene activity. He also noted a partial correlation between the extent of differences in major proteins and differences in cell, tissue, organ, and the whole animal shape. To date, the most dramatic evidence for a direct role of hormones in genetic processes has been found in insect metamorphosis where a direct effect on the giant chromosomes of *Chironomus tentans* was reported for ecdysone, the hormone that induces molting (Clever and Karlson, 1960).

A most convenient, but not necessarily the only, site for hormonal influence on genetic expression is an effect on the synthesis or function of the chief mobile informational macromolecule, messenger RNA. Modification of the type or rate of synthesis of mRNA would be reflected in terms of the synthesis of specific proteins and/or enzymes. The early studies of Finamore and Frieden (1960) suggested an increased rate of total liver RNA biosynthesis and a reduction in RNA synthesis during the later period of tail resorption. However, Paik et al. (1961) reported a decrease in adenine uptake into RNA, as well as a decrease in ATP levels. Tata (1965 and 1966) has now confirmed the early increase in RNA biosynthesis in both the liver and the tail. For the present, it has not been possible to attribute these changes specifically to mRNA. Tata (1965) finds a higher fraction of the total ribosomal RNA can be recovered as polysomes associated with membranous material after T_3 treatment. Recently, we have obtained evidence for a difference in the kind of liver RNA being synthesized during induced metamorphosis since the AMP/GMP labeling ratio was significantly changed soon after T_3 treatment (Eaton et al., 1967).Thus, while it is likely that there is a modification of RNA synthesis during metamorphosis, the initiating step in the temporal sequence outlined below remains to be identified:

Gene —▸ —▸ DNA —————▸ mRNA —▸ —▸ ribosomes

—▸ —▸ proteins (enzymes) —▸ —▸ —▸ intracellular structures

The DNA and RNA steps are currently the earliest in the genetic lineup that our current methodology permits us to examine experimentally. Examination of the role and function of the ribosomal-cell membrane interaction should also prove to be valuable in the future.

Genetic Repressor Control by the Thyroid Hormone

Another closely related avenue of approach is the search for effects on gene repressors. The logic here is that certain tadpole genes are inactive because of the presence of repressors of the operator genes that are modified during metamorphosis. The large increase in activity of a number of protein synthetic systems in the liver and other tissues could be reflected in a change in the amount and type of these repressors. The basic proteins of the nucleus, the so-called histones, have been implicated as a major type of genetic repressor, particularly by Bonner et al. (1965). Specific mechanisms that might lead to the decrease in the amount or activity of these repressors, including the methylation and acetylation of the basic proteins (histones) of the nucleus, are now being explored in several laboratories (Cohen, 1966; Frieden et al., 1966). Kim and Cohen (1966) have recently reported that chromatin prepared from the liver nuclei of T_4-treated tadpoles was more efficient in the synthesis of RNA by DNA-directed polymerase. Modification of DNA or RNA activity produced by different histones could account for this shift in AMP/GMP RNA labeling patterns cited above (Eaton et al., 1967).

Repression can be a two-way metabolic street. The simplest interpretation of the data of Ohtsu, Naito, and Wilt (1964) on the loss of the ability of the developing tadpole eye to form retinene$_2$ leading to a predominance of retinene$_1$ and rhodopsin is that a repressor for the retinene$_2$ system must become activated during metamorphosis. Similarly, the fall in liver tryptophan pyrrolase observed during metamorphosis by Spiegel and Spiegel (1964) is attributed to the prior release of a genetic repressor substance. Both repression and derepression (induction) may be involved in the switch from tadpole to frog hemoglobins, as will be described in more detail later (Moss et al., 1965; Theil et al., 1966; Trader, 1966).

There may be some useful correlations between the metabolic effects produced by thyroid hormones in the tadpole and those now being proposed for mammals from the contemporary work of Ackerman, Barker, Bronk, Sokoloff, Tapley, Tata, Wolff, and their associates. There is agreement that protein biosynthesis in rat liver microsomes and mitochondria is eventually increased when a thyroidectomized or euthyroid animal is given T_3 or T_4. The precise mechanism of this greater protein synthesis is, however, under vigorous debate. Sokoloff (1965) reports that the stimulated amino acid uptake occurs during the reactions involved in the transfer of soluble RNA-bound amino acids into microsomal proteins and is not dependent on any stimulation of RNA polymerase. Tata and Widnell (1966) provide evidence that the earliest effect of T_4 in vivo is the increase in DNA-dependent RNA polymerase activity that leads to an increased mRNA production and protein biosynthesis. Ackerman et al. (1966) propose that the role of thyroid hormones is to control endogenous synthesis of purine nucleotides by inhibiting GMP formation and stimulating AMP formation. As will be discussed in detail later, many of these thyroid effects seem to have their counterparts in various tadpole tissues, particularly the tadpole liver.

In the preceding pages, we have considered some of the promising approaches in attempting to find a common effect for the thyroid hormones on their target tissues during metamorphosis. Let us now examine several of the specific biochemical systems and tissues listed in Table 1 about which considerable information has accumulated.

THE QUESTION OF RESPIRATION

Early expectations of associating an increase in respiration with the metamorphic process in amphibia have not been realized even though oxygen uptake is historically correlated with thyroid function (Bennett and Frieden, 1962; Frieden, 1961). What experimental evidence that can be marshalled on this subject now suggests two major conclusions, which are outlined below.

No Increase in Oxygen Uptake During Spontaneous Metamorphosis

First, there is no increase in oxygen consumption during spontaneous metamorphosis. Fletcher and Myant (1959) concluded that there is no change in respiration before or during metamorphosis in the three species, *Xenopus laevis*, *Rana temporaria*, and *Bufo vulgaris*, regardless of whether the data were calculated per unit wet or dry weight. This confirmed the earlier evidence of Etkin (1934). A close inspection of their data suggests that there is a reduction in QO_2 (dry weight) during the intermediate stages of metamorphosis. Lewis and Frieden (1959) found no difference in the respiration of various stages of *B. americanus* or bullfrog tadpoles. There was evidence of a higher oxygen uptake in very young toad tadpoles, which might be due to a higher rate of feeding at the early larval stages. In a recent study, Funkhouser (1966) reported an actual decrease in oxygen consumption in two South American anurans, *Phyllobates subpunctatus* and *Leptodactylus podicipinus*. As shown in Fig. 3, Funkhouser reports a careful study of Phyllobates at 15°, showing a drop in microliters O_2 uptake per gram dry weight per hour of 2,100 to 750 and from 130 to 90 μl O_2/g. wet wt/hour. Fletcher and Myant (1959) also found a decrease in the respiration of whole tadpole liver as metamorphosis proceeded. On the other hand, Barch (1953) found almost a twofold increase in the metabolic rate of *R. pipiens* skin during normal and induced metamorphosis. Thus, with one exception, the current evidence consistently supports the lack of an increase in oxygen utilization

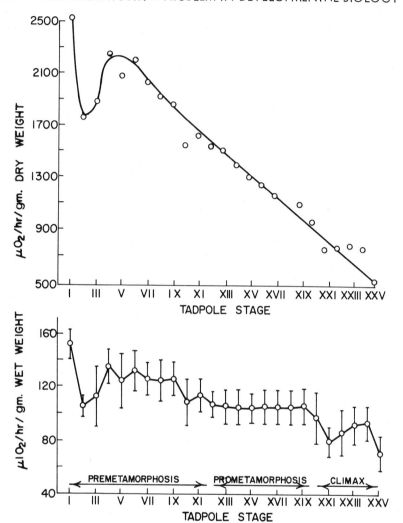

FIG. 3. Oxygen uptake in Phyllobates subpunctatus in terms of dry weight and wet weight. Data from Funkhouser (1966).

during noninduced metamorphosis; in certain species there is a strong suggestion that respiration may decrease during this process.

Calorigenic Response of Tadpoles

The second point is that the tadpole is capable of an increase in oxygen consumption in response to calorigenic agents.

This is, however, not unanimously accepted. Fletcher and Myant (1959) reported a decrease in QO_2 after immersion in T_4 or T_3 prop. in $X.$ *laevis* and $R.$ *temporaria* tadpoles. Funkhouser (1966) could only obtain a modest increase (25 percent) in respiratory rate after injection of T_3. Using isolated tail tips from $X.$ *laevis*, Heinemann and Weber (1966) obtained a 50 percent increase in respiration rate after T_4 administration. Dinitrophenol (10^{-5} M) also produced a significant but transient increase in O_2 uptake during the first two hours of treatment. Lewis and Frieden (1959) reported significant increases in tadpole respiration after T_3 and T_4 injection, regardless of the unit of tissue used for the basis of calculation. The ability of tadpoles to respond to calorigenic agents was amply confirmed with 2,4-dinitrophenol, which in a 30 nmoles/g dose produced a 100 percent increase in oxygen utilization. When the experimental technique used by these groups was challenged (Etkin; 1964), Lipner et al. (1965) rechecked this using an oxygen electrode system described by Lipner and coworkers. A 50 to 70 percent increase in oxygen consumption in $R.$ *grylio* tadpoles was found five days after the injection of T_3 or T_4, 1.0 nmoles/g of tadpole. However, as the T_3 dose was reduced (below 0.2 nmoles/g of tadpole) the morphological response remained, although it was somewhat reduced, but the increase in oxygen uptake disappeared. Thus, certain features of induced metamorphosis can proceed without any evidence for an increase in oxygen consumption. Our conclusion is that a metamorphic response can proceed without any concomitant increase in oxygen uptake. However, larger doses of T_3 or T_4 can force a calorigenic response in the tadpole.

There remains one conflict in data arising from the report of Fletcher and Myant (1959) of a decrease in respiration after immersion in T_4. First, their dose levels, 10^{-8} to 10^{-9} M by immersion, probably corresponded to a level of hormone intake incapable of producing a calorigenic response. Second, in contrast to Lewis and Frieden (1959), they fed their animals during their experiments, and it has been found that feeding desensitizes animals to the effects of T_3. Funkhouser (1966) further suggests that the decrease in respiratory activity might be due to the fact that "tadpoles subject to T_4 treatment would reach metamorphic climax more rapidly, and if oxygen consumption normally decreases at this time, the respiratory activity of these treated tadpoles would decrease." (For a discussion of the effects of starvation see the chapter by Dent in this volume).

Thus it appears that normal metamorphosis is accompanied by either no increase in or, in certain species, an actual decrease in respiration. However, when sufficient T_3, T_4, or 2, 4-dinitro-phenol is appropriately administered, a calorigenic response resulting in an increased oxygen uptake can be obtained. This data, when considered together with the latency of the calorigenic response to exogenous T_3 or T_4, suggests the absence of a causal relation between oxidative metabolism and the metabolic and morphological changes involved in anuran metamorphosis. As will be emphasized later, the mechanisms underlying thyroid hormone action in the tadpole are now believed to involve a modification of genetic expression via DNA or RNA utilization and/or synthesis or in some other essential feature of protein synthesis.

These observations are not as contradictory as they might seem. When sufficient T_3 or T_4 is injected, there is a flood of metabolites that are immediately available for rapid protein and nucleic acid biosynthesis and/or oxidation. During normal metamorphosis, metabolites are gradually used for new protein and other macromolecular reconstruction. While the enzymic machinery involved in oxidation may be poised for greater activity, the absence of metabolites available for oxidative pathways may not allow any increase in oxygen uptake. The elimination of the large surface area of the tail and the extensive modification of skin cells might also contribute to a decrease in oxygen utilization during metamorphosis. Thus, despite a steadily increasing level of thyroid hormone secretion, it is possible to rationalize the increased protein and nucleic acid biosynthesis with the lack of increased oxygen uptake in the tadpole during spontaneous metamorphosis.

INCREASE IN ALBUMIN, CERULOPLASMIN, AND OTHER SERUM PROTEINS

The physiological versatility of the serum proteins is well known. Among their more important functions, particularly that of serum albumin, is the maintenance of blood volume through osmotic regulation. Therefore, it was not unexpected that in the transition from fresh water to land there would be significant adjustment of the osmotic regulatory mechanisms. Evidence for a large increase in serum albumin concentration and an overall increase in serum proteins during metamorphosis has been found for numerous amphibian species by Herner and Frieden (1960) and confirmed by Manwell (1966), Hahn (1962), and others. In fact, it appears that aquatic forms, in general, have less serum albumin than any related land form. In such species as *R. grylio* and *R. heckscherii,* there is almost a total absence of serum albumin in the early tadpole. Just after metamorphosis the albumin increases to a point where it comprises about one half of the total serum proteins. In other species such as *R. catesbeiana,* the typical American bullfrog, and *X. laevis* there is evidence of a small amount of serum albumin in the tadpole and a large increase during metamorphosis. Data on the protein content and the albumin to globulin ratio in these species is summarized in Table 4. More details on the electrophoretic patterns of these serum proteins may be found in the paper by Herner and Frieden (1960). The mechanism of this increased albumin biosynthesis in liver cells, however, remains to be explained.

An increase in serum ceruloplasmin comparable to that of albumin has also been observed by Inaba and Frieden (1967). As shown in Fig. 4, the catalytic activity of this copper protein in tadpole serum increases up to a hundredfold at the metamorphic climax. This increase begins early in metamorphosis and appears to precede the changes in hemoglobins. The enzymic activity of ceruloplasmin is masked by a dialyzable inhibitor that has not yet been identified. This observation may portend an important role for ceruloplasmin in the utilization of iron in hemoglobin biosynthesis and in metalloprotein metabolism during metamorphosis. It is also of interest that the levels of serum transferrin and blood carbonic anhydrase are substantially elevated during metamorphosis.

THE HEMOGLOBIN TRANSITION

The study of the structure and function of the hemoglobins in the vertebrates has become one of the more fruitful and enjoyable pastimes of the biochemist, geneticist, and taxonomist. The amino acid sequence of the hemoglobins is proving to be a valuable tool in the morphological classification and the evolutionary history of different vertebrates. While this key information about tadpoles and frog hemoglobin is presently lacking, the development of greatly improved chromatographic methods for the separation of similar proteins and the identification of their amino acid sequence should eventually permit the elucidation of the complete structure of tadpoles and frog hemoglobins and their chains. Thus, any decision on the chemistry of these hemoglobins is necessarily incomplete at this time.

The functional differences between tadpole and frog hemoglobins have been known for more than 30 years. In 1951,

TABLE 4

TOTAL SERUM PROTEIN CONCENTRATIONS AND ALBUMIN/GLOBULIN RATIOS OF ANURAN LARVAE DURING METAMORPHOSIS

Species and Description	Leg/Tail	Protein Concentration, gm/100 ml	Albumin/Globulin
R. grylio			
Early metamorphosis	0.09 ± 0.04	1.42 ± 0.30[a]	0.12 ± 0.03[a]
3 days after T_3 injection[b]	0.18 ± 0.03	1.28 ± 0.27	0.16 ± 0.04
5 days after T_3 injection	0.28 ± 0.08	1.47 ± 0.10	0.22 ± 0.05
6 days after T_3 injection	0.36 ± 0.07	1.41 ± 0.40	0.35 ± 0.08
Intermediate	1.22 ± 0.12		0.54 ± 0.14
Postmetamorphosis		2.19 ± 0.17[c]	0.81 ± 0.11
Adult		1.97 ± 0.12[c]	0.90 ± 0.01
R. catesbeiana			
Early metamorphosis	0.04 ± 0.03	1.16 ± 0.19	0.12 ± 0.02
6 days after T_3 injection	0.39 ± 0.09	1.74 ± 0.39	0.23 ± 0.08
Postmetamorphosis		2.56 ± 0.50	0.64 ± 0.09
Adult		2.56 ± 0.53	0.70 ± 0.07
R. heckscheri			
Early metamorphosis	0.11 ± 0.02	0.35 ± 0.04	0.02 ± 0.02
2 days after T_3 injection	0.10 ± 0.05		0.08 ± 0.05
3 days after T_3 injection	0.14 ± 0.05		0.07 ± 0.02
5 days after T_3 injection	0.18 ± 0.03		0.09 ± 0.02
6 days after T_3 injection	0.41 ± 0.16	0.92 ± 0.22	0.11 ± 0.03
Intermediate	0.60		0.14
Adult		2.03 ± 0.19	0.38 ± 0.05
X. laevis			
Early metamorphosis		0.2	0.20
Weight about 3 g		2.3	0.52
Weight about 20 g		3.5	1.49

[a]Data from Herner and Frieden (1960), including standard deviations—groups averaged 3 to 10 animals.

[b]10^{-9} molesT_3/g injected at zero time.

[c]Later experiments, as in Fig. 4, suggest that this figure is closer to 3.0% in the young frogs.

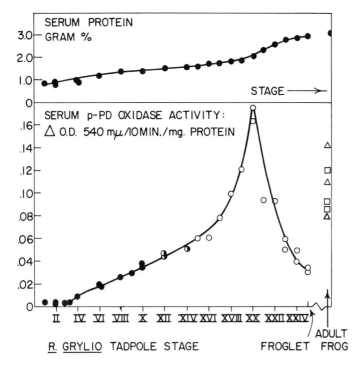

FIG. 4. Serum proteins and ceruloplasmin activity levels in the Florida bullfrog tadpole (R. grylio) at different stages of spontaneous metamorphosis. Serum protein was determined by the well-known Lowry method. The p-phenylene-diamine oxidase activity at 30° was determined at pH 5.2 on dialyzed serum. Solid circles on the left refer to a pooled group of 10 tadpoles; half circles—4 animals; open circles—1 to 2 animals. Data from Inaba and Frieden (1966).

Riggs confirmed the fact that tadpole hemoglobin had a greater affinity for oxygen and also noted the absence of a Bohr effect in the tadpole. Later, Herner and Frieden (1961) reported on the differential chemistry of these hemoglobins, noting significant differences in electrophoretic mobility (Chieffi et al., 1960), the degree of heterogeneity, sensitivity to alkali denaturation, and differential biosynthesis. Subsequent papers by Trader et al. (1963 and 1966) repeated comparative amino acid analyses, reactivities of —SH groups, molecular weight heterogeneity, the mechanism of the dimerization reaction, and other chemical properties. Differences in peptide "fingerprint" patterns have also been reported by Baglioni and Sparks (1963) and Hamada et al. (1964, 1966). N-terminal groups have also been studied by Elzinga (1964), Hamada et al. (1964, 1966), and Trader et al. (1963 and 1966). During the last two years, numerous papers

applying more current techniques to the comparative biochemistry of tadpole and frog hemoglobins have appeared and will
be summarized here.

Comparative Chemical Properties of Tadpole and Frog Hemoglobins

Table 5 presents a detailed comparison of the properties
of both tadpole and frog hemoglobins. Since the hemes appear
to be the same, the differences occurring are in the globin
part of the molecule. This is reflected in a variety of different
properties arising from differences in amino acid composition.
The problem of precise quantitative data on the amino acid
composition and other properties is greatly complicated by the
presence of multiple hemoglobins in both the tadpole and frog
and the tendency of bullfrog hemoglobin to dimerize. Using
virtually every known micromethod of protein separation, four or
five apparently discrete hemoglobins have been observed in both
animals (Baglioni and Sparks, 1963; Elzinga, 1964; Trader et al.,
1966), yet the possibility that some of these are analytical
artifacts has not been excluded. Elzinga (1964) has noted many
distinctive hemoglobin components in tadpoles resulting from
individual genetic differences or from the metamorphic process
itself.

Certain properties such as the relative sensitivity to alkali
denaturation and relative oxygen binding fit some of the generalizations usually observed when comparing fetal to adult forms.
The key to these and other differences is the extensive alteration
in amino acid composition shown in Table 6. The difference in
electrophoretic mobility is due to the greater negative charge
at pH 8.6 of tadpole hemoglobin arising from fewer arginine
and lysine and more aspartate residues. More tryptophan in
tadpole hemoglobin probably accounts for the distinctive absorption at 290 mμ (Trader et al., 1963; Hamada et al., 1966).

Molecular Evolution of Anuran Hemoglobins

The differences in amino acid composition of anuran hemoglobins along with fetal and human hemoglobins are summarized in Table 7 (Trader et al., 1966). *R. grylio* tadpole and
frog hemoglobins differ greatly from human Hb A and Hb F,
as might be expected. *R. grylio* tadpole hemoglobins have large
differences from all frog hemoglobins studied, although fewer

TABLE 5

COMPARISON OF THE PROPERTIES OF TADPOLE AND BULLFROG HEMOGLOBINS

Property	Tadpole	Bullfrog
1. pO_2 for 50% saturation	4 mm	14 mm
2. Bohr effect[a]	None	Typical
3. Heme spectrum	Same	Same
4. Methemoglobin formation	Resistant	Less resistant
5. Alkali denaturation	Resistant	Less resistant
6. Paper electrophoretic Mobility (relative)	11 cm	7.5 cm
7. Starch block electrophoretic Mobility	Fast	Slower
No. of Protein Bands	3–5	3–5
8. Average molecular weight	68,000	68,000
9. Dimerizable	0	80%
10. Protein chains	$\alpha_2^T \beta_2^T$	$\alpha_2^T \beta_2^F$
11. N terminus	gly-leu	gly-leu
	val-ala	gly-ser
12. C terminus	his, ala	his, glu
13. Amino acid analysis Residues of acidic AA in 65,000 g	104	98
Residues of basic AA in 65,000 g (–his)b	52	62
1/2 cystine	0	8
Tryptophan "fine structure" (about 290 m)	Definite peak	Weak shoulder

[a]A typical Bohr effect refers to the decrease in oxygen binding affinity as the pH is decreased.

[b]Histidine is omitted from this calculation since it is assumed to be essentially uncharged at the electrophoretic pH, 8.6.

when compared to the adult of the same species. The bullfrogs *R. grylio* and *R. catesbeiana* have hemoglobins that also appear to be very similar in other properties such as electrophoresis and chromatographic behavior.

The similarity of the amino acid composition of hemoglobins of closely related species, e.g., *R. grylio* and *R. cates-*

TABLE 6

AMINO ACID COMPOSITIONS OF AMPHIBIAN AND HUMAN HEMOGLOBINS

Amino Acid[a]	R. grylio Tadpole (4)[b] Ref. Trader and Frieden (1966)	R. grylio Adult (3) Ref. Trader and Frieden (1966)	R. catesbeiana Adult (1) Ref. Trader and Frieden (1966)	R. catesbeiana Tad. (1) Ref. Homada and Shukuya (1946)	R. catesbeiana Adult (1)	R. pipiens Adult (2) Ref. Trader and Frieden (1966)	R. esculenta Adult Ref. Tentori et al. (1965)	Human Adult Ref. Trader and Frieden (1966)
Aspartic acid	57.5 (1.2)[c]	52.0 (3.4)	56	57	55	61	58	50
Glutamic acid	46.0 (2.2)	46.0 (1.7)	46	83	66	45	44	32
Lysine	34.0 (1.1)	36.4 (2.2)	38	35	35	41	41	44
Histidine	30.5 (2.5)	43.4 (5.8)	43	26	38	44	52	38
Arginine	18.1 (0.7)	25.9 (0.9)	25	21	25	18	17	12
Half-cystine[d]	0.1	9.0 (0.6)	8–9	0	4	9	6	6
Threonine[d]	27.2 (1.0)	20.5 (1.3)	19	26	24	22	21	32
Serine[d]	38.4 (1.9)	37.1 (0.5)	35	32	32	36	29	32
Proline	26.1 (1.7)	19.5 (1.0)	20	13	20	20	21	28
Glycine	41.9 (1.0)	35.2 (1.3)	37	48	40	36	38	40
Alanine	58.4 (0.4)	63.3 (2.0)	63	50	69	63	74	72

Valine[e]	42.7 (1.2)	37.7 (2.2)	41	42	41	44	38	62
Methionine	1.7 (0.9)	5.0 (1.2)	4	2	4	3	4	6
Isoleucine[e]	28.3 (2.1)	16.3 (0.9)	19	28	17	16	17	0
Leucine[e]	64.7 (1.7)	68.7 (2.0)	66	58	69	63	69	72
Tyrosine	14.3 (0.7)	19.6 (1.3)	20	11	12	18	20	12
Phenylalanine	30.9 (0.5)	29.8 (1.2)	31	28	25	30	30	30
Ammonia[d]	59.0 (3.7)	61.3 (5.7)	58			59	49	28

aTryptophan was not determined.
bThe figures in parentheses are the number of analyses performed.
cStandard deviation.
dExtrapolated values, corrected for losses during hydrolysis.
eValues calculated from long-term hydrolysis to correct for incomplete hydrolysis.

TABLE 7

NUMBER OF DIFFERENT RESIDUES BETWEEN ANURAN
AND HUMAN HEMOGLOBINS[a]

Species	No. of Different Residues/mole Hb
R. grylio tadpole—human adult	108
R. grylio frog—human adult	106
R. grylio tadpole—human fetal	97
R. grylio frog—human fetal	95
R. grylio tadpole—*R. esculenta* adult	86
Human fetal—human adult	68
R. grylio tadpole—*R. catesbeiana* adult	63
R. grylio tadpole—*R. pipiens* adult	58
R. grylio tadpole—*R. grylio* adult	52
R. grylio adult—*R. esculenta* adult	38
R. grylio adult—*R. pipiens* adult	27
R. grylio adult—*R. catesbeiana* adult	8

[a]From Trader and Frieden (1966). The differences reported
were determined by calculating the differences between the two
hemoglobins for each amino acid and summing these values. By
using the standard deviations from the mean, the least possible
difference was calculated in each case. The averages of the
standard deviations were 1.3 ± 0.4 and 1.7 ± 1.5 for the *R. grylio*
tadpole and frog hemoglobins, respectively. The known compositions of the human hemoglobins were used in the calculations.
The average values reported by Tentori et al. (1965) were used
in the calculations for *R. esculenta* hemoglobins.

beiana adults, and the large differences in animals far apart in
evolution, e.g., human and frog, support the scheme of hemoglobin evolution proposed by Ingram (1961) and E. Zuckerhandl, and
the value of homology in trying to relate amino acid identity and
sequence as discussed recently by Hill and Buettner-Janusch
(1964). The difference of 52 residues that characterizes the shift
from tadpole to frog hemoglobin in *R. grylio* emphasizes that the
switch mechanism, which must occur during metamorphosis,
compares significantly with the change from fetal to adult hemoglobin.

Hemoglobin-Sulfhydryl Groups and the Dimerization Reaction

A striking difference between tadpole and frog hemoglobin is the total absence of cysteine (or 1/2 cystine) in the tadpole. As metamorphosis proceeds, at least eight cysteines (or 1/2 cystines) appear. The appearance of Hb-SH's can be used as a sensitive method for following the appearance of frog hemoglobin (Fig. 5 Ashley and Frieden, 1967). A rapid increase in Hb-SH occurred during stages XXIII and XXIV, the last two stages of bullfrog metamorphosis. Sakai et al. (1964) have studied this process after T_4 treatment and noted the appearance of 4 SH's per Hb 12 to 16 days after immersion in 24 nM T_4. The only point of disagreement is the number of −SH's reported. In the work of Ashley and Frieden (1968) and Trader et al. (1963 and 1966), 8 moles of SH were detectable per mole of Hb. Sakai et al. (1965) and Hamada et al. (1966) report only 4 moles −SH/Hb or 1 mole −SH/heme.

The appearance of Hb-SH is also accompanied by an unusual dimerization reaction associated exclusively with frog hemoglobin (Trader et al., 1966; Riggs et al., 1964). The presence in amphibian blood of hemoglobin species heavier than 4.3 S (68,000) had been noted earlier by Svedberg et al. but was first associated with the change in hemoglobin structure accompanying metamorphosis by Trader et al. (1963 and 1966). The hemoglobin dimer is now believed to be formed in vitro after red cell lysis (Riggs et al., 1964; Trader et al., 1966). The dimerization reaction has been studied in detail (Trader et al., 1966) and found to be associated with the disappearance of at least 2 SH groups per Hb. The dimer can be reconverted to monomer by mercaptoethanol. While 80 percent or more dimer is observed in bullfrog and *Xenopus* hemoglobin, no dimer is found in *R. pipiens* and *L. pentadactylus*. From numerous considerations, a mechanism for dimer formation was proposed as follows:

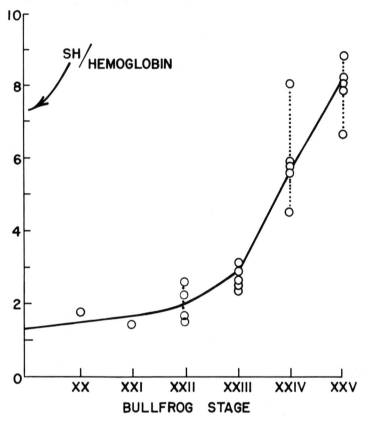

FIG. 5. The appearance of–SH groups in tadpole hemoglobin during normal metamorphosis. The red blood lysates were sephadexed and then titrated with p-chloromercuribenzoate according to Boyer's method. The nonhemoglobin sulfhydryls were estimated to be less than one per hemoglobin molecule. Data from Ashley and Frieden (1967).

Do Tadpole and Frog Hemoglobins
Have a Common Protein Chain?

The evolution of the hemoglobin molecule as proposed by Ingram (1961) emphasized the genetic stability of the α chain and the greater mutability of the β chain. Thus, the normal variants in the hemoglobins of humans are $\alpha_2\sigma_2$ (prefetal hemoglobin, $\alpha_2\gamma_2$ (Hb F), $\alpha_2\beta_2$ (Hb A) and $\alpha_2\delta_2$ (Hb A$_2$). Accordingly, an important evolutionary principle is involved in the question of whether tadpole and frog hemoglobins have an α chain in common. From the amino acid composition, it is obvious that at least one chain must be different. The remaining question is whether there are any identical chains, i.e., tadpole Hb = $\alpha_2^T\beta_2^T$; frog Hb = $\alpha_2^T\beta_2^F$ or $\alpha_2^F\beta_2^F$. Herner and Riggs (1963) were unable to detect new hybrids after mixing tadpole and frog chains, suggestive of one highly similar or identical chain. Hamada and Shukuya (1966) have reported evidence for a common α chain with no —SH groups. They reported solving the difficult problem of isolating the principal α and β chains by chromatographic separation on carboxymethylcellulose columns using formic acid-pyridine elution method of Dintzis.

The data in support of a common α chain included the similarity of peptide maps, the identity of C and N terminal amino acids (his and gly-leu, respectively), similar ultraviolet absorption spectra and, finally and most important of all, a highly similar amino acid composition. We have compared their amino acid analysis data with that reported for several *Rana* species and find that it corresponds closely with several exceptions. The most significant difference is in the —SH groups of the frog β chain which is reported to have only 2 SH per chain. This accounts for the total of 4-SH/Hb they report; but as noted earlier, the other reports give at least 6 to 8 for other Ranidae.

As an independent check for the presence of a peptide chain in bullfrog hemoglobin with no —SH groups, Stratton (1967) and Frieden have devised a sensitive radioautographic technique for detecting SH's in hemoglobin peptide chains. Hemolysates were treated with chlormerodrin Hg^{203} overnight in the cold to permit the following reaction:

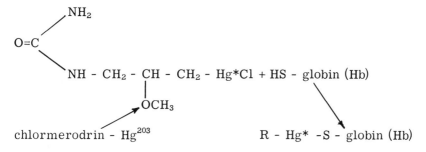

Hb chains were then separated by starch gel electrophoresis in pH 3.5 formic acid-HCl and 6 M urea. None of the major protein bands obtainable from tadpole hemolysates show any fixing of Hg^{203} as indicated by radioautography, although two of the minor, slow moving bands, different from frog bands, exhibited a small amount of labeled Hg. All of the five protein bands from frog hemolysates, representing peptide chains, contain the label. While all the possible alternatives have not yet been excluded, this preliminary data indicates that all frog chains have—SH groups in contrast to the data of Hamada and Shukuya (1966).

Biosynthesis of Hemoglobins

Finally, we turn to the problem of hemoglobin biosynthesis. The knowledge that the globin portions of the tadpole and frog hemoglobins differed greatly in amino acid composition led to the realization that there was a substantial "switch" mechanism during metamorphosis, comparable to the transition from fetal hemoglobin (Hb F) to adult hemoglobin (Hb A). From Fe^{59} uptake studies, Herner and Frieden (1961) suggested that hemoglobin biosynthesis occurred in both tadpole and frog erythrocytes and switched during anuran development.

Recently, three laboratories (Moss and Ingram, 1965; Sakai et al., 1964; Theil, 1967; Frieden et al., 1965) have reported preliminary data on the change in the biosynthesis of hemoglobins during metamorphosis. Moss and Ingram (1965) reported that T_4 first repressed tadpole hemoglobin synthesis and later induced frog hemoglobin production in tadpole erythrocytes. Theil and Frieden (1966) found that the amount of phe-U-C^{14} in proteins from tadpole erthyrocytes was suppressed by T_4 and by puromycin and chloramphenicol. Induction of new protein synthesis in the latter stages of T_4 treatment or during spontaneous metamorphosis was also noted (Theil, 1967; Theil and Frieden, 1966).

In addition Theil (1967) studied the significance of nonheme protein reported earlier by Herner and Frieden (1961). During spontaneous metamorphosis, the nonhemoglobin proteins of tadpole erythrocytes become labeled with C^{14} when the cells are incubated in phe-U-C^{14}. The proteins disappear between stages XXIII and XXIV, the time when tadpole hemoglobin is replaced by frog hemoglobin. These nonheme proteins have no cysteine (or 1/2 cystine) and a molecular weight of about 30,000 or equivalent to 2α or 2β chains. They could represent unused tadpole α or β chains or apo-ferritin subunits (Theil, 1967).

The tadpole-frog hemoglobin transition is one of the most promising experimental systems for the study of the switch mechanism in animals (Baglioni, 1966; Moss and Ingram, 1965; Herner and Frieden, 1961; Theil and Frieden, 1966). This has led to considerable speculation as to its molecular basis. A shift in cell lines synthesizing hemoglobins from the kidney in the tadpole to the spleen in the frog was noted earlier by

Jordan and Speidel (1923). Thus, a simple and convenient hypothesis is that the thyroid hormone blocks the proliferation of erythroid cells that make tadpole hemoglobin while simultaneously, or later, stimulating the development of erythroid cells that synthesize frog hemoglobins exclusively (Moss and Ingram, 1965). However, Shukuya (1966) reported evidence for the presence of both tadpole and frog hemoglobins in a single type of cell. To account for the rapid replacement of tadpole red cells by frog red cells, T_4 must also accelerate the aging and, thus, the cell destruction process. In genetic terms, we need to know whether T_4 directly or indirectly represses tadpole hemoglobin genes and derepresses frog hemoglobin genes. Other alternative suggestions (Moss and Ingram, 1965; Theil, 1967; Herner and Frieden, 1961) include the possibility that the erythroid cells that proliferate after T_4 stimulation are already determined for the synthesis of frog hemoglobin or that there are relatively indirect effects on the appropriate cells of the spleen or liver.

DEVELOPMENTAL CHANGES IN THE LIVER

During metamorphosis, the amphibian liver undergoes a major metabolic reorganization. A summary of these changes appeared in several recent reviews (Bennett and Frieden, 1962; Brown, 1964; Cohen, 1966; Frieden, 1967). A comprehensive survey and general discussion of amphibian metabolism was presented by Brown (1964). The extensive experimental contributions on amphibian liver changes by Cohen and his associates have been summarized by Cohen in the 1965 Harvey Lectures so recently that only a brief resumé need be presented here. Most of the changes in liver function have been studied in terms of differences in amounts of certain proteins and enzymes and in alterations in the metabolism of proteins, polynucleotides and their constituents. We have previously described changes in certain important blood proteins such as serum albumins and globulins, ceruloplasmin and the hemoglobins, several of which originate in the liver. In a survey of protein relationships from several tissues, including tadpole and frog liver, Manwell (1966) also found differences in the electrophoretic characteristics of numerous proteins and enzymes. While most protein systems examined show an extraordinary increase during metamorphosis, an unusual contrast in enzyme development was observed by Spiegel and Spiegel (1964) in a study of liver tryptophan pyrrolase in embryonic, larval, and adult *R. catesbeiana*.

Constitutive tryptophan pyrrolase activity appeared after Shum-
way stage 22 (free-swimming tadpole stage) disappeared during
metamorphosis and reappeared in the adult. Thyroxine caused
the suppression of this enzyme activity in the very young tadpole.

The shift from aquatic to terrestrial habitat of many
amphibians has resulted in a drastic change in nitrogenous
excretory products. This transition from ammonotelism to
ureotelism has become a classical fact of comparative and
developmental biochemistry (Baldwin, 1940). The extensive
development of the ornithine-urea cycle in the liver, which
accounts for this transformation during metamorphosis, has
now been extensively explored (Cohen, 1966) and is reviewed
next.

The Enzymes of Urea Biosynthesis and Related Systems

Figure 6 shows the metabolic interrelationships of the
ornithine-urea cycle and the metabolites indirectly involved in
urea biosynthesis and the relative activities of certain key

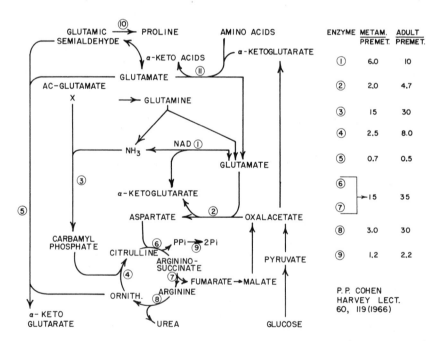

FIG. 6. Interrelations of metabolic cycles that produce urea and
involve related compounds. On the far right are the comparative enzyme
levels before and after metamorphosis. Adapted from Cohen (1966).

enzymes. All the enzymes of the urea cycle are significantly increased during either normal or induced metamorphosis, especially carbamylphosphate synthetase and the arginine synthetase system (Brown et al., 1959). Dolphin and Frieden (1955) had earlier reported a tenfold increase in arginase after T_3 or T_4 treatment. Brown et al. (1959) identified argininosuccinate synthetase as the rate-limiting enzymic step in the overall biosynthesis of urea. Brown (1964) also showed the striking correlation between the development of the enzymes of the urea cycle and the formation of urea-C^{14} from $C^{14}O_2$ by slices of tadpole livers at different stages of development.

The carbamylphosphate synthetase enzyme has proved to be a useful system for the study of the hormonal induction of protein synthesis and metamorphic development. In order to explore the de novo synthesis of this enzyme in tadpoles, Cohen et al., (1966) prepared the pure enzyme and its specific antibody. This antibody was then used to precipitate specifically newly synthesized carbamylphosphate synthetase labeled with leucine-C^{14} in thyroxinized tadpole liver. Tadpole liver slices will also synthesize carbamylphosphate synthetase in vitro as shown by leucine-C^{14} incorporation (Metzenberg et al., 1961). The synthesis appears to be confined to a mitochondrial fraction, at least in the latter steps (Cohen, 1966).

Several crucial enzymes indirectly involved in urea biosynthesis primarily concerned with the related metabolism of aspartate, ornithine, glutamate, and glutamine have also been studied by Cohen and his associates (1966). The significant increases in glutamate dehydrogenase (Degroot and Cohen, 1962) and glutamate-oxalacetate transaminase (Cohen, 1966) are consistent with their positive role in the mechanism of ureotelism, as is the reduction of ornithine-α-ketoglutarate transaminase (Cohen, 1966). A penetrating study of glutamate dehydrogenase has revealed several important differences between the tadpole and frog liver enzymes (Wiggert and Cohen, 1966). Relatively little significant change in the biosynthesis of the free and protein amino acids or in the amino acid activating enzymes have been reported (Cohen, 1966). However, Eaton (1967) noted about a 40 percent increase in the uptake of C^{14}-phenylalanine into liver protein five days after a single T_3 injection (1.0 nmoles/g).

RNA and DNA Biosynthesis

The enzymic and other changes associated with the shift to urea formation provide a clear and consistent picture of these metabolic events. The metabolic directions involving the nucleic acids are less clearly defined. Even before the widespread acceptance of the key role of DNA and RNA in the control of differentiation and development, several laboratories had initiated studies in this direction. In 1960, Finamore and Frieden (1960) had reported an increased uptake of P^{32}-phosphate into the RNA, DNA, and protein of the tadpole after T_3 treatment and prior to the onset of discernible morphological transformations (Fig. 7). In 1961, Paik et al. (1961) reported a decrease in adenine-8-C^{14} incorporation into RNA and a decrease in the amount of ATP during T_4 treatment. Both groups found that the nucleotide composition of RNA remained essentially the same during thyroid hormone treatment. Further studies have been in progress in several laboratories (Cohen, 1966; Eaton et al., 1967; Frieden, 1967; Tata, 1965), which will be summarized here. More recently, Kim and Cohen (1966) state that it has been found that thyroxine treatment increases the rate of synthesis of various types of RNA in tadpole liver.

Tata (1965a and b) has confirmed the early increase in RNA biosynthesis during induced metamorphosis. With H^3-uridine, a 100 percent increase in the specific activity of the nuclear RNA fraction was observed after two days of T_3 treatment. Microsomal and soluble RNA showed no change. The newly synthesized RNA was found in the 78 S fraction of sucrose density gradient centrifugation of liver RNA. A higher fraction of total ribosomal RNA is recovered as polysomes associated with membranous material. Tata has also emphasized that the RNA effects precede other key protein synthetic events in both the liver and the tail, accounting for the lag in thyroid hormone effects in the tadpole as well as other systems. A postulated sequence of events is shown schematically in Fig.8. The order of events may be similar to the changes in rat liver except that the enhanced protein biosynthesis is directed to many new proteins in a genetically predetermined pattern.

The role of T_3 in the possible regulation of protein biosynthesis was reviewed earlier in this chapter. While efforts have been made to account for hormonal induction mechanisms in terms of messenger-RNA, it is recognized that mRNA may not be the initial step in the stimulation of metamorphosis by the thyroid hormone (Frieden, 1967). It is, however, the earliest step in nucleic acid metabolism that our current methodology permits us to study. Kim and Cohen (1966) have recently reported that the chromatin prepared from liver nuclei of thyroxine-treated tadpoles was more efficient in the synthesis of RNA by DNA-directed RNA polymerase. Promising work is now in pro-

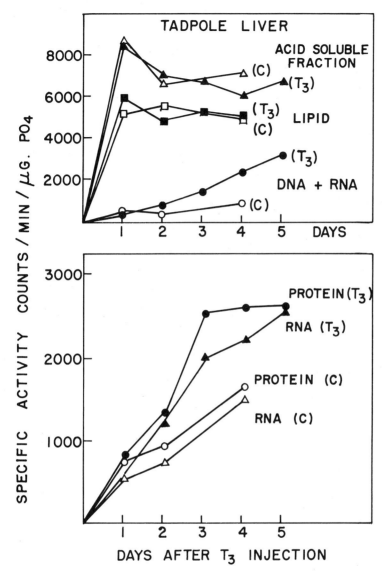

FIG. 7. Specific activity of different liver fractions at various times after $P^{32}O_4$ injection. Groups of about 20 animals received single injections of 1×10^{-8} moles/g of body weight of triiodo-L-thyronine at zero time to induce metamorphosis, and approximately 1 hour later they were administered 100 μc of carrier-free P^{32} as orthophosphate. Comparable control groups received only P^{32}. Open symbols (C), control group; closed symbols (T_3), hormone group. Data from Finamore and Frieden (1960).

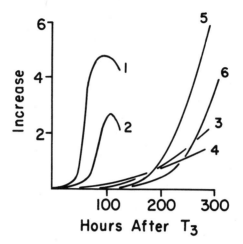

FIG. 8. Relative increases in some hepatic cellular activities and amounts of constituents in R. *catesbeiana* tadpoles expressed schematically as a function of time after the induction of metamorphosis with triiodothyronine. Curves 1: RNA synthesis in the nucleus; 2: ribosomal RNA synthesis; 3: cytochrome oxidase per milligram mitochondrial protein; 4: total liver protein; 5: carbamyl phosphate synthetase (and other urea cycle enzymes); 6: appearance in the blood of adult hemoglobin. The downward trend in curves 1 and 2 does not represent a true decline in the rate of RNA synthesis. It merely reflects the dilution caused by nucleotides and acid soluble phosphorus (released from the tail undergoing rapid regression) of the radioactive precursors used for measuring their incorporation into RNA. Data from Tata (1965).

gress in several laboratories examining the role of "histones" in the regulation of tadpole liver DNA activity (Cohen, 1966; Frieden, 1967).

Metabolism of Nucleotides and Their Constituents

In an effort to establish the role of purine metabolism in the thyroid hormone response, Eaton et al. (1967) at Florida State University have recently studied the entry of labeled adenine, guanine, and hypoxanthine into the acid-soluble nucleotide pool and the RNA in tadpole liver. These results show that T_3 reduces the specific activity of adenine and hypoxanthine in the acid soluble pool. However, the stimulated rate of RNA synthesis compensates for this, producing a RNA of specific activity similar to control groups. Guanine, however, retains its activity in the pool and, thus, more label appears in RNA after T_3 treatment. The most striking result is the shift in the relative radioactivity appearing in the AMP and GMP of liver RNA. A severalfold shift in the ratio of AMP*/GMP* appears as early as two days after T_3 injection. In an earlier paper (Finamore and Frieden, 1960), we found that the ratio of adenine to guanine in liver RNA was 0.54; thus, the specific activity change would almost double the relative activity effects. One interpretation of this data is that T_3 is greatly modifying the kind of RNA being synthesized, favoring the turnover of adenine-rich RNA. Paik et al. (1961) had suggested that T_4 caused a rearrangement of RNA molecules based on a decreased rate of incorporation of adenine-8-C^{14} into liver RNA and the lack of any change in the amount of RNA. But this would have led to an RNA deficient in labeled adenine, contrary to the results described. An alternative explanation is that the difference in labeling patterns of the purine nucleotides in liver RNA is due to the change in the labeling pattern of the purine nucleotide pool. The latter explanation is in accord with the data of Ackerman et al. (1966), in which thyroid hormones stimulated AMP formation and inhibited GMP production in certain rat tissues. They further reported remarkable in vitro effects of T_3 and T_4 in inhibiting inosinic acid dehydrogenase and in stimulating adenylosuccinate synthetase. The control of the intracellular level of purine nucleotides could reorient the synthesis of liver RNA so as to produce the different kinds of proteins and enzymes observed in tadpole liver and other tissues during metamorphosis.

Pyrimidine metabolism has been studied by Cohen and his coworkers (1966). Lindsay et al. (1964) demonstrated the similarity between the pathways of pyrimidine biosynthesis in the tadpole and rat livers. Uridine phosphorylase activity increased while uridine kinase activity remained unchanged both during normal and induced metamorphosis (Akamatsu et al., 1964). On the basis of an enhancement of the rate of formation of carbamylphosphate synthetase by uracil, uridine, and orotic acid, when given in the immersion water with T_4, it was concluded that there appeared to be a relative deficiency of pyrimidines during T_4-induced metamorphosis. Thiouracil inhibits the production of carbamylphosphate synthetase, probably due to an interference with pyrimidine nucleotide biosynthesis (Akamatsu et al., 1964).

TAIL RESORPTION

The versatility of the metamorphosing tadpole as a model for the study of differentiation and development arises not only from the presence of numerous anabolic tissues such as liver and limbs but also from the variety of tissues such as tail, gut, and gills in which ultimately numerous catabolic reactions predominate. The possibility that tail resorption is a controlled expression of the activity of intracellular catabolic enzymes has long been entertained. Most tissues seem to contain the enzymes responsible for their destruction when cells die or are directed into certain pathological or physiological states. The unique feature in the tadpole is, of course, the conversion of the event to a useful biological purpose. An extensive review of the background and history of this subject has recently been published by Weber (1967a and b).

Tissue Acidity and Tail Hydrolases

The impressive nature of tail resorption led to experimental work more than 40 years ago. Alterations in the tissue acidity of tadpole tail has long been associated with the demolitive changes in the tail triggered by the thyroid hormone. Heightened metabolic processes in the tadpole tail could increase the production of acidic metabolites such as lactic acid and pyruvic acid. The resulting increased acidity from pH 7.1 to 6.6 during tail resorption might activate acid proteases or modify certain intracellular structures to release degradative enzymes. During tail resorption, there is also a conspicuous increase in amino acid and polypeptide nitrogen, reflecting an increase in protein hydrolysis of tail tissue. The transport of these acidic products contributes to the decrease in blood pH from 7.5 to 7.2 during metamorphosis.

These autolytic and pH changes and the other early studies on enzymic hydrolysis have been summarized in an earlier review (Frieden, 1961; Frieden, 1964) and even more recently by Weber (1967a and b). Numerous studies later suggested a definitive role for the hydrolytic enzymes present in the tail itself (Eeckhout, 1965; Kubler and Frieden, 1964; Salzmann and Weber, 1963; Weber, 1957 and 1963). A major contribution has emerged from the work of Weber and his associates (Weber, 1963 and 1967a and b) in establishing the significance of alterations in cathepsins and phosphatase activity during tail resorption. Thus, evidence accumulated rapidly that there was a generalized

TABLE 8

CHANGES IN TADPOLE TAIL ENZYMES AFTER META-
MORPHOSIS[a]

| | Postmetamorphic / Premetamorphic | |
	Specific Activity	Total Amount
β-glucuronidase	34	3–4
DNase	30	2–3
Cathepsin	22	2–3
Phosphatase (acid)	18	2–3
Collagenase	10	
RNase (acid)	9	1.3
Protease (acid)	9	
Catalase	6	.3
Di-and-tri-peptidases (several kinds)	3–7	
Phosphatase (alkaline)	3	
Amylase, lipase	1.1–1.6	
Succinate dehydrogenase	1	
Glutamate dehydrogenase	1	
Aldolase	0.2	0.2
ATPase (Mg^{++})	0.5	

[a]Data assembled mainly from Eeckhout (1965), Frieden (1964), Kubler and Frieden (1964), and Weber (1967a).

increase in most hydrolytic enzymes, as summarized in Table 8. The 34-fold increase in β-glucuronidase during normal metamorphosis was particularly spectacular (Kubler and Frieden, 1964).

The Lysosomal Hypothesis

The numerous mechanisms proposed for the control and regulation of the degradative action of the intracellular hydrolases have also been summarized by Frieden (1964) and Herner and Riggs (1963). A recent attractive hypothesis was that of deDuve, who earlier had proposed the existence of an intracellular entity, the lysosome, which contained numerous lytic enzymes. The controlled disintegration of this subcellular particle could produce cytolysis and tissue disappearance. Support for this idea also came from observations in which lysosomolytic agents such as cortisone and vitamin A either promoted tail resorption or otherwise enhanced the thyroid hormone effect. Salzmann and Weber (1963) found some evidence to support the existence of hydrolase-rich "phagosomes" among the macrophages of the subepidermal connective tissue. During metamorphosis, a progressive activation of these cells begins in the connective tissue of the tail fin and spreads to the tail muscle. Weber (1967a) recently concluded that "the increase in the activity of acid hydrolase reflects the progressive transition of histocytes into active macrophages, which apparently are important sites of synthesis of acid hydrolases in the regressing tadpole tail."

Stimulation of Protein Synthesis

In the absence of definitive cytological evidence for the presence and modifications of typical lysosomes in the tadpole tail during metamorphosis, Weber (1963) and Frieden (1964) and their associates also tested this hypothesis at the biochemical level using several lysosomal enzymes—namely, cathepsin, β-glucuronidase, and phosphatase—as indicator enzymes. Both groups reached essentially similar conclusions as follows:

1. The distribution of and the changes in these enzymes did not correspond to the prediction of the "lysosomal hypothesis." The enzymes were almost uniformly distributed throughout the mitochondrial-lysosomal, microsomal, and supernatant fractions. Tadpole tail β-glucuronidase was even less "releasable" than the corresponding enzyme of froglet tail stump.

2. An unexpected observation in this regressing tissue was the demonstration by both groups of an increase in the synthesis of these enzymes. For example, Kubler and Frieden (1963) found that while the tail was decreasing to one tenth of its original weight and protein content, the specific activity of β-glucuronidase was increasing by a factor of 34-fold. Weber (1963) reported a twofold increase in cathepsin and phosphatase activities. Typical tests precluded the role of activators or other modifiers of these enzymes' activity; a careful comparison of several key kinetic properties of partially purified β-glucuronidase revealed no differences in the tadpole and froglet enzymes (Price and Frieden, 1963). Thus, an initial synthesis of certain tail enzymes appeared to precede the dissolution of tail tissue.

Prevention of Tail Regression by Protein Synthesis Inhibitors

Support for this idea has now come from several sources. A comprehensive study of tail metamorphosis comprised the PhD dissertation of Y. Eeckhout (1965), a student of C. DeDuve. Eeckhout confirmed the huge increase in the following hydrolases: cathepsin, β-glucuronidase, phosphatase, RNase, and DNase, as shown in Fig. 9. He also concluded that protein synthesis was a prelude to tail resorption. To prove this further, Eeckhout employed an organ culture of tadpole tail pieces as suggested by Shaffer and Weber. He observed that actinomycin D, an inhibitor of RNA biosynthesis, puromycin which suppresses both protein and nuclear RNA synthesis, and ethionine which blocks protein biosynthesis, blocked the morphological effect of thy-

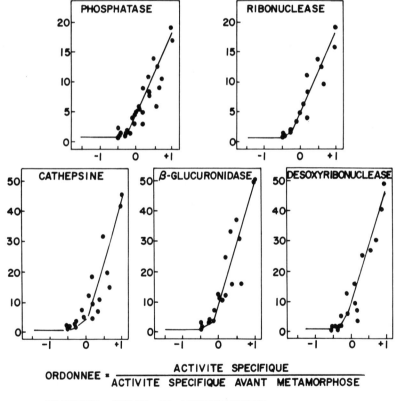

$$\text{ORDONNEE} = \frac{\text{ACTIVITE SPECIFIQUE}}{\text{ACTIVITE SPECIFIQUE AVANT METAMORPHOSE}}$$

ABSCISSE = INDICE DE METAMORPHOSE

FIG. 9. The increase in five tail enzymes during spontaneous metamorphosis. Each horizontal axis is the log of the ratio of the hind-leg to tail measurements. Data from Eeckhout (1965).

roxine. This is illustrated in Fig. 10, taken from Eeckhout's work in which the resorptive effects of thyroxine are shown to be inhibited by puromycin. About the same time, Weber (1965) showed that actinomycin D prevented tail atrophy in *Xenopus* larvae during metamorphosis.

Requirement of RNA and Protein Synthesis

More recently, Tata (1966) has provided further evidence that tail resorption has a requirement for RNA and protein synthesis. Using *R. temporaria* tadpole tails in organ culture, he confirmed the fact that the protein synthesis blocking agents, cycloheximide, actinomycin D, and puromycin interfered with tail regression and hydrolase production induced by T_3. Tata also found that T_3 added to the medium increased the rate of protein and RNA biosynthesis. The incorporation of C^{14}-amino acids into protein increased before H^3-uridine incorporation into RNA. This sequence of events is unexpected if the new RNA is serving as the messenger for additional protein synthesis. Perhaps T_3 must first induce the synthesis of enzymes that are necessary for RNA biosynthesis. Tata also reported that puromycin and cycloheximide prevented the C^{14}-amino acid uptake, whereas actinomycin D and cycloheximide inhibited the H^3-uridine incorporation:

Usual Sequence

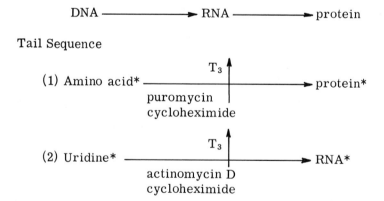

Tail Sequence

Changes in Collagen and Related Enzymes

Thus far our consideration of the mechanism of tail resorption has been general with specific references for illustrative

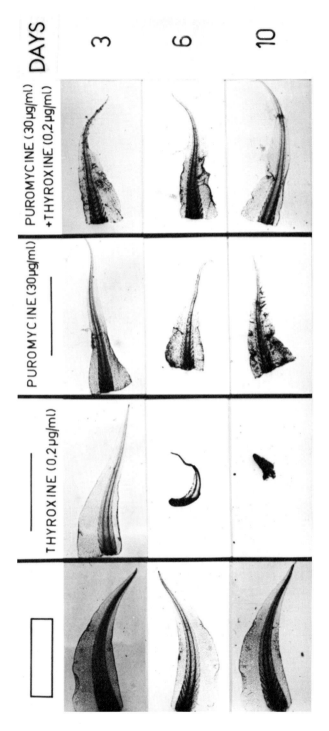

FIG. 10. The inhibition of the T_3-induced resorption of isolated tadpole tail pieces by puromycin. Data from Eeckhout (1965).

purposes only. We should not leave this subject without mentioning a most interesting change occurring in tail collagen during metamorphosis as elucidated by J. Gross and his associates (1964). Lapiere and Gross (1963) have noted increased degradation in collagen metabolism of the tail fin during resorption in contrast with constant biosynthesis in the back skin. The first animal collagenase has been isolated from the epithelial cells of tail cultures undergoing metamorphosis. This enzyme has been purified and shown to have a highly specific and characteristic mode of action on the collagen molecule. A hyaluronidase has been detected in the mesenchymal cells of the tail fin.

Overall Biochemical Changes in the Tail

In summary, tail resorption, as induced by T_3 or T_4, involves an initial phase of protein synthesis, as already observed for tadpole liver at metamorphosis and in other systems. The synthetic phase is followed by demolitive processes, leading ultimately to tail dissolution, as shown:

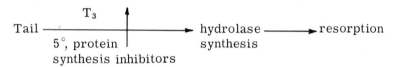

The entire process can be turned off at 5°, as described earlier. Our tentative prediction is that the synthetic steps are cut off at 5°. As expected, the metabolic blocking agents also appear to affect the synthetic step. A possible unique feature in this system is that protein synthesis precedes RNA synthesis in contrast to the usually accepted sequence of events (see previous section). The changes in the tadpole tail thus reflect not only the ability of the thyroid hormone to produce a controlled stimulation of protein biosynthesis but also to trigger the degradative reactions leading to tail resorption.

OTHER BIOCHEMICAL DEVELOPMENTS

Numerous other biochemical areas have been explored during metamorphosis. Wilt and his associates (Ohtsu et al., 1964) have examined the mechanism of the alterations in visual pigments reported earlier by Wald and coworkers (1958). Of particular interest is the finding that in the developing tadpole there is a progressive loss of the ability of eye tissue to form retinene$_2$, leading to a predominance of retinene$_1$ and rhodopsin in the adult form.

In an investigation of the development of the subepidermal granular glands of *X. laevis* larvae, Vanable (1964) found a large increase in 5-hydroxytryptamine concentrations and a somewhat smaller increase in the activity of the decarboxylase that produces 5-hydroxytryptamine from 5-hydroxytryptophane.

Urbani (1962) has published a recent summary emphasizing the work of the Camerino, Italy, group on enzymes and metabolite changes in the embryonic development and metamorphosis of *B. vulgaris* and *R. esculenta*. Most of this work deals with whole animal analyses and does not distinguish between the various tissues or organs as do most of the experiments in this field. Total lipids, total nitrogen, and total carbohydrates fall to less than one half during both the embryonic and metamorphic period. Except in the tail, amylases, lipases, and proteases of the tadpole decrease during metamorphosis. While these descriptive changes provide useful biochemical information, they appear to be remote from the key reactions responsible for spontaneous or induced amphibian metamorphosis.

Taylor and Barker (1965) have observed that the active sodium ion transport system, as revealed by the potential difference of bullfrog skin, develops during metamorphosis after the emergence of the forelimbs. T$_4$ accelerates the appearance of the transepidermal potential difference in tadpole skin. Since the skin potential is associated with sodium ion conservation, the absence of this system in the tadpole was unexpected.

SUMMARY

Amphibian metamorphosis is accompanied by dramatic adaptive changes in numerous biochemical systems, many of which appear to be highly temperature sensitive. Several of these developmental transitions have been considered in detail, including the trends in respiration, the increase in serum proteins and ceruloplasmin, the switch from tadpole to frog hemoglobins, the developmental changes in the liver including the inducement of those enzymes responsible for the advent of ureotelism and, finally, the mode of tail resorption. Common mechanisms that appear to involve genetic control of protein and RNA biosynthesis and their repressors have emerged to account for the changes observed in such diverse tissues as the liver and the tail. It is hoped that further search among these and related events will identify the reaction(s) that enable the thyroid hormones to initiate metamorphosis.

ACKNOWLEDGMENTS

The published and unpublished research cited in this chapter from the author's laboratory has been supported in part by U.S. Public Health Service grant HD-01236, National Science Foundation grant GB-2690, and by the Division of Biology and Medicine, U.S. Atomic Energy Commission. Paper No. 28 in a series on the biochemistry of amphibian metamorphosis.

A more complete series of acknowledgments and references appears in Frieden (1967). I am especially grateful to Dr. R. Weber for a copy of his excellent review (1966), "Biochemistry of Amphibian Metamorphosis," in advance of publication.

REFERENCES

Ackerman, C. J., S. Al-Mudhaffar, and V. Mah. 1966. Fed. Proc., 25:618.

Akamatsu, N., R. H. Lindsay, and P. P. Cohen. 1964. J. Biol. Chem., 239:2246.

Ashley, H., and E. Frieden. 1967. Unpublished observations.

_____, P. Katti, and E. Frieden. 1968. Develop. Biol., in press.

Baglioni, C. 1966. J. Cell Phys., 67:169.

_____, and C. E. Sparks. 1963. Develop. Biol., 8:272.

Baldwin, E. 1940. Introduction to Comparative Biochemistry, vol. 4, 483, New York, Cambridge Univ. Press.

Barch, S. H. 1953. Physiol. Zool., 26:223.

Bennett, T. P., and E. Frieden. 1962. _In_ Florkin, M., and H. S. Mason, eds., Comparative Biochemistry, vol. 4, pp. 483–556. New York, Academic Press.

Bonner, J. 1965. The Molecular Biology of Development, New York, Oxford University Press.

Brown, G. 1964. _In_ Moore, J. A., ed., Physiology of Amphibia, pp. 1–98. New York, Academic Press.

Brown, G. W., Jr., W. R. Brown, and P. P. Cohen. 1959. J. Biol. Chem., 234:1775.

Chieffi, G., M. Siniscalco, and M. Adinolfi. 1960. Atti Accad. Nazl. Lincei Rend. Classe Sci. Fis. Mat. Nat., 28:233.

Clever, U., and P. Karlson. 1960. Exp. Cell Res., 20:623.

Cohen, P. P. 1966. Harvey Lect., 60:119-154.

Degroot, N., and P. P. Cohen. 1962. Biochim. Biophys. Acta, 59:588-595.

Delsol, M., and J. Flatin. 1962. C. R. Soc. Biol., (Paris) 156:53.

Dolphin, J., and E. Frieden. 1955. J. Biol. Chem., 217:735.

Dodd, J. M., and A. J. Matty. 1964. In Pitt-Rivers, R., and W. R. Trotter, ed., The Thyroid Gland, vol. I, 303, London, Butterworth.

Eaton, J., J. G. Cory, and E. Frieden. 1967. Fed. Proc., 26:392.

Eeckhout, Y. 1965. Contribution a l'etude de la metamorphose caudale des amphibians anoures, Dissertation, Louvain, Faculty of Science, Catholic University.

Elzinga, M. 1964. PhD dissertation, Urbana, University of Illinois.

Etkin, W. 1934. Physiol. Zool., 7:129-148.

_____. 1964. In Moore, J. A., ed., Physiology of the Amphibia, pp. 427-469, New York, Academic Press.

_____, and A. G. Gona. 1967. J. Exptl. Zool., 165:249.

Finamore, F. J., and E. Frieden. 1960. J. Biol. Chem., 235:1751.

Fletcher, K., and N. B. Myant. 1959. J. Physiol., 145:353.

Flickinger, R. A. 1964. Gen. Comp. Endocr., 4:285.

Frieden, E. 1961. Amer. Zool., 1:115.

_____. 1964. Proceedings of the Second International Congress on Congenital Malformations, pp. 191-190, New York, International Medical Congress.

_____. 1967. Recent progress in hormone research, Montreal, Canada, The Laurentian Hormone Conference.

_____, et al. 1967. Sixth International Biochemical Congress, Tokyo, in press.

_____, A. Wahlborg, and E. Howard. 1965. Nature, 205:1173.

, and G. W. Westmark. 1961. Sci., 133:1487.

, and E. Theil. 1966. Fed. Proc. 25:7980.

Funkhauser, A. 1966. PhD dissertation, Norman, University of Oklahoma.

Goldstein, A., D. B. Goldstein, and L. I. Lowrey. 1964. J. Mol. Biol., 9:213.

Gross, J. 1964. Med., 43:291

Hahn, E. W. 1962. Comp. Biochem. Physiol., 7:55.

Hamada, K., Y. Sakai, R. Shukuya, and K. Kaziro. 1964. J. Biochem. (Japan), 55:213, 636.
_____, and R. Shukuya. 1966. J. Biochem. (Japan), 59:397.
Heinemann, F., and R. Weber. 1966. Helv. Physiol. Pharmacol. Acta, 24:124.
Herner, A. E. and E. Frieden. 1960. J. Biol. Chem., 235:2845.
_____, and E. Frieden. 1961. Arch. Biochem. Biophys., 95:25.
_____, and A. Riggs. 1963. Nature, 198:35.
Hill, R. L., and J. Buettner-Janusch. 1964. Fed. Proc., 23:1236.
Inaba, T., and E. Frieden. 1967. J. Biol. Chem., 242:218.
Ingram, V. M. 1961. Nature, 189:704.
Jordan, H. E. and C. C. Speidel. 1923. J. Exp. Med., 38:529.
Kaltenbach, J. C., and N. B. Clark. 1965. Gen. Comp. Endocr., 5:74.
Kaye, N. W. 1961. Gen. Comp. Endocr., 1:1.
Kaywin, L. 1936. Anat. Rec., 64:413.
Kim, K. H., and P. P. Cohen. 1966. Proc. Nat. Acad. Sci. USA, 55:1251.
Kollros, J. 1961. Amer. Zool., 1:107.
_____. 1963. Gen. Biol., 7:1.
Kubler, H., and E. Frieden. 1964. Biochim. Biophys. Acta, 93:635.
Lapiere, C. M., and J. Gross. 1963. Mechanism of Hard Tissue Destruction, p. 663, Washington, D. C., American Association for the Advancement of Science.
Lewis, E. J. C., and E. Frieden. 1959. Endocrinology, 65:273.
Lindsay, R. H., H. Nakagawa, and P. P. Cohen. 1964. J. Biol. Chem., 239:2239.
Lipner, H. J., P. Katti, and E. Frieden. 1965. Unpublished observations.
Mah, B., and C. J. Ackerman. 1965. Life Sci., 4:573.
Manwell, C. 1966. Comp. Biochem. Physiol., 17:805.
Metzenberg, R. L., M. Marshall, W. K. Paik, and P. P. Cohen. 1961. J. Biol. Chem., 236:162.
Money, W. L., S. Kumahoa, R. W. Rawson, and R. L. Kroc. 1960. Ann. N.Y. Acad. Sci., 86:316.
Moss, B., and V. M. Ingram. 1965. Proc. Nat. Acad. Sci. USA, 54:967.
Nishimura, S., T. M. Jacob, and H. G. Khorana. 1966. Proc. Nat. Acad. Sci., 55:1251.
Ohtsu, K., K. Naito, and F. H. Wilt. 1964. Develop. Biol., 10:216–232.
Paik, W. K., and P. P. Cohen. 1960. J. Gen. Physiol., 43:683.
_____, R. L. Metzenberg, and P. P. Cohen. 1961. J. Biol. Chem., 236:536.

Pitt-Rivers, R., and J. R. Tata. 1959. The Thyroid Hormones, London, Pergamon Press.

Price, S., and E. Frieden. 1963. Comp. Biochem. Physiol., 10:245.

Riggs, A. 1951. J. Gen. Physiol., 35:23.

_____, B. Sullivan, and J. R. Agee. 1964. Proc. Nat. Acad. Sci. USA, 51:1127.

Sakai, Y., K. Hamada, R. Shukuya, and R. Kaziro. 1964. J. Jap. Biochem. Soc., 36:698.

Salzmann, R., and R. Weber. 1963. Experientia, 19:352.

Shellabarger, C. 1964. In Pitt-Rivers, R., and W. R. Trotter, eds., The Thyroid Glands, vol. I, 187, London, Butterworth.

_____, and J. R. Brown. 1959. J. Endocr., 18:98.

Shukuya, R. 1966. 11:228.

Sokoloff, L. 1965. Proceedings of the Second International Congress, Part I, 87, London, International Medical Congress.

Spiegel, M., and E. S. Spiegel. 1964. Biol. Bull., 126:307.

Stratton, L. P., and E. Frieden. 1967. Nature, 216:932.

Tata, J. R. 1965. Proceedings of the Second International Congress of Endocrinology, Part I, No. 83, London, International Medical Congress.

_____. 1965. Nature, 207:378.

_____. 1966. Develop. Biol., 13:77.

_____, and C. C. Widnell. 1966. Biochem. J., 98:604.

Tatibana, M., and P. P. Cohen. 1965. Proc. Nat. Acad. Sci. USA, 53:104.

Taylor, A. C., and J. J. Kollros. 1946. Anat. Rec., 94:7.

Taylor, R. E., Jr., and S. B. Barker. 1965. Sci., 148:1612.

Tentori, L., S. Vivaldi, S. Carta, A. M. Salvati, M. Sorcini, and S. Velani. 1965. Arch. Biochem. Biophys., 108:404.

Theil, E. 1967. Biochim. Biophys. Acta, 138:175.

_____, and E. Frieden. 1966. Fed. Proc., 25:798.

Trader, C. D., J. S. Wortham, and E. Frieden. 1963. Sci., 139:918.

_____, and E. Frieden. 1966. J. Biol. Chem., 241:357.

Urbani, E. 1962. In Abercrombie, M., and J. Bradiet, eds., Advances in Morphogenesis, vol. 2, 61–109, New York, Academic Press.

Vanable, J. 1964. Develop. Biol., 10:331.

Wahlborg, A., C. Bright, and E. Frieden. 1964. Endocrinology, 75:561.

Wald, G. 1958. Science, 128:1481.

Weber, R. 1957. Experientia, 13:153.

_____. 1963. Ciba Foundation Symposium on Lysosomes, p. 282, London, Churchill.

_____. 1965. Experientia, 21:665.

_____. 1967a. *In* Florkin, M., and E. Statz, eds., Comprehensive Biochemistry, vol. 26, in press.

_____. 1967b. *In* Weber, R., ed., The Biochemistry of Animal Development, vol. II, New York, Academic Press, pp. 227–301.

Wiggert, B. O., and P. P. Cohen. 1966. J. Biol. Chem., 241:210.

Yamamoto, K., D. Kanski, and E. Frieden. 1966. Gen. Comp. Endocr., 6:312.

ten

NATURE OF HORMONE
ACTION IN AMPHIBIAN
METAMORPHOSIS

Jane C. Kaltenbach

Department of Biological Sciences
Mount Holyoke College
South Hadley, Massachusetts

INTRODUCTION

The prime importance of thyroid hormone in accelerating metamorphic changes in amphibian larvae has long been known (Gudernatsch, 1912), and the morphological and biochemical details of many such changes have been well established (see Chapters 7 and 9); yet the precise nature of hormone action in stimulating metamorphic events remains to be determined. Various approaches to this problem have increased our understanding of the relationship of thyroxine to specific metamorphic events but have not revealed the basic mechanism by which the hormone participates in or triggers these differentiating processes. Factors characterizing the nature of the role played by thyroxine in the mediation of metamorphosis have been considered in reviews (e.g., Lynn and Wachowski, 1951; Frieden, 1961; Kollros, 1961; Etkin, 1964; Dodd and Matty, 1964; Cohen, 1966) and constitute the subject matter of the present chapter.

DIRECT ACTION OF THYROXINE ON METAMORPHIC EVENTS

Hormone Implantation Method

Before discussing the metamorphosing action of thyroid hormone it is well to recall the following points: (1) metamorphosis is not an isolated phenomenon in the life of an amphibian but rather is normally the sum of a host of reactions taking place in different tissues and organs in a definite orderly sequence, resulting in the transformation of an aquatic larva into a terrestrial adult; (2) thyroxine initiates metamorphic reactions and, as hormone concentration increases, it accelerates the rate but does not change the nature of such reactions.

The question arises as to whether the hormone stimulates individual metamorphic events by acting directly upon specific target organs rather than indirectly by way, for example, of the liver or another endocrine gland. This question was first approached by Hartwig (1940) by means of the local application of hormone to specific sites in salamander larvae. The rate of hormone diffusion from thyroxine-soaked agar blocks implanted under the skin or in the tail fin was such that metamorphic changes occurred precociously in localized regions about the implants. Such changes were attributed to the direct local action of thyroid hormone upon the tissues concerned. Localized metamorphic responses were also evoked in various regions by implants of mammalian and amphibian thyroid glands (e.g., Kollros, 1942; Lüke, 1944). Radioautographs of gland implants containing I^{131} indicated that localized responses in the surrounding tissues were most advanced when diffusion into the body fluids and away from the area of the implant was minimal (Kaltenbach, 1950). In order to provide an improved local hormone source, one which would promote marked and still more sharply localized metamorphic responses, thyroxine was mixed with an inactive, somewhat adhesive vehicle, cholesterol, and tamped into the form of small pellets (Kollros and Kaltenbach, 1952). Pellets of cholesterol alone served as controls. Analysis of a number of metamorphosing structures by means of thyroxine-cholesterol implants has been effective in demonstrating local responses to thyroid hormone. Such direct hormone-tissue relationships are discussed below.

External Changes in Form. A metamorphic event involving primarily a reorganization of cells and tissues, namely, transformation of larval skin into the adult type, was produced precociously and locally in the vicinity of thyroxine implants. Such a response represented a gradient of change, being maximal overlying an implant and progressively less advanced at increasing disctances from it; no local changes developed over control pellets. In urodele larvae, the local skin changes consisted of disappearance of glandular Leydig cells, as well as stratification, cornification, and molting of the epidermis (Hartwig, 1940; Lüke, 1944; Kuhn, 1952). Similar reactions plus dermal changes and development of glands, dermal plicae, and adult pigment occurred near subcutaneous implants in anuran larvae (Kollros and Kaltenbach, 1952; Kaltenbach, 1953a, b, and c). Localized areas of molting were also induced in adult thyroidectomized newts by thyroxine-cholesterol implants, indicating a direct response of adult skin to thyroxine (Fig. 1; Clark and Kaltenbach, 1961).

Normal and thyroxine-induced metamorphosis is expressed in certain organs mainly as growth phenomena, e.g., in the eye and its adnexa, the forelimbs, and the hind limbs. As might be expected, an increase in mitotic activity is one of the characteristics of such metamorphosing structures (e.g., Champy, 1922). A complex of changes in the eye and orbital region was induced precociously by intraorbital and intraocular thyroxine-cholesterol implants, resulting in striking differences between thyroxine-treated and contralateral control eyes (Fig. 2). This was attributed to thyroxine acting directly upon a target area rather than acting indirectly through stimulation of systemic

FIG. 1. Dorsal view of a thyroidectomized newt undergoing a local molt over a thyroxine-cholesterol implant. × 2½. From Clark and Kaltenbach (1961).

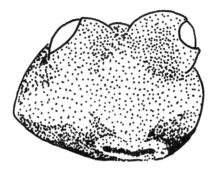

F IG. 2. Anterior view of a tadpole containing a thyroxine-cholesterol pellet in the left orbit and a cholesterol control pellet in the
right orbit. Premature metamorphosis of the thyroxine-treated eye is
evidenced by marked bulging of the eye and development of eyelids
and a nictitating membrane. Only a slight bulge and incipient lids developed over the control eye. Other structures remained larval in character, e.g., the small, rounded mouth; the broad, rounded head outline;
and the absence of an adult skin pigment pattern. × 8. From Kaltenbach
(1953).

factors such as other hormones. Interactions within the tissues
were not ruled out, however. Localized changes included growth
of extrinsic ocular muscles, eyelids, and nictitating membrane,
fusion of the two larval corneal layers, and bulging of the eyeball (Kaltenbach, 1953b), as well as marked stimulation of mitosis
in the ora serrata of the retina (Kaltenbach and Hobbs, unpublished) and an increase in the uptake of tritiated thymidine in
the treated eyeball (Kaltenbach and Harding, unpublished).
Whether each of these components represents an individual response to thyroxine independent of possible stimuli from other
structures within the local area was not determined. If individual
regions of the eye could be isolated and maintained in culture,
an effect of thyroxine upon one alone might be revealed.
        Since larval forelimbs in most anurans are not only small
but are enclosed along with the gills in the opercular chamber,
they are not readily accessible for pellet implantation. However,
in *Xenopus* tadpoles each forelimb develops in a small brachial
sac just posterior to the gill chamber. A thyroxine pellet inserted
into the sac immediately adjacent to the enclosed limb results in
enlargement of the sac and growth of the limb, in contrast to the
lack of response in the contralateral control limb (Kaltenbach,
unpublished). This indicates that forelimb growth is not caused
by a stimulus from the degenerating gills, as proposed earlier

FIG. 3. Ventral view of the hind limbs of a tadpole with a thyroxine-cholesterol implant in one shank and a cholesterol control implant
in the other. The tissues were cleared with potassium hydroxide, and
bone was stained with alizarin red. The femur, tibio-fibula, and tarsal
bones in the thyroxine-treated limb are longer than in the control limb.
× 8. From Kaltenbach (1953).

by Blacher et al. (1931), but instead is caused by direct hormone
action.

Hind limbs of larval anurans and urodeles in early stages
of development are sufficiently large for pellet implantation.
The marked growth and ossification of a thyroxine-treated limb
results in striking disharmonies between the hormone treated
and control limbs and is evidence of a direct effect of thyroxine
upon the limb (Fig. 3; Kaltenbach, 1953a; Beaudoin, 1956; Kuhn
and Hammer, 1956).

Thus, by applying hormone locally in the form of pellets to various structures such as eyes and limbs, the direct action of hormone upon growth of these structures was established.

Also under direct control of thyroid hormone are various processes involving resorption of larval structures no longer of use to a land-dwelling animal. For example, thyroxine-cholesterol and cholesterol control pellets implanted circumorally on opposite sides of *Rana pipiens* larvae induced unilateral loss of larval mouth furnishings (Fig. 4); pellets implanted postorally brought about striking asymmetries in head outline due to resorption of subcutaneous material near the thyroxine implants (Kaltenbach, 1953a).

The cause of thinning and perforation of the opercular wall, a phenomenon which enables the forelimbs to emerge from the opercular chamber, has been a source of conflicting theories. These have included such varied causative agents as mechanical pressure from the forelimbs, histolytic influence from the degenerating gills, secretion from cutaneous glands on the forelimbs, loss of opercular blood supply due to degeneration of aortic arches, and endocrine stimulus upon tissue specified to

FIG. 4. Ventral view of the circumoral area of a tadpole with thyroxine-cholesterol and cholesterol control implants beneath the skin on either side of the mouth. Note the precocious loss of labial fringe and teeth on the right thyroxine-treated side. Larval characteristics still exist elsewhere, e.g., the small mouth; the broad, rounded head outline; and the labial fringe and teeth on the control side. × 8. From Kaltenbach (1953).

degenerate (see reviews of Newth, 1949; Kaltenbach, 1953c). However, implantation of thyroxine pellets near the operculum showed that its degradation is caused by direct hormonal action upon the operculum (Kaltenbach, 1953c). Such an experiment also afforded an interesting example of tissue specificity for two different responses in skin, namely, maturation of body skin immediately above the pellet and degeneration followed by perforation of adjacent opercular skin were brought about by a single subcutaneous thyroxine implant (Fig. 5; Kaltenbach 1953c).

Hormone pellets in the tail fin of urodele and anuran larvae induced resorption of the fin immediately overlying the implants (Fig. 6; Hartwig, 1940; Kaltenbach, 1959). Such a sharply localized response ruled out previously proposed causative factors of fin resorption such as growth of the urostyle and subsequent interference with the blood supply of the tail, degeneration of the nervous system in the tail, atrophy of underlying tail muscle, and a generalized lowering of the pH (see discussion by Kaltenbach, 1959) and demonstrated a specific response of the fin to the direct

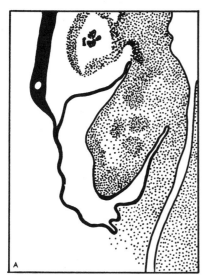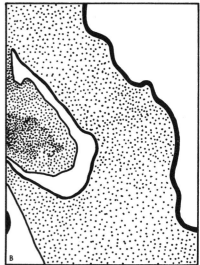

FIG. 5. Cross sections through the opercular region of a tadpole containing subcutaneous thyroxine-cholesterol and cholesterol control implants. A: thyroxine-treated side; B: control side. Note the encapsulated thyroxine-cholesterol pellet and the thickening of the overlying skin. The opercular wall beneath the thyroxine implant has undergone marked thinning in contrast to the opercular wall on the control side, which has retained its larval character. × 88. From Kaltenbach (1953).

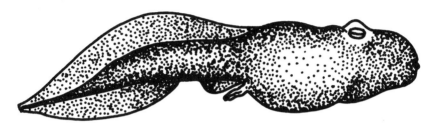

FIG. 6. Lateral views of tadpoles showing local resorption of dorsal and ventral tail fins in the regions of thyroxine-cholesterol implants. × 3. From Kaltenbach (1959).

action of thyroxine. (See also the discussion of pH effects in Chapter 9.)

Thus, numerous external individual metamorphic events involving such diverse phenomena as growth of the limbs and resorption of the tail fin are caused by the direct action of thyroid hormone upon specific target organs.

Internal Morphological Changes. Differential activation of nerve cells in the central nervous system occurs during normal and thyroxine-induced metamorphosis. However, due to the small size of the larval brain and spinal cord it is difficult to dissociate responses in specific neuron systems from each other; hormone diffusing from an implant is apt to reach not only the adjacent side of the brain but the opposite side as well. Nevertheless, by careful control of hormone concentration and of pellet location, neurons in specific regions of the brain and spinal cord have been shown to respond directly to thyroid hormone.

In anuran larvae the corneal reflex, retraction of the eyeball into the orbit upon stimulation of the cornea, is initiated about the time of metamorphic climax. No such response is elicited when the corneas of younger tadpoles are stimulated, even though the peripheral components of the reflex are fully functional in those animals. Therefore, it has been assumed that the time at which the reflex appears is contingent upon maturation of the reflex center in the hindbrain. To determine whether this center is under direct hormonal control, thyroxine was applied locally to the medulla. Such treatment advanced the onset of the reflex more than it did other metamorphic events; moreover, implants near one side of the medulla caused earlier development of the reflex on that side of the body than on the opposite side (Kollros, 1942 and 1943). Thus, with onset of the corneal reflex as a criterion of maturation or setting into operation of a reflex center in the medulla, it was possible to demonstrate a localized action of thyroxine upon a specific brain center.

Support for the thesis that certain morphological changes occur in the tadpole brain as a direct response to thyroxine was afforded by the specific neural responses to thyroxine implants near the midbrain. The cell bodies of the mesencephalic V nucleus enlarged significantly; in fact, a gradation of response was induced, cell sizes varying inversely with increasing distance from the hormone source (Kollros and McMurray, 1956). Other regions of the tadpole, including the jaw musculature to which the V nucleus cells send proprioceptor fibers, were only mildly stimulated, indicating that growth of these particular sensory cells was stimulated by the direct action of thyroxine, independently of any influence from their periphery. However, it does not exclude the possibility of more than one causative agent, e.g., change in size of the peripheral field. Moreover, reduction in size of mesencephalic V cells after withdrawal of hormone (Kollros and McMurray, 1956) or after thiourea treatment (Kollros, 1957) indicated that maintenance of size of these larval cells is dependent upon the continuous presence of thyroxine. Such a condition is unexpected because, according to Kollros and McMurray (1956), "no other metamorphic change has yet been shown to be reversible."

Other examples of local hormone stimulation were the marked growth of neurons and the increased mitotic activity of ependymal cells near thyroid implants in the tadpole medulla (Weiss and Rossetti, 1951; Pesetsky and Kollros, 1956). In contrast to these stimulatory effects was the decrease in size of Mauthner's cells (M-cells), a pair of giant neurons in the same locality; in fact, the member of the pair nearest the thyroxine implant was smaller than the somewhat more distant member (Pestsky and Kollros, 1956). M-cells are associated with movements in the trunk and tail and normally disappear at the time of tail resorption. However, their size is apparently not influenced by peripheral losses, as evidenced by the constancy of their size in tail removal experiments (Weiss and Rossetti, 1951) and in head grafts containing only a few lateral line organs and no tail motor centers (Kollros, unpublished; Pesetsky, 1960). On the other hand, the M-cells proved to be unexpectedly larger in tadpoles immersed in strong thyroxine solutions (Pesetsky, 1962) and smaller in thyroidectomized tadpoles (Pesetsky, 1966b). Such findings led Pesetsky (1962) to propose that hormonal control of these cells is analogous to that of mesencephalic V cells, i.e., that their growth is stimulated directly by thyroxine, their size dependent upon its presence, and their regression a result of hormone withdrawal (in the case of implantation studies, of hormone depletion of the pellets). Further support for this idea may be forthcoming from analyses of M-cell sizes following temporary thyroxine stimulation and thiourea treatment.

Hormonal control of motor neurons in the spinal cord is of particular interest because the size and number of these neurons can be altered by changes in the peripheral load. Precocious growth of one thyroxine-implanted tadpole limb was accompanied by an increase in size of cells in the corresponding lateral motor column—an illustration of an indirect effect of thyroxine upon motor neurons (Beaudoin, 1956). Moreover, thyroxine implants adjacent to one side of the lumbo-sacral region of the cord directly stimulated cell enlargment in the lateral motor column on that side. Such experiments indicate that thyroxine exerts a direct as well as an indirect effect upon size of certain motor cells in anuran larvae.

The pellet implantation method has afforded an experimental approach to expand our understanding of the influence of thyroxine upon maturation of specific components of the nervous system in the developing anuran. The examples above illustrate local effects of thyroid hormone upon the corneal reflex center, the mesencephalic V nucleus, Mauthnerian and nonMauthnerian cells in the medulla, and lateral motor column cells in the spinal cord. Other cells and regions of the nervous system remain to be explored in this manner. Two such examples are spinal ganglion cells and Rohon-Beard cells (large sensory cells in the larval spinal cord), shown to be responsive to general thyroxine treatment by Tusques (1949) and Stephens (1965).

The digestive system undergoes striking alterations during metamorphosis, the most obvious being a tremendous shortening of the long, coiled larval intestine and thickening of its wall. Whether such changes are accelerated by the direct action of thyroxine upon specific organs is difficult to determine by the pellet implantation method. The wall of the larval gastrointestinal tract is too thin to hold an implant effectively, and hormone diffusion from an intraperitoneal implant is generally too rapid to induce a localized effect in an adjacent organ. However, Barry (1952) reported that thyroxine pellets implanted in the body cavity next to the duodenum did produce localized metamorphic changes; in fact, histological sections revealed a gradient of response within the duodenum. In order to achieve a more sharply localized effect, Lipson (1965) used the anterior and the vitreous chambers of the tadpole eye for "culturing" pieces of intestine for as long as nine days. A thyroxine pellet in one eye induced marked metamorphic changes in the intestine in that eye in contrast to the lack of change in the control intestine in the contralateral eye. Tissue culture might prove to be an even better method for analysis of the relationship between hormone action and changes occurring in the digestive tract during metamorphosis.

Biochemical Changes. Studies on the biochemical aspects of anuran metamorphosis provide a description of chemical developments and serve as a basis for investigating and clarifying the mechanism by which thyroxine stimulates metamorphic events (see Chapter 9; Frieden, 1961; Cohen, 1966). Although many examples have been cited that demonstrate a direct local action of thyroxine upon morphological changes, there are only a few studies indicating metabolic and enzymic changes that occur as a direct response of a peripheral tissue to thyroxine. Care must be taken in deciding whether such biochemical reactions are a result of other changes induced locally in the tissue or whether they are a part of the mechanism by which the hormone acts.

Although the influence of thyroxine upon the metabolic rate of mammals is well established, evidence for metabolic effects of thyroxine in amphibians is conflicting. However, Barch (1953) provided a clear-cut example of a local thyroxine effect upon metabolism of tadpole skin. By implanting thyroxine-cholesterol pellets under the dorsal skin on one side of the body, she demonstrated an increase in oxygen consumption on that side as compared to the contralateral control side. Furthermore, this response appeared before morphological changes in the local area were discernible. (For a contrasting view of thyroxine action on metabolic rate, see Chapter 9.)

During metamorphosis a change occurs in the type of visual pigment in the anuran eye (Wald, 1946). Porphyropsin, a conjugated protein containing vitamin A_2 aldehyde (retinene$_2$) is gradually replaced by rhodopsin, a compound with vitamin A_1 aldehyde (retinene$_1$) as the chromophore group. Rhodopsin has one less double bond than the larval pigment. (See Chapter 9 for further

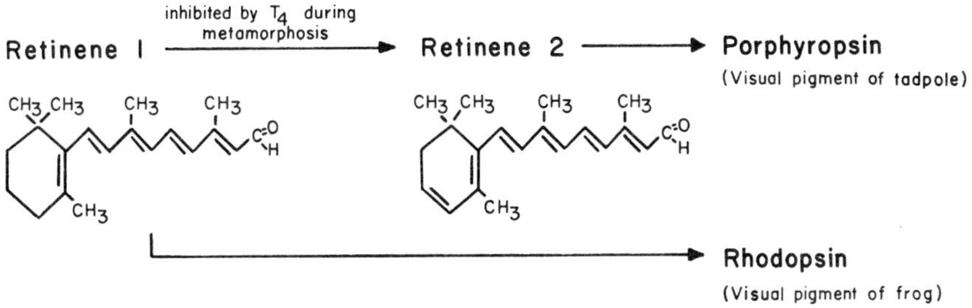

Retinene I — inhibited by T_4 during metamorphosis → Retinene 2 ———→ **Porphyropsin**
(Visual pigment of tadpole)

→ **Rhodopsin**
(Visual pigment of frog)

FIG. 7. Possible relationships of the visual pigments, according to Ohtsu et al. (1964).

discussion of the biochemical changes.) Thyroxine, administered by immersion or by placing thyroxine agar in the vitreous of one eye, led to an increase in the amount of vitamin A_1 (an index of rhodopsin) in both eyes (Wilt, 1959a). Moreover, a thyroxine-cholesterol implant in one eye, from which hormone diffusion is more localized than it is from agar base pellets, brought about a greater increase in vitamin A_1 in the treated eye than in the con-tralateral control eye (Wilt, 1959b). It was concluded that "photo-pigment conversion is a direct response of the eye to thyroxine." Further studies with radioactive vitamin A and carotenoids in-dicated that retinene$_1$ may be involved in the synthesis of reti-nene$_2$ and that during metamorphosis thyroxine decreases the ability of the eye to form retinene$_2$, thereby leaving retinene$_1$ available for rhodopsin formation (Fig. 7; Ohtsu et al., 1964).

Another interesting example of a local biochemical response to thyroxine concerns the loss of a blue pteridine pigment, Pleu-rodele blue, from larval salamander skin. Analysis by paper chromatography revealed a reduction in the amount of this sub-stance in skin overlying thyroxine-cholesterol implants but not in skin somewhat distant from them (Bagnara, 1964). Since other changes, such as molting, were also induced locally in the over-lying skin, it remains to be determined if the pteridine loss was caused indirectly by other locally induced skin changes or di-rectly by thyroxine acting upon an enzyme involved in pteridine metabolism.

Investigations of biochemical changes in tissue stimulated by the direct action of thyroxine should contribute further insight into the nature of thyroid action in amphibian metamorphosis.

Tissue Culture Method

Another way of demonstrating direct local action of thyroxine on morphological and biochemical changes in the metamorphosing tadpole is to isolate organs or tissues and maintain them in culture to which hormone has been added.

Morphological Changes. Isolated tails were cultured as early as 1859 by Vulpian, and interest in this method was renewed in 1962 by Hauser and Lehman, who used such preparations for a study of tail regeneration. The addition of thyroxine (Weber, 1962 and 1963; Flickinger, 1963) or triiodothyronine (Shaffer, 1963; Tata, 1966) to the medium resulted in a dramatic shortening of the cultured tails, thereby providing a demonstration of the direct action of thyroid hormone upon a metamorphic change at the morphological level (Fig. 8).

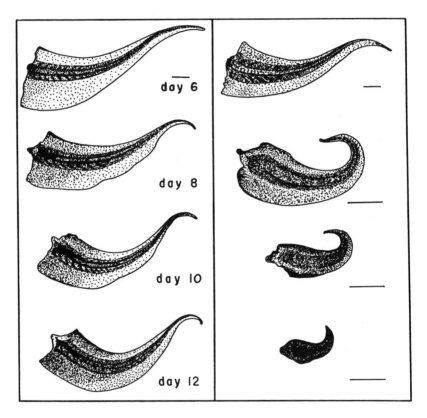

FIG. 8. Isolated tails of *X. laevis* maintained in culture. Left: Control tails; right: Regressing tails cultured for corresponding periods of time and treated with thyroxine for three, five, seven, and nine days. — = 1 mm. From Weber (1963).

Biochemical Changes. Tail culture has also been used as a model to study the direct metamorphosing action of thyroid hormone at the biochemical level. Shortening of the isolated tail was accompanied not only by loss of total protein per tail—decrease in total nitrogen (Weber, 1963)—but by an increase in activity of various hydrolytic enzymes, namely, cathepsin, acid phosphatase, and ribonuclease—per unit protein and per unit wet weight (Weber, 1963; Tata, 1966). Such changes in isolated tails were similar to those in tails of intact metamorphosing tadpoles (see Chapter 9 and Weber, 1966). Moreover, experiments with labeled uridine and labeled amino acids showed that synthesis of both RNA and protein was elevated in metamorphosing cultured tails; the addition of compounds known to block such synthetic activities (actinomycin D, puromycin, and cycloheximidine) prevented tail resorption (Tata, 1966). Such studies suggest that RNA and protein synthesis are closely associated with regression of the tail and that the increase in activity of hydrolytic enzymes may be due to necessary, newly synthesized hydrolytic enzyme molecules.

Cultures of tail tips were also used to compare the effects of thyroxine and dinitrophenol (an agent that uncouples oxidative phosphorylation) on histolysis and tissue respiration by Heinemann and Weber (1966). A significant increase in oxygen consumption occurred three days after the addition of thyroxine to the culture medium, in contrast to a transient rise two hours after the addition of dinitrophenol. From experiments of this type, Heinemann and Weber (1966) proposed that thyroxine acts "by controlling the release of biosynthetic messages from the genome rather than by interfering with energy metabolism."

A somewhat different type of culture method was used to investigate the mechanism of connective tissue resorption in the tadpole tail fin. By use of reconstituted collagen gels and hyaluronic acid as culture substrates, the fin was found to contain an enzyme with collagenolytic activity and another with hyaluronidase activity (Gross and Lapiere, 1962; Silbert et al., 1965). Culturing epithelial and mesenchymal components of the fins separately and determining the effects of puromycin upon enzyme activity showed the epidermal cells to be responsible for the production of the collagenase and the mesenchymal cells for the release of hyaluronidase (Eisen and Gross, 1965). Thus, the two main extracellular components of connective tissue, namely, collagen fibers and ground substance, are attacked by different enzymes produced by different type cells (see also Chapter 9). The effects of thyroxine upon this system have not yet been reported.

Culture of various larval organs and tissues should provide an opportunity for further research on the metamorphosing action of thyroxine at various levels of organization. Although balanced saline solutions were adequate for maintenance of tails in culture, a nutrient medium may be required for maintenance and growth of other organs. Urodele larval organs such as pancreas (Foote and Foote, 1965), *Rana* tadpole eyes (Ohtsu et al., 1964), and *Xenopus* larval skin (Vanable, 1965 and 1966), and whole hearts of tadpoles (Stephenson, 1967), have been cultured on enriched media for varying lengths of time up to three weeks, thereby providing a means for analyzing the action of thyroxine and its analogs upon metamorphic changes in these organs.

Experimental evidence, as cited in the preceding pages, clearly indicates that thyroid hormone acts directly upon peripheral tissues to accelerate metamorphic changes at both a morphological and biochemical level. Understanding that the metamorphosing organs themselves are the direct sites of thyroid action was a first, albeit distant, step in the fundamental task of searching for the mechanism by which the hormone achieves its stimulation of metamorphosis.

METAMORPHOSING ACTION OF THYROXINE ANALOGS

General Metamorphosis

Another aspect in elucidating the nature of thyroid hormone action is that of relating the chemical structure of the hormone with its metamorphosing activity. The isolation (Kendall, 1915) and synthesis (Harington and Barger, 1927) of thyroxine opened the way for such studies, and interest was renewed by the discovery of $3, 5, 3'$-triiodothyronine (Gross and Pitt-Rivers, 1952a) and the finding that it was more active than thyroxine both in mammals (Gross and Pitt-Rivers, 1952b) and in tadpoles (Roth, 1953). In the last few years organic chemists have produced innumerable alterations in the thyroxine molecule, resulting in the production of thyroxinelike compounds (Fig. 9). Assays of the metamorphosing potencies of such thyroxine analogs have allowed generalizations of the following types to be made (see, e.g., reviews of Selenkow and Asper, 1955; Money et al., (1960). Replacement of the alanine side chain of thyroxine with propionic, acetic, or acrylic acid results in greater activity. Values ranging from 2 to 300 times that of thyroxine have been reported. On the other hand, substitution of a carboxyl or an amino group

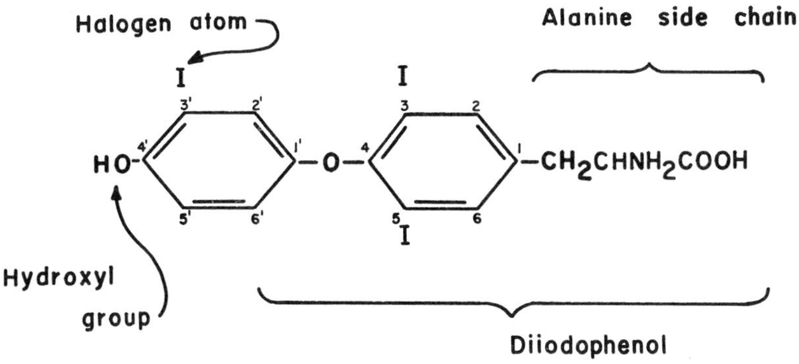

FIG. 9. Thyroxine (a diphenyl ether). Its metamorphosing potency can be altered by changes in the alanine side chain, the number and type of halogen atoms, the nature and position of the end group, and the number of benzene rings.

for the alanine side chain, replacement of iodine with other halogen atoms, removal of two halogen atoms (at the $3'$ and $5'$ positions), or replacement of the hydroxyl group with a methoxy group bring about decreases in activity. Diiodophenols, i.e., single-ring compounds likely to condense to active diphenyl ethers, have very weak activity; single-ring compounds unlikely to condense, as well as analogs devoid of halogen atoms, or with changes in the configuration of the molecule are inactive.

Care must be taken in considering analog assays in a strictly quantitative manner. Variations in results may be attributed to differences in the species of test amphibian, the criterion chosen for metamorphosis, the strength of serum protein-analog bonds, and consequent differences in availability of analogs to peripheral tissues, as well as purity, solubility, stability, and method of administration of the compounds. Therefore, some of the quantitative data may reflect factors other than the actual metamorphosing potency of the thyroxine analogs. For example, acetic and propionic acid analogs were found to have much greater activity relative to thyroxine when tested by immersion (compounds added to the tadpole bath) rather than by intraperitoneal injection, a finding attributed to the assumed lower permeability of thyroxine than of acid side-chain analogs (Frieden and Westmark, 1961; Wahlborg et al., 1964). However, the role of permeability in immersion experiments may be eclipsed by another factor, namely, different equilibria undoubtedly established between hormone concentrations within the tadpole and within its surroundings, a phenomenon that varies according to the concentration of hormone in the external medium (Kollros, 1963; Kollros and Reiter, 1965). It was concluded that immersion was effective in providing a relatively constant, continuous hormone source. Yet, the small but variable amounts of radioactive thyroxine and triiodothyronine absorbed by tadpoles from the surrounding medium indicated to Yamamoto et al. (1966) that immersion was less satisfactory than injection as a means of hormone administration (see also Chapter 9). Further studies in absorption and equilibria, as well as stability, of various analogs should aid in evaluating the suitability of immersion and injection methods for analog assay.

Local Metamorphosis

Whether the metamorphosis-stimulating activity of thyroxine analogs is due to a direct effect of the analogs upon peripheral tissues was answered by the implantation of analog pellets. Such implants in the dorsal tail fin of tadpoles induced localized fin resorption, a response attributed to the direct action of the analog upon the target organ, namely, tail fin (Fig. 10; Kaltenbach, 1966). Any change the analog may have undergone must have occurred within the peripheral tissues. Similarly, thyroxine analogs act directly upon skin in stimulating molting in adult thyroidectomized newts (Kaltenbach and Clark, 1965). Results from analog implant studies are consistent with more quantitative data on general metamorphosing potencies of analogs presented in numerous other studies.

According to Frieden et al. (1957), the metamorphosing activity of diiodophenols, single-ring compounds, is probably dependent upon their conversion to active diphenyl ethers either "in the tadpole incubation medium or in the organism." Such condensation reactions are known to occur in vitro, e.g., diiodotyrosine

FIG. 10. Lateral view of a tadpole showing a striking degree of local resorption of the dorsal tail fin in the region of a tetraiodothyropropionic acid-cholesterol implant. × 3. From an unpublished experiment of J. C. Kaltenbach.

to thyroxine (first shown by von Mutzenbacher, 1939). However, metamorphosis of skin near diiodophenol implants indicated that if such an effect were produced by the condensation of the implanted compounds, the condensation must have occurred in vivo. In fact, it must have occurred not only within the tadpole, but within its peripheral tissues; moreover, implants of single-ring compounds unlikely to condense were ineffective in stimulating metamorphic changes (Kaltenbach, 1966).

Analog Selection of Target Organs

Very few studies have been designed to test the possibility that thyroxine analogs may act selectively upon target organs. Kollros (1958a and 1961) reported that a different sequence of metamorphic events was induced by propionic and formic acid analogs; this was attributed, not to differences in the activities of the compounds, but rather to selectivity of specific peripheral tissues by different compounds. Although various analogs may not be equally effective in stimulating all metamorphic events, no analog has been reported that will stimulate either growth or resorptive changes but not both. However, diverse metamorphic phenomena may all be brought about by similar means, e.g., by direct or indirect stimulation of protein synthesis. Even tail regression has been attributed to increased synthesis of certain (hydrolytic) enzymes (Weber, 1963; Tata, 1966). New experimental approaches to this problem may offer more conclusive evidence. Until then, the question may still be asked: To what extent, if at all, do analogs act selectively upon specific sites in the tadpole.

However, analog studies to date have indicated that the direct metamorphosing activity of thyroid hormone is retained, lessened, or even facilitated by alterations in the thyroxine molecule.

CONTROL OF METAMORPHIC PATTERN

Reactivity of Target Organs to Thyroxine

Specificity of Response. As we have seen, target organs respond independently and directly to thyroxine. Moreover, the response is highly specific: in anurans the hind limbs grow; the tail is resorbed. Furthermore, the specificity of response is independent of the type of tissue involved in the reaction. Thus, growth occurs in the striated muscle in the developing limbs and tongue, while the same type of tissue in the anuran tail degenerates and is resorbed. However, the response of a particular tissue is not the same in all amphibians, as evidenced by the different response of the tail in anuran and urodele larvae. In the latter the tail does not shorten but is retained in adult life.

At least two types of experimental approach have lent support to the fundamental concept of tissue specificity. Transplantation of larval tissues to various sites in the tadpole and observations of their reactions provide one type of evidence. Most transplants of this type responded to thyroxine in a manner typical of their origin rather than typical of their new surroundings, indicating that specificity was an inherent quality of the grafted tissue. For example, hind-limb bud and eyecup transplants on the tadpole tail continued to grow and were gradually moved forward to the sacral region as metamorphosis proceeded and the tail shortened (Schubert, 1926; Schwind, 1933). Thus, the growth response of the transplanted organs was specific and was not altered by the adjacent regressing tail tissues. Experiments involving skin transplants showed that localized regions of skin are specific with regard to pigment formation (Lindeman, 1929) and plical gland formation (Helff, 1931). A second type of evidence for the concept of tissue specificity was that afforded by the implantation of thyroxine pellets. As described in the preceding pages, the type of response elicited by thyroxine implants varied, depending upon their location. In particular, one might be reminded of the dual response provoked by subcutaneous implants near the operculum, i.e., maturation of the overlying body skin and resorption of the adjacent opercular skin (Kaltenbach, 1953c).

However, there are a few exceptions in which the expected specificity of a tissue was not realized (Kollros, 1961). With immersion in very low thyroxine concentrations for long periods of time, the perforated opercular skin, rather than fusing with skin at the base of the shoulder, was almost entirely resorbed. In fact, resorption occasionally extended beyond the midline (Kollros, personal communication). On the other hand, skin of a partially resorbed tail, instead of undergoing histolysis, may have molted.

Onset of Sensitivity. It is generally agreed that the capacity of anurans to metamorphose in response to thyroid hormone is first acquired late in embryonic life at the time of opercular formation. This is well before the tadpoles own thyroid glands show any appreciable activity. Whether all parts of the animal acquire sensitivity to thyroxine simultaneously or whether there is a progressive sensitization of various organs has been questioned. According to Etkin (1950), the onset of sensitivity "appears to occur in all tissues at about the same time." However, Moser (1950) reported small differences in the times at which hormone sensitivity developed in certain organs, e.g., responsiveness of the tail eight hours before that of the limbs. More recently, Kollros and McMurray (1956) showed that the onset of responsiveness of mesencephalic V cells of the anuran midbrain occurred still later. These cells did not begin to react to thyroxine until larval stages III to IV (stages of Taylor and Kollros, 1946), and their response was not complete until stage V or afterward. Moreover, the progressive development of maximal sensitivity by these cells, as well as by future plical gland cells in the skin (Heady and Kollros, 1964), indicated that sensitivity of an individual responding system is acquired gradually rather than in an all-or-none fashion. Still more recently, Etkin (1966) showed that the median eminence in the floor of the hypothalamus is not competent to react to thyroxine until a late tadpole stage. This contrasts with the early development of responsiveness in other structures and affords further evidence for the concept of progressive acquisition of hormone sensitivity by different anuran tissues. Differences have also been reported with respect to the times at which various urodele (axolotl) tissues first become sensitive to thyroxine (Prahlad and DeLanney, 1965).

Early studies on the onset of tissue responsiveness to thyroxine are difficult to evaluate (see discussion of Etkin, 1955; Kollros, 1961); the conditions of different investigations varied with regard to the species of amphibian, method of staging, temperature, dosage of hormone, method of hormone administration, and time of exposure to the hormone. The data of Verma (1965), showing responses of rudimentary skin glands in the sequence of plicae, thigh, shank, and finally foot, at constant hormone concentrations, emphasize regional specificities in either developing sensitivity or in capacity to respond.

This is an area that warrants further investigation, but perhaps with new approaches. The response of tissue transplants of specific regions from precisely staged embryos might offer some information. What differences exist between the reactive and unreactive states of tissues? An answer to such a question, especially at the fine structural level or the biochemical level, might enable one to predict if a tissue from a particular embryo had the wherewithal to respond to thyroxine. If we knew the mechanism by which thyroxine works, what particular organelles and biochemical reactions are involved, a more meaningful analysis of the tissues and their capacities to react to hormonal stimulus would be possible.

Threshold of Response. Not only do different peripheral structures acquire hormone sensitivity at different times, but the degree of sensitivity acquired varies widely among individual structures. In general structures that metamorphose early are more sensitive than those that undergo change later. Although this variation long has been recognized, whether it is related to differences in threshold values or to differences in total thyroxine requirements has led to much debate. The concept that each target organ has its own threshold, as indicated by the minimal level of hormone needed for response, was favored by early investigators. However, interpretation of their results, which were usually obtained from short periods of hormone administration, was questioned by Etkin (1955). As a strong proponent of the stoichiometric view, Etkin (1935, 1955, and 1964) believed that each tissue had a different total thyroxine requirement that could be met either by a high concentration of thyroxine acting for a short time or a low concentration acting for a long time. Accordingly, a hormone concentration just adequate to stimulate early metamorphic events would also stimulate late ones if its administration were continued sufficiently long. This held true for the thyroxine concentrations and the times of administration used by Etkin.

However, by using greatly lower hormone concentrations for extended lengths of time (up to a year), Kollros (1958b and 1961) showed conclusively that different tissues do have different thresholds. In hypophysectomized tadpoles, early metamorphic events were accelerated but later ones were only stimulated slightly, if at all. This state of partial metamorphosis was maintained for long periods of time even though hormone treatment was still continued. In fact, by careful selection of hormone levels successive metamorphic events were shown to have different and somewhat higher thresholds. For example, the threshold for onset of the corneal reflex was found to be lower than that for perforation of the operculum (Kollros, 1958b), and the latter threshold was lower than that for gill resorption (Kollros, 1961). Not only did such experiments demonstrate the existence of individual thresholds for different target organs, but they also established the idea of progressively increasing thresholds at different stages of development of a particular organ (Kollros, 1961). Thus, in the case of the hind limb, long exposure to a very low concentration of thyroxine promoted differentiation to the stage of three digits. At this new level of differentiation, threshold requirements had altered; a higher hormone concentration was needed for development of five toes and a still higher one was needed for formation of the interdigital webs and toe pads.

New investigations in this area will probably be concerned with subcellular and biochemical differences that may exist between organs with high and low sensitivities to thyroxine. Such information might throw light on the mechanism of thyroxine action. On the other hand, knowledge of how the hormone acts might help in elucidating the physical bases of tissue sensitivity.

Rate of Response. Individual target organs differ, not only in their sensitivities, but in their rates of response to effective concentrations of thyroxine (see, e.g., Etkin, 1935; Kollros, 1961). Generally speaking, the responses of early metamorphic events are less rapid than are those of later one. For example, the legs, although highly sensitive, respond slowly to the hormone; the tail, a relatively insensitive structure, responds rapidly. Moreover, the rates of response vary directly with changes in hormone concentration above threshold levels. Responses become progressively more rapid as concentrations are raised, until at high concentrations maximal rates are attained. Moreover, the increases in rates of responses in various organs are not necessarily the same. At high thyroxine concentrations, all metamorphic events are therefore crowded together, resulting in asynchronous development. For example, the tail begins to resorb before the limbs become well developed. The animal is thereby left without a satisfactory means of locomotion, a rather sorry state for an animal. In fact, a very abnormal metamorphic pattern usually results in death. Kollros (personal communication, 1966) questioned: "If metamorphosis is realizable in a concentration time basis, as proposed by Etkin, should asynchronies occur?" (For a contrary interpretation, see Chapter 8.) One might hope for further quantitative studies on rates of response of individual target organs to different thyroxine concentrations above the threshold levels.

It is well to keep in mind that peripheral structures differ from each other, and from one stage of development to another, with respect to sensitivity and rate of response to thyroxine and possibly to the length of the latent period before a response is first discernible. Therefore, in analyses of thyroxine-induced metamorphosis consideration should be given to choice of criteria by which metamorphic progress is to be gauged.

Thyroxine Concentration

The preceding discussion has called attention to the importance of hormone concentration in controlling the overall metamorphic pattern, in particular by influencing the onset of individual metamorphic events and the rates at which they occur. Lengthy treatment with low concentrations of thyroxine only advanced metamorphic progress slowly and to a limited degree. Those structures with low thresholds of response were stimulated; others with high thresholds did not respond, regardless of the length of hormone treatment. On the other hand, with high concentrations of thyroxine all threshold values were exceeded, and all tissues responded. Moreover, late metamorphic events proceeded so rapidly that abnormal tadpoles resulted. A normal metamorphic pattern could not be achieved by the administration of any single thyroxine concentration. It could be produced, however, by the administration of progressively higher levels of thyroxine (Etkin, 1935 and 1964).

Such a matching of the normal metamorphic pattern by means of graded increases in exogenous thyroxine concentrations provided evidence for the concept of increasing hormone levels during normal metamorphosis, maximum levels being reached at metamorphic climax. Early support for this idea was based on morphological studies of the larval thyroid gland (see Etkin, 1936 and 1964). Histological indices showed that gland activity increased gradually, becoming most intense during metamorphic climax, at which time the epithelium was high columnar and the colloid vacuolated, indicating hormone discharge. In contrast, after climax the histological picture became typically that of an inactive gland—flattened epithelium and colloid-distended follicles. Such studies on gland activity were later substantiated by chemical investigations (e.g., see Etkin, 1964). To cite one such example, in *R. pipiens* tadpoles thyroidal uptake of I^{131} was found to be forty times greater during climax than during early larval stages (Kaye, 1961).

Thus, two different types of experimental approaches, namely, administration of varying concentration of thyroxine to tadpoles and analysis of thyroid gland activity during various phases of normal metamorphosis, serve to emphasize the important controlling role that hormone concentration plays in metamorphosis.

Summary: Response of Target Organs to Varying
Thyroxine Concentrations

The normal metamorphic pattern is the result of direct specific responses of individual target organs to varying concentrations of thyroid hormone. The timing of these responses is due to variations of certain qualities inherent in the tissues. As seen from the preceding discussion, these include time of onset of sensitivity as well as threshold and rate of response. Moreover, these factors are not constant for a particular organ but vary with its stage of development. Further work aimed at uncovering the nature of the target organs and their hormone-mediated reactions will undoubtedly be focused at the molecular level of biological organization. The unfolding of metamorphic events considered as one of the important aspects of cellular differentiation becomes a fundamental problem for all developmental biologists. Information on such problems as nucleocytoplasmic interactions and the mechanism of embryonic inductions will undoubtedly increase our understanding of the molecular bases of metamorphic processes. Meanwhile, all we can say is that on a tissue level, the general characteristics as mentioned earlier, together with the progressively increasing concentrations of thyroid hormone, are responsible for the definite sequence and spacing of metamorphic events that result in the overall metamorphosis of the tadpole.

FACTORS THAT INFLUENCE THE METAMORPHIC RESPONSE

Even though metamorphic reactions are initiated by thyroxine, they may be either facilitated or inhibited by other factors. Some may affect the activity of the thyroid gland directly, such as iodine, thiourea, and thiouracil; others may have an indirect effect upon it through the pituitary or hypothalamus. Prolactin (Etkin, Chapter 8), steroid hormones, crowding, diet, and temperature are among the factors whose mode of action and importance in the regulation of normal metamorphosis are still unknown.

Steroid Hormones

Of the hormones, those from the adrenal cortex and the gonads have probably been implicated most often as modifiers of thyroxine-induced metamorphosis. Steroids alone, administered to tadpoles in early stages of development, did not accelerate metamorphosis—they either produced no effect or an inhibitory effect (e.g., Kobayashi, 1958). However, metamorphosis of later-stage tadpoles was hastened by desoxycorticosterone acetate, an effect probably associated with relatively high endogenous levels of thyroxine (Kobayashi and Okubo, 1954). Moreover, certain steroids administered along with thyroxine facilitated its accelerating action, e.g., cortin (Bock, 1938), the mineralocorticoid desoxycorticosterone (Gashe, 1942; Kobayashi, 1958), the gluco-corticoids cortisone and hydrocortisone (Frieden and Naile, 1955), and the estrogenic hormones estrone and stilbesterol (Frieden and Naile, 1955). Degenerative changes were particularly enhanced by such steriods. On the other hand, thyroxine-induced metamorphosis was reported to be unaffected by des-oxycorticosterone (Frieden and Naile, 1955), the estrogens (Roth, 1942, 1943, and 1948), and progesterone (Frieden and Naile, 1955) and to be inhibited by cortisone (Dastoli and Tector, 1959), prednisolone acetate (Manner, 1958), and testosterone (Roth, 1941, 1942, and 1943; Frieden and Naile, 1955). Inconsistencies among reports may be due to differences in the concentrations of thyroxine and steroids administered, the order and manner of their administration, or the species and stage of amphibian used for testing. A biphasic effect of hormones depending upon their concentration is not new in the records of endocrinology.

Assay of a large series of natural and synthetic steroids might aid in assessing the effective parts of the steroid molecule, although conversion of one steroid to another in the water or in the tadpole has not been ruled out. Whether the effectiveness of certain steroids is due to a reaction with thyroxine, to a systemic effect (e.g., by a primary action on the pituitary, thyroid, or liver), or to an effect upon the target organs is unknown. However, the induction of localized tail fin resorption by pellets containing subthreshold amounts of thyroxine plus desoxycorticost-erone, cortisone, or hydrocortisone suggests that the enhancing effect of such steroids takes place within the target organs (Kaltenbach, 1958). Do certain steroids lower the thresholds of response of the target organs to thyroxine or affect intracellular binding of the hormone? Do they increase the permeability of the extracellular components of connective tissue? Do they alter the permeability of cell membranes or of intracellular membranes? Changes in permeability might allow thyroxine diffusing from the implants, or key metabolities in the body fluids, to reach their sites of action more readily. The nature of the enhancing effect of the steroids on thyroxine-induced metamorphosis remains an unsolved problem.

Crowding

It has been well established by numerous studies that crowding of tadpoles results in a reduced growth rate (see Richards, 1958). The animals remain small; in addition, metamorphosis is delayed (Adolph, 1931; Lynn and Edelman, 1936). Early investigators attributed growth inhibition to such factors as lack of oxygen, reduced feeding, and overstimulation due to increased number of collisions. However, the finding that water in which crowded tadpoles had been raised retarded growth of other tadpoles suggested a factor of a different type, namely, growth-inhibiting products in the water (Richards, 1958). Growth retardation was most pronounced if water from larger tadpoles was used on smaller ones (Rose, 1959). That water-borne inhibitory products are cellular and algalike in nature and located in tadpole fecal material was reported by Richards (1958 and 1962). However, according to Akin (1966) inhibitory products are probably produced by the tadpoles themselves and only secondarily become associated with algal cells that pass through the intestine. (For further discussion of this point, see Chapter 7.)

Although studies relating space to growth are prevalent, very few detailed studies relating space to metamorphosis have been carried out. Identification of growth-inhibiting substances and their effects upon metamorphosis, on pituitary and thyroid gland histology, on the uptake or radioactive iodine, and on tissue sensitivity are some of the areas yet to be explored. The importance of crowding under natural conditions should also be taken into consideration since, according to Rose (1959), "A new genome that favored growth might spread rapidly, for its bearers would inhibit their more slowly growing relatives without being inhibited by them. This may be a relationship favoring rather rapid evolutionary advances in aquatic organisms."

Diet

The effects of starvation and of various diets upon growth of tadpoles have been investigated for more than 100 years, but the effects of such factors upon metamorphosis have not always been taken into consideration. Moreover, controlled conditions in nutritional experiments are difficult to maintain because of variations in the amount of food consumed by individual tadpoles, the type and number of microorganisms in the water, and so forth. However, the inconsistencies among early reports on the effects of starvation on metamorphosis were resolved by D'Angelo et al. (1941), who showed that the stage of the tadpole at the time of food withdrawal was critical. Starvation before the critical stage caused a delay in metamorphosis, but after that stage it accelerated metamorphosis. These effects were found to be related to the degree of differentiation of the pituitary and thyroid glands.

Similar effects on metamorphosis followed the feeding of vitamin poor diets during early and late larval life (Doetsch, 1938).

Specific elements in the diet seem to affect metamorphic progress. For instance, metamorphosis was delayed by certain fats (Emmet and Allen, 1919; Kneibe, 1920; McCarrison, 1921) but was accelerated by the amino acids phenylalanine, tyrosine, and tryptophan (Gudernatsch and Hoffman, 1936), by glucose and organic phosphorus (Perichanjanz and Sudzilowskaja, 1936), by vitamin B_{12} (Medda et al., 1956), and by vitamin E (Bounhiol et al., 1958).

Interesting metamorphic effects followed immersion of *Xenopus* (Weissmann, 1961) and *Rana* tadpoles (Henry and Kaltenbach, unpublished) in solutions of vitamin A. Tails underwent a partial metamorphosis associated with loss of metachromatic material from the fins. On the other hand, the mucosal epithelial cells in the intestine increased in height, and a remarkable number of goblet cells developed; such changes are normally associated with metamorphosis. Weissman (1961) theorized that changes in the tail were probably caused by the action of vitamin A on lysosomal membranes, thereby allowing release of lytic enzymes capable of degrading the protein-polysaccharide complex in the ground substance of the fins. The vitamin may also be needed for the synthesis of the mucopolysaccharide of which the mucus of the goblet cells is composed. Such work opens the way for future studies, e.g., finding the metamorphic effect of other agents known to weaken or to stabilize lysosomal membranes, analyzing (histochemically and biochemically) the activity of lysosomal enzymes in various tissues after vitamin A treatment and determining quantitiatively the hyaluronic acid content of the fins of vitamin-treated and control tadpoles.

Temperature

That normal metamorphosis and growth are influenced by temperature changes has long been known. For example, in cold environments larval life is longer than in warmer ones (see, e.g., Adler, 1916), and tadpoles raised at $16°C$ grew larger than those that metamorphosed more rapidly at warmer temperatures (Etkin, 1955). By accelerating metamorphosis and thereby shortening the larval period, thyroid administration has facilitated study of temperature effects on metamorphosis. Thus, in both anurans and urodeles the effects of thyroid treatment are hastened by increased temperatures (see review of Lynn and Wachowski, 1951) and almost completely inhibited by cold about $+5°C$ (e. g. , Huxley, 1929; Hartwig, 1936).

That responses at low temperatures are also delayed in hypophysectomized tadpoles treated with thyroxine is an indication that temperature effects are probably reflections of sensitivity changes in peripheral tissues and may occur independently of the pituitary and thyroid glands (Kollros, 1961). Moreover, in such tadpoles the threshold of response of a particular organ was higher, i.e., more thyroxine was required to induce a specific metamorphic event at 15°C than at 25°C (Kollros, 1961). However, variation in histologic structure of thyroid glands from tadpoles raised at different temperatures have been described (e.g., Adler, 1916).

A recent detailed analysis of temperature effects by Frieden et al. (1965) involved single injections of hormone followed by transfer of tadpoles to different temperatures. The metamorphic response of cold-inhibited tadpoles could be restored by transferring the animals to room temperature, thereby clearly indicating that metamorphic inhibition by cold is reversible. Tadpoles treated with various analogs of thyroxine responded similarly to changes in temperature. (For further discussion of the biochemical aspects of temperature dependence, see Chapter 9.)

Not only does cold impede morphological changes but biochemical changes as well (see Chapter 9). For example, this is true with regard to oxygen uptake of normal tadpoles (see Frieden et al., 1965) and to specific activity of liver carbamylphosphate synthetase in thyroxine-treated tadpoles (Paik and Cohen, 1960). Moreover, both the uptake of radioactive thyroxine and triiodothyronine from the water and its elimination from the tadpole were slower at 6°C than at 25°C (Yamamoto et al., 1966). This was attributed to "differences in diffusion rates, in concentration in the gut and liver, and in the fecal loss of these hormones at these two temperatures" (Yamamoto et al., 1966).

Studies involving assessment of metamorphic progress at different temperatures may be important tools in elucidating the mechanism by which thyroxine initiates metamorphic reactions. For example, Kollros (1958b) found that by altering temperature and hormone concentration metamorphic events normally occurring within a few days of each other—e.g., corneal reflex onset and forelimb emergence—could be separated by an interval of almost six months. Such a demonstration supports the theory that metamorphic events are individual, separate occurrences, each directly responsive to thyroid hormone.

Are metabolic reactions that comprise a given metamorphic event also individual reactions, able to be separated by experimental manipulation? The reversibility of temperature effects in hormone-treated tadpoles led Frieden et al. (1965) to ask if thyroid hormone might not induce preparatory changes, e.g., messenger RNA(s) synthesis, at 5°C, but not complete the total response involving protein synthesis until higher temperatures became available. These are basic questions, answers to which await further experimentation. Perhaps further details relating to experimental procedures, such as time intervals between hormone injection and transfer of tadpoles to lower temperatures, frequency of water changes, and constancy of light at different temperatures, would be helpful in evaluating and interpreting results.

The adaptive value of tadpole responses to temperature changes, as well as to crowding and starvation, has been pointed out by Etkin (1964). During "inappropriate cold seasons" metamorphosis and emergence from ponds is inhibited, and during warm seasons exitus from overheated ponds is promoted.

To conclude, little is known with regard to the mechanism by which metamorphic responses are affected by temperature. As the mechanism of hormone action is elucidated, the way in which other factors affect metamorphic responses should become clearer.

METAMORPHOSING ACTION OF THYROXINE ON A CELLULAR AND SUBCELLULAR LEVEL

It is well established that the metamorphosing action of thyroid hormone is reflected by specific changes in structure at both gross and histological levels and by specific chemical changes in certain organs such as the eye, liver, and tail. New techniques applied to metamorphosing organs may enable identification of cellular and subcellular sites of hormone action. To date, electron microscopic and histochemical studies have indicated that metamorphosis is accompanied by alterations in fine structure and in chemical reactions occurring within specific tissues and cells.

Fine Structural Changes

Electron microscopy of body and tail skin undergoing normal and thyroxine-induced metamorphosis has revealed that the basement lamella, composed of layers of orthogonally arranged collagenic fibrils, is invaded by underlying mesenchymal cells; in head and body skin adult stratum spongiosum and stratum compactum are then formed (Weiss and Ferris, 1954; Kemp, 1961 and 1963; Usuku and Gross, 1965; Pflugfelder and Schubert,

1965). However, the exact mechanism by which these changes are brought about is still open to speculation. Fine structural changes of Lydig cells have also been described (Kelly, 1966). These are large cells specialized for mucus or fluid secretion, located in urodele larval epidermis; their final disappearance was coincident with metamorphic alterations in other epidermal cells (Kelly, 1966).

That tympanic membrane formation is a metamorphic event brought about directly by a chemical influence from the growing annular tympanic cartilage and only indirectly by action of thyroid hormone was proposed by Helff in 1928 on the basis of skin graft experiments. This theory prevailed for more than 30 years until Goldsmith's (1965) electron microscopic study showed that the ultrastructure of the tympanic membrane was identical to that in the surrounding head skin. Formation of such adult-type integument is brought about directly by thyroid hormone. Only quantitative differences were detected between the skin of the tympanum and that elsewhere in the body, the tympanic membrane being thinner and containing fewer glands. Goldsmith (1965) attributed this to tension exerted by the growing tympanic cartilage and to the shorter developmental period of the tympanic skin. Thus, the direct stimulus for tympanic membrane formation, as for other metamorphic events, appears to be thyroid hormone.

Not only have metamorphic changes in skin fallen under the scrutiny of the electron microscope, but so have those occurring in intestinal epithlium, tail muscle, and heart muscle. Studies of Bonneville (1962 and 1963) indicated that during natural and thyroxine-induced metamorphosis degeneration of the larval intestinal epithelial cells is associated with increased numbers of lysosomelike bodies, followed by sloughing of the dying cells into the intestinal lumen. Meanwhile, proliferation and differentiation of basal cells results in the appearance of adult epithelium with a different fine structural organization than that of larval epithelium.

Weber's (1964) observations on tadpole tail muscle showed that changes in its fine structure, involving myofibrils, mitochondria, and sarcoplasm, occurred before any appreciable shortening of the tail took place. Absence of lysosomes in the cells suggested that such changes were not dependent upon activity of lysosomal enzymes. Weber postulated that extrusion of peripheral sarcoplasm stimulated phagocytic activity of nearby mesenchymal cells; macrophages increased in number as tail resorption advanced. Moreover, a combination of electron micro-scropic and histochemical techniques showed that acid phosphatase activity was specifically localized within inclusion bodies, "phagosomes," of the macrophages. Such observations aid in elucidating the mechanism by which tail muscle is resorbed during metamorphosis; they do not indicate which, if any, changes in cellular organelles occur as a direct response to thyroid hormone.

Differences in fine structure of cardiac muscle cells at various stages of metamorphosis have also been reported (Kaye and Copenhaver, 1966). Certainly the future will bring a great many more studies on fine structural changes in other metamorphosing organs.

Histochemical Changes

Alkaline phosphatase activity has been thoroughly studied in the developing intestine of birds and mammals by biochemical and histochemical methods (see Moog, 1962). The pattern of its distribution in the intestine of amphibian larvae is of interest because of the extensive remodeling of the intestine and the changes in feeding habits that occur during metamorphosis. Although no alkaline phosphatase activity was found in the larval duodenum anterior to the entrance of the bile duct, a positive reaction was obtained in the striated border of the mucosal epithelial cells just posterior to this location; such activity disappeared during metamorphic climax and reappeared in the new adult epithelial cells (Chieffi and Carfagna, 1959 and 1960; Kaltenbach and Lipson, 1962). The pattern of localization of this enzyme, as well as of leucine aminopeptidase, nonspecific esterase, and polysaccharides, was also determined for the stomach and esophagus during normal and thyroxine-accelerated metamorphosis (Lipson and Kaltenbach, 1965).

Histochemical techniques applied to the metamorphosing tail have indicated that cathepsinlike esterase and acid phosphatase are not distributed uniformly throughout the various tissues of the tail but are confined mainly to the macrophages within it (Salzmann and Weber, 1963; Weber, 1964).

Furthermore, histochemical means have demonstrated that precocious maturation of the anuran hind brain, induced by exogenous thyroxine, is accompanied by increased activity of TPNH (NADPH) diaphorase, glucose 6-phosphate dehyrogenase, and thiamine pyrophosphatase (Pesetsky, 1965 and 1966a). Enzyme activity was present in small neurons of the mantle and was particularly marked in ependymal cells. Since the latter represent the main glial elements of the amphibian brain, activation of their enzyme systems could, according to Pesetsky (1966a) "be interpreted as signs of glial activation, and thus may indicate a particular significant locus of thyroxin's action in the central nervous sytem."

CONCLUDING REMARKS

Countless studies have afforded careful descriptions of morphological and biochemical changes initiated by thyroid hormone during metamorphosis. Ideas concerning the basic mechanism by which such changes are brought about have centered upon hormonal control of enzyme synthesis and enzyme activity, of cellular and intracellular membrane permeability, and of genic expression. Evidence from amphibian and mammalian material suggests that the nucleus (possibly genetic material and the nuclear membrane) and messenger RNA may be important sites of thyroid hormone action (e.g., Chapter 9; Siegel and Tobias, 1966). Different hypotheses need not be mutually exclusive, since a hormone might conceivably have more than one locus of action. Few tools for probing the role of thyroxine at a molecular level include metabolic inhibitors to block specific steps in the DNA-RNA-protein scheme, as well as radioautographic and immunological techniques to pinpoint specific sites of hormonal action. Future studies will certainly clarify the mechanism by which thyroid hormone induces larval structures to metamorphose into those of the adult amphibian, but at the present time the frog, cocky creature that he is, still has not revealed many of his secrets.

ACKNOWLEDGMENT

Many thanks are due to Miss Maryanne Pendergast, New York University Medical Center, for preparing Figures 1 to 10.

REFERENCES

Adler, L. 1916. Untersuchungen über die Entstehung der Amphibienneotenie. Zugleich ein Beitrag zur Physiologie der Amphibienschilddrüse. (Inaugural-Dissertation zur Erlangung der Doctor würde Kgl. Universitat zu Frankfurt A. M.) Pfleugers Arch. Ges. Physiol. 164:1–101.

Adolph, E. F. 1931. Body size as a factor in the metamorphosis of tadpoles. Biol. Bull., 61:376–386.

Akin, G. C. 1966. Self-inhibition growth in *Rana pipiens* tadpoles. Physiol. Zool., 39:341–356.

Bagnara, J. T. 1964. Analyse des transformations des pteridines de la peau au cours de la vie larvaire et à la métamorphose chez le Triton *Pleurodeles waltlii* Michah. Changements induits par l'action localisée d'implants de thyroxine-cholestérol. C. R. Acad. Sci. (Paris), 258:5969–5971.

Barch, S. H. 1953. Oxygen consumption of normal and thyroxin-stimulated *Rana pipiens* skin. Physiol. Zool., 26:223–231.

Barry, D. G. 1952. Local action of thyroxin on metamorphosis of the amphibian gut. Dissertation Abstr., 12:605.

Beaudoin, A. R. 1956. The development of lateral motor column cells in the lumbo-sacral cord in *Rana pipiens*. II. Development under the influence of thyroxin. Anat. Rec., 125:247–259.

Blacher, L. J., M. A. Woronzowa, L. D. Liosner, and W. N. Samarajew. 1931. Resorptionsprozesse als Quelle der Formbildung. VII. Die Mitogenetischen Ausstrahlungen als Stimulus des Wachstums des Vorderbeines bei der Metamorphose von *Rana temporaria*. Arch. Entwicklungsmech. Org., 124:138–153.

Bock, K. A. 1938. Die Einwirkung von Nebennierindenextrakt auf den Ablauf der Thyroxinmetamorphose bei Froschlarven und beim Axolotl. Klin. Wochr. 17:1311–1314.

Bonneville, M. A. 1962. Cytological responses during thyroxine-accelerated metamorphosis. Proceedings of the Fifth International Congress for Electron Micros., New York, Academic Press.

_____. 1963. Fine structural changes in the intestinal epithelium of the bullfrog during metamorphosis. J. Cell Biol., 18:579–597.

Bounhiol, J. J., P. Disclos, and G. Disclos. 1958. La vitamine E stimule la croissance larvaire et rend plus précoce la métamorphose du Crapud accoucheur (*Alytes obstetricans* Laur.). C. R. Soc. Biol., (Paris) 152:1685–1687.

Champy, C. 1922. L'action de l'extrait thyroïdien sur la multiplication cellulaire. Arch. Morph. Gen. Exp., 4:1–58.

Chieffi, G., and M. Carfagna. 1959. Variazioni del contenuto della fosfatasi alcalina nell'intestino di *Rana esculenta* durante la metamorfosi. Rend. Accad. Naz. Lincei (Ser. 8), 26:94–98.

_____, and M. Carfagna. 1960. The alkaline phosphatase of the intestinal epithelium of Bufo vulgaris tadpoles during metamorphosis. The influence of hydrocortisone on the epithelial in vitro. Acta Embryol. Morph. Exp., 3:213–220.

phosphatase in vitro. Acta Embryol. Morph. Exp., 3:213–220.

Clark, N. B., and J. C. Kaltenbach. 1961. Direct action of thyroxine on skin of the adult newt. Gen. Comp. Endocr., 1:513–518.

Cohen, P. P. 1966. Biochemical aspects of metamorphosis: Transition from ammonotelism to urotelism. *In* Harvey Lect., 60:119–154.

D'Angelo, S. A., A. S. Gordon, and H. A. Charipper. 1941. The role of the thyroid and pituitary glands in the anomalous effect of inanition on amphibian metamorphosis. J. Exp. Zool., 87:259–277.

Dastoli, F. R., and A. J. Tector, Jr. 1959. The effect of cortisone on amphibian metamorphosis. Bios, 30:27–31.

Dodd, J. M., and A. J. Matty. 1964. Comparative aspects of thyroid function. *In* Pitt-Rivers, R., and W. R. Trotter, The Thyroid Gland, vol. 1, 303–356, London, Butterworths.

Doetsch, H. 1938. Der Einfluss der Schilddrüse auf Entwicklung und Wachstum von Amphibienlarven unter verscheidenen Ernahrungsbedingungen. Z. Ges. Exp. Med., 103:163–169.

Eisen, A. Z., and J. Gross. 1965. The role of epithelium and mesenchyme in the production of a collagenolytic enzyme and a hyaluronidase in the anuran tadpole. Develop. Biol., 12:408–418.

Emmet, A. D., and F. P. Allen. 1919. Nutritional studies on the growth of frog larvae (*Rana pipiens*). J. Biol. Chem., 38:325–344.

Etkin, W. 1935. The mechanisms of anuran metamorphosis. I. Thyroxine concentration and the metamorphic pattern. J. Exp. Zool., 71:317–340.

_____. 1936. The phenomena of anuran metamorphosis. III. The development of the thyroid gland. J. Morph., 59:69–89.

_____. 1950. The acquisition of thyroxine-sensitivity by tadpole tissues. Anat. Rec., 108:541.

_____. 1955. Metamorphosis. *In* Willier, B. H., P. A. Weiss, and V. Hamburger, Analysis of Development, pp. 631–663, Philadelphia, Saunders.

_____. 1964. Metamorphosis. *In* Moore, J. A., Physiology of the Amphibia, pp. 427–468, New York, Academic Press.

_____. 1966. Hypothalamic sensitivity to thyroid feedback in the tadpole. Neuroendcr., 1:293–302.

Flickinger, R. A. 1963. Iodine metabolism in thyroidectomized frog larvae. Gen. Comp. Endocr., 3:606–615.

Foote, F. M., and C. L. Foote. 1965. Organs of the larval axolotl (*Siredon mexicanum*) grown singly or in combination *in vitro*. Trans. Illinois State Acad. Sci., 58:164–175.

Frieden, E. 1961. Biochemical adaptation and anuran metamorphosis. Amer. Zool, 1:115–149

_____, and B. Naile. 1955. Biochemistry of amphibian metamorphosis: I. Enhancement of induced metamorphosis by gluco-corticoids. Science, 121:37–39.

_____, and G. W. Westmark. 1961. On the anomalous activity of thyroxin analogs in tadpoles. Science, 133:1487–1489.

_____, A. Wahlborg, and E. Howard. 1965. Temperature control of the response of tadpoles to triiodothyronine. Nature, 205:1173–1176.

_____, H. M. Walborsky, and J. E. McRae. 1957. Conversion of diiodophenols to side-chain analogs of thyroxin. Science, 125:887–888.

Gasche, P. 1942. Die Beeinflussung der Thyroxinmetamorphose durch Steroidhormone. Verhandl. Schweiz. Naturforsch. Ges. 122:158–159.

Goldsmith, M. 1965. The ontogeny of the tympanic integument during metamorphosis in *Rana pipiens:* a cytological and ultra-structural investigation. PhD dissertation. Providence, Rhode Island, Brown University.

Gross, J., and C. M. Lapiere. 1962. Collagenolytic activity in amphibian tissues: A tissue culture assay. Proc. Nat. Acad. Sci. USA, 48:1014–1022.

_____, and R. Pitt-Rivers. 1952a. The identification of 3, 5, 3'-L-triiodothyronine in human plasma. Lancet, 1:439–441.

_____. 1952b. Physiological activity of 3, 5, 3'-L-triiodothyronine. Lancet, 1:593–594.

Gudernatsch, J. F. 1912. Feeding experiments on tadpoles. I. The influence of specific organs given as food on growth and differentiation. A contribution to the knowledge of organs with internal secretion. Arch. Entwicklungsmech. Org., 35:457–483.

_____, and O. Hoffman. 1936. A study of the physiological value of α-amino acids during the early periods of growth and differentiation. Arch. Entwicklungsmech. Org., 135:136–177.

Harington, C. R., and G. Barger. 1927. Chemistry of thyroxine. III. Constitution and synthesis of thyroxine. Biochem. J. 21:169–183.

Hartwig, H. 1936. Über die Beziehungen zwischen Schilddrüse und Entwicklung bei Salamanderlarven unter dem Einfluss verscheidener Temperaturen. Arch. Entwicklungsmech. Org., 134:562–587.

_____. 1940. Metamorphose-Reaktionen auf einen lokalisierten Hormonreiz. Biol. Zentr. 60:473–478.

Hauser, R., and F. E. Lehman. 1962. Regeneration in isolated tails of *Xenopus* larvae. Experientia, 18:83–84.

Heady, J. E., and J. J. Kollros. 1964. Hormonal modification of the development of plical skin glands. Gen. Comp. Endocr., 4:124–131.

Heinemann, F., and R. Weber. 1966. Der O_2-Verbrauch im regredierenden Schwanzgewebe von Xenopuslarven bei spontaner Metamorphose und bei thyroxinbedingter Rückbildung *in vitro*. Helv. Physiol. Parmacol. Acta, 24:124–138.

Helff, O. M. 1928. Studies on amphibian metamorphosis. III. The influence of the annular tympanic cartilage on the formation of the tympanic membrane. Physiol. Zool., 1:463–495.

_____. 1931. Studies on amphibian metamorphosis. IX. Integumentary specificity and dermal plicae formation in the anuran, *Rana pipiens*. Biol. Bull., 60:11–22.

Huxley, J. S. 1929. Thyroid and temperature in cold-blooded vertebrates. Nature, 123:712.

Kaltenbach, J. C. 1950. Localized metamorphic changes in the skin of *Rana pipiens* larvae by subcutaneous implants of mouse and frog thyroid glands containing radioactive iodine. Anat. Rec., 108:526–527.

_____. 1953a. Local action of thyroxin on amphibian metamorphosis. I. Local metamorphosis in *Rana pipiens* larvae effected by thyroxin-cholesterol implants. J. Exp. Zool., 122:21–39.

_____. 1953b. Local action of thyroxin on amphibian metamorphosis. II. Development of the eyelids, nictitating membrane, cornea, and extrinsic ocular muscles in *Rana pipiens* larvae effected by thyroxin-cholesterol implants. J. Exp. Zool., 122:41–51.

_____. 1953c. Local action of thyroxin on amphibian metamorphosis. III. Formation and perforation of the skin window in *Rana pipiens* larvae effected by thyroxin-cholesterol implants. J. Exp. Zool., 122:449–467.

_____. 1958. Direct steroid enhancement of induced metamorphosis in peripheral tissues. Anat. Rec., 131:569–570.

_____. 1959. Local action of thyroxin on amphibian metamorphosis. IV. Resorption of the tail fin in anuran larvae effected by thyroxine-cholesterol implants. J. Exp. Zool., 140:1–17.

_____. 1966. Local action of thyroxine analogues on amphibian metamorphosis. Gen. Comp. Endocr., 7:329–344.

_____, and N. B. Clark. 1965. Direct action of thyroxine analogues on molting in the adult newt. Gen. Comp. Endocr., 5:74–86.

_____, and M. S. Lipson. 1962. Alkaline phosphatase in the epithelium of the digestive tract during normal and thyroxin-induced metamorphosis. Amer. Zool., 2:418–419.

Kaye, N. W. 1961. Interrelationships of the thyroid and pituitary in embryonic and premetamorphic stages of the frog, *Rana pipiens*. Gen. Comp. Endocr., 1:1–19.

_____, and W. M. Copenhaver. 1966. Heart muscle development in *Rana pipiens* tadpoles studied with the electron microscope. Anat. Rec., 154:366.

Kelly, D. E. 1966. The Leydig cell in larval amphibian epidermis. Fine structure and function. Anat. Rec., 154:685–699.

Kemp, N. E. 1961. Replacement of the larval basement lamella by adult-type basement membrane in anuran skin during metamorphosis. Develop. Biol., 3:391–410.

_____. 1963. Metamorphic changes of dermis in skin of frog larvae exposed to thyroxine. Develop. Biol., 7:244–254.

Kendall, E. C. 1915. A method for the decomposition of the proteins of the thyroid, with a description of certain constitutents. J. Biol. Chem., 20:501–509.

Kneibe, I. L. 1920. Der Einfluss verscheidener Fettsäuren und fettsäurer Salze sowie des Cholesterins und Cholins auf Wachstum und Entwicklung von Froschlarven. Z. Biol., 71:165–192.

Kobayashi, H. 1958. Effect of desoxycorticosterone acetate on metamorphosis induced by thyroxine in anuran tadpoles. Endocrinology, 62:371–377.

_____, and K. Okubo. 1954. Effects of desoxycorticosterone acetate on broodiness, molting, and pituitary lactogen content in the canary, and on metamorphosis of the toad tadpole. Annotationes Zool. Japon., 27:173–179.

Kollros, J. J. 1942. Localized maturation of lid-closure reflex mechanism by thyroid implants into tadpole hindbrain. Proc. Soc. Exp. Biol. Med., 49:204–206.

_____. 1943. Experimental studies on the development of the corneal reflex in Amphibia. II. Localized maturation of the reflex mechanism effected by thyroxin-agar implants into the hindbrain. Physiol. Zool., 16:269–279.

_____. 1957. Influence of thiourea on growth of cells of midbrain in frogs. Proc. Soc. Exp. Biol. Med., 95:138–141.

_____. 1958a. Selectivity in sites of action of thyroxine analogues in induced anuran metamorphosis. Anat. Rec., 130:327.

_____. 1958b. Hormonal control of onset of corneal reflex in the frog. Science, 128:1505.

_____. 1961. Mechanisms of amphibian metamorphosis: Hormones. Amer. Zool., 1:107–114.

_____. 1963. Immersion as a method of thyroxine administration in amphibian metamorphosis studies. Develop. Biol., 7:1–10.

_____, and J. C. Kaltenbach. 1952. Local metamorphosis of larval skin in *Rana pipiens*. Physiol. Zool., 25:163–170.

_____, and V. M. McMurray. 1956. The mesencephalic V nucleus in anurans. II. The influence of thyroid hormone on cell size and cell number. J. Exp. Zool., 131:1–26.

_____, and R. Reiter. 1965. Thyroid hormone exchange between environment and tadpoles of *Rana pipiens*. Anat. Rec., 151:374.

Kuhn, O. 1952. Erkenntnisquellen für die Reaktionsweise der Haut als äussere Körperbedeckung. Phot. Wiss., 1:1–8.

_____, and H. O. Hammer. 1956. Über die Einwirkung des Schilddrüsenhormons auf die Ossifikation. Experientia, 12:231–233.

Lindeman, V. F. 1929. Integumentary pigmentation in the frog, *Rana pipiens*, during metamorphosis, with especial reference to tail-skin histolysis. Physiol. Zool., 2:255–268.

Lipson, M. S. 1965. A histochemical study of the digestive tract of amphibian larvae throughout normal and thyroxin-induced metamorphosis. PhD dissertation. Amherst, Four College Cooperative PhD Program, University of Massachusetts.

_____, and J. C. Kaltenbach. 1965. A histochemical study of the esophagus and stomach of *Rana pipiens* during normal and thyroxin-induced metamorphosis. Amer. Zool., 5:212.

Lüke, M. 1944. Über die Wirkung und das Verhalten von Schilddrüsengewebe des Axolotl im Transplantationsversuch. Arch. Entwicklungsmech. Org., 142:730–762.

Lynn, W. G., and A. Edelman. 1936. Crowding and metamorphosis in the tadpole. Ecology, 17:104–109.

_____, and H. E. Wachowski. 1951. The thyroid gland and its functions in cold-blooded vertebrates. Quart. Rev. Biol., 26:123–168.

Manner, H. W. 1958. The effect of prednisolone acetate on amphibian metamorphosis. Anat. Rec., 132:472.

McCarrison, R. 1921. Observations on the effects of fat excess on the growth and metamorphosis of tadpoles. Proc. Roy. Soc. (London), Series B, 92:295–303.

Medda, A. K., G. C. Bhattacharya, and P. N. Nandi. 1956. On the action of penicillin on the retardation of metamorphosis of tadpoles. Sci. Cul. (Calcutta), 22:173–174.

Money, W. L., S. Kumaoka, and R. W. Rawson. 1960. Comparative effects of thyroxine analogues in experimental animals. Ann. N.Y. Acad. Sci., 86:512–544.

Moog, F. 1962. Developmental adaptations of alkaline phosphatases in the small intestine. Fed. Proc., 21:51–56.

Moser, H. 1950. Ein Beitrag zur Analyse der Thyroxinwirkung im Kaulquappenversuch und zur Frage nach dem Zustandekommen der Frübereitschaft des Metamorphose-Reaktionssystems. Rev. Suisse Zool., Suppl. 2, 57:1–144.

Newth, D. R. 1949. A contribution to the study of fore-limb eruption in metamorphosing anura. Proc. Zool. Soc. London, Part III, 119:643–659.

Ohtsu, K., K. Naito, and F. H. Wilt. 1964. Metabolic basis of visual pigment conversion in metamorphosing *R. catesbeiana.* Develop. Biol., 10:216–232.

Paik, W. K., and P. P. Cohen. 1960. Biochemical studies on amphibian metamorphosis. I. The effect of thyroxine on protein synthesis in the tadpole. J. Gen. Physiol., 43:683–696.

Perichanjanz, J., and O. Sudzilowskaja. 1936. Über die Gemeinsame wirkung von Glukose und Organischen Phosphorverbindungen auf den Wuchs und die Differenzierung von Kaulquappen der *Rana temporaria.* Arch. Int. Pharmcodyn., 54:349–354.

Pesetsky, I. 1960. Maintenance and regression of Mauthner's neuron in larval *Rana pipiens.* Anat. Rec., 136:257.

_____. 1962. The thyroxine-stimulated enlargement of Mauthner's neuron in anurans. Gen. Comp. Endocr., 2:229–235.

_____. 1965. Thyroxine-stimulated oxidative enzyme activity associated with precocious brain maturation in anurans. A histochemical study. Gen. Comp. Endocr., 5:411–417.

_____. 1966a. Thyroxin-stimulated thiamine pyrophosphatase activity in the ependymal cells of anuran amphibians. Anat. Rec., 154:401.

_____. 1966b. The role of the thyroid in the development of Mauthner's neuron. A karyometric study in thyroidectomized anuran larvae. Z. Zellforschung, 75:138–145.

_____, and J. J. Kollros. 1956. A comparison of the influence of locally applied thyroxine upon Mauthner's cell and adjacent neurons. Exp. Cell Res., 11:477–482.

Pflugfelder, O., and G. Schubert. 1965. Elektronenmikroskopische Untersuchungen an der Haut von Larven und Metamorphosestadien von *Xenopus laevis* nach Kaliumperchloratbehandlung. Z. Zellforschung, 67:96–112.

Prahlad, K. V., and L. E. DeLanney. 1965. A study of induced metamorphosis in the axolotl. J. Exp. Zool., 160:137–146.

Richards, C. M. 1958. The inhibition of growth in crowded *Rana pipiens* tadpoles. Physiol. Zool., 31:138–151.

_____. 1962. The control of tadpole growth by alga-like cells. Physiol. Zool., 35:285–296.

Rose, S. M. 1959. Failure of survival of slowly growing members of a population. Science, 129:1026.

Roth, P. 1941. Action antagoniste du propionate de testostérone dans le métamorphose expérimentale des batraciens provoquée par la thyroxine. Bull. Mus. Nation. Hist. Nat. (Paris), 13:500–502.

_____. 1942. Les antagonistes de la thyroxine dans la metamorphose des Batraciens anoures. La diiodotyrosine, le propionate de testostérone et le benzoate d'oestradiol. Bull. Mus. Nation. Hist. Nat. (Paris), 14:480–483.

_____. 1943. Action antagoniste du propionate de testostérone dans la métamorphose expérimentale des Batraciens anoures provoquée par la thyroxine. Bull. Mus. Nation. Hist. Nat., (Paris), 15:99–100.

_____. 1948. Sur l'action antagoniste des substances oestrogènes dans la métamorphose expérimentale des amphibiens. Bull. Mus. Nation Hist. Nat. (Paris), 20:408–415.

_____. 1953. Action de la 3:5:3' triiodothyronine sur la métamorphose des têtards de Rana temporaria L. Ann. Endocr., 14:857–864.

Salzmann, R., and R. Weber. 1963. Histochemical localization of acid phosphatase and cathepsin-like activities in regressing tails of Xenopus larvae at metamorphosis. Experientia, 19:352–354.

Schubert, M. 1926. Untersuchungen über die Wechselbeziehungen zwischen wachsenden und reduktiven Geweben. Z. Mikr. Anat. Forsch., 6:162–189.

Schwind, J. L. 1933. Tissue specificity at the time of metamorphosis in frog larvae. J. Exp. Zool., 66:1–14.

Selenkow, H. A., and S. P. Asper, Jr. 1955. Biological activity of compounds structurally related to thyroxine. Physiol. Rev., 35:426–474.

Shaffer, B. M. 1963. The isolated Xenopus laevis tail: A preparation for studying the central nervous system and metamorphosis in culture. J. Embryol. Exp. Morp., 11:77–90.

Siegel, E., and C. A. Tobias. 1966. End-organ effects of thyroid hormones: subcellular interactions in cultured cells. Science, 153:763–765.

Silbert, J. E., Y. Nagai, and J. Gross. 1965. Hyaluronidase from tadpole tissue. J. Biol. Chem., 240:1509–1511.

Stephens, L. B., Jr. 1965. The influence of thyroxin upon Rohon-Beard cells of Rana pipiens larvae. Amer. Zool., 5:222–223.

Stephenson, E. M. 1967. Effects of temperature on tadpole hearts in vitro. J. Embryol. Exp. Morph. 17:147–159.

Tata, J. R. 1966. Requirement for RNA and protein synthesis for induced regression of the tadpole tail in organ culture. Develop. Biol., 13:77–94.

Taylor, A. C., and J. J. Kollros. 1946. Stages in the normal development of *Rana pipiens* larvae. Anat. Rec., 94:7–23.

Tusques, J. 1949. Corrélation entre le développement des membres et le développement des structures nerveuses centrales correspondantes (axe gris medullaire, ganglions spinaux et cervelet) sous l'action de la thyroxine chez les tetards de *Rana esculenta*. C. R. Soc. Biol. (Paris), 143:380–382.

Usuku, G., and J. Gross. 1965. Morphologic studies of connective tissue resorption in the tail fin of metamorphosing bullfrog tadpole. Develop. Biol., 11:352–370.

Vanable, J. W., Jr. 1965. Organ culture of *Xenopus laevis* larval skin. Amer. Zool., 5:663.

_____. 1966. Development of *Xenopus laevis* skin glands in organ culture. Exp. Cell Res. 44:436–442.

Verma, K. 1965. Regional differences in skin gland differentiation in *Rana pipiens*. J. Morph.. 117:73–85.

von Mutzenbecher, P. 1939. Über die Bildung von Thyroxin aus Dijodtyrosin. Hoppe-Seylers Z. Physiol. Chem., 261:253–256.

Vulpian, M. A. 1859. Note sur les phénomènes de développement qui se manifestent dans la queue des très jeunes embryons de grenouille, après qu'on l'a séparée du corps par une section transversale. C. R. Acad. Sci. (Paris), 48:807–811.

Wahlborg, A., C. Bright, and E. Frieden. 1964. Activity of some new triiodothyronine analogs in the tadpole. Endocrinology, 75:561–564.

Wald, G. 1946. The chemical evolution of vision. *In* Harvey Lect., 41:117–160.

Weber, R. 1962. Induced metamorphosis in isolated tails of *Xenopus* larvae. Experientia, 18:84–85.

_____. 1963. Zur Aktivierung der Kathepsine im Schwanzgewebe von Xenopuslarven bei spontaner und *in vitro* induzierter Rückbildung. Helv. Physiol. Pharmacol. Acata., 21:277–291.

_____. 1964. Ultrastructural changes in regressing tail muscles of *Xenopus* larvae at metamorphosis. J. Cell Biol., 22:481–487.

_____. 1966. Biochemische und zellbiologische Aspekte der Geweberückbildung in der Entwicklung. Bull. Schweiz. Akad. Med. Wiss., 22:27–46.

Weiss, P., and W. Ferris. 1954. Electron-microscopic study of the texture of the basement membrane of larval amphibian skin. Proc. Nat. Acad. Sci. USA, 40:528–540.

_____, and F. Rossetti. 1951. Growth responses of opposite sign among different neuron types exposed to thyroid hormone. Proc. Nat. Acad. Sci. USA, 37:540–556.

Weissmann, G. 1961. Changes in connective tissue and intestine caused by vitamin A in Amphibia, and their acceleration by hydrocortisone. J. Exp. Med., 114:581–592.

Wilt, F. H. 1959a. The differentiation of visual pigments in metamorphosing larvae of *Rana catesbeiana*. Develop. Biol., 1:199–233.

_____. 1959b. The organ specific action of thyroxin in visual pigment differentiation. J. Embryol. Exp. Morp., 7:556–563.

Yamamoto, K., D. Kanski, and E. Frieden. 1966. The uptake and excretion of thyroxine, triiodothyronine and iodide in bullfrog tadpoles after immerson or injection at 25° and 6°C. Gen. Comp. Endocr., 6:312–324.

Author Index

Complete references are given on pages indicated by italics.

443

Subject Index

Complete references are given on pages indicated by italics.